Preface

This book is a completely revised version of the very successful *Engineering Technology* which was first published by the same authors in 1985. The revised book charts a theoretical course in engineering technology, treating essential concepts and important aspects of the subject. It is designed to meet the demands of education programmes which respond to continuous change in our society.

In our revision, we have retained our objectives set for the first book: to present the student with a format which is easy to read and well illustrated. We have taken into account the helpful comments and suggestions of many practising teachers. Many of the graphic illustrations have been completely redesigned and all are presented in a manner which will enable the student to acquire a clear impression of the topics and concepts they are dealing with. Inset in some of the more complicated graphics are schematic diagrams which the student will find easy to reproduce. Photographs are included to add realism and provide a context for the subject matter under discussion.

As in the earlier edition, safety is not treated as a separate topic in the book. We feel strongly that the concept of safety must be totally integrated into a course of study. References to safety arise incidentally in some chapters to highlight important safety implications and make sure that students fully appreciate the absolute necessity to always work safely with tools and equipment. It should be clearly understood that these brief references do not represent a definitive consideration of the health and safety aspects of the topic. They merely serve to remind the reader of the more stringent precautions that need to be taken.

Students and teachers should keep pace with government policies of continuously revising and upgrading safety standards. In areas such as machine tool operation and welding, it is imperative that students following a practical course in engineering, be familiar with current safety regulations and standards that apply to them as students. These regulations can be obtained from government publications offices and safety organisations.

We wish to express our sincere thanks to our many colleagues and friends who have given us encouragement, advice and valuable criticism. We acknowledge the specialist help of the following: Professor Michael Hillery, University of Limerick, Professor Evan Petty, University of Limerick, Mr Charlie Cannon, Letterkenny Vocational School; Mr Martin Gormley, Milford Vocational School, Mr Jack Lynch, Cork Regional Technical College; Mr Bernard McCallion, Falcarragh Community School; Mr John McCarthy, Limerick City VEC; Mr Joe McGrath, Ardscoil, Lorgan, Castleblayney; Mr Hugh McLean, Pobalscoil Ghaothdobhair; Eugene O'Brien, St Nessan's Community College.

A special thanks to Mary and Rosaleen – we appreciate their support and encouragement while we were working on the book.

Liam Hennessy, Lawrence C. Smyth

The Structure of Materials

INTRODUCTION

There is a close relationship between the structure of atoms within a material and the properties that the material possesses. Indeed, the name atom evolved from a very early attempt to understand the nature of materials. The theory that matter could be divided, or cut up, until a stage is reached that the parts are so small that they can no longer be divided, or cut, is credited to *Democritus* and *Leucippus* (circa 4th century BC). They called these uncuttable parts atoms, from the Greek word *atomos*, meaning uncuttable.

However, shortly after these two men put forward their idea, another man, who was much better known, came up with the rare idea that all matter consisted of *earth*, *fire*, *air* and *water*. This was the idea of none other than the great *Aristotle*, and because of his far-reaching reputation as a philosopher, his idea grew to be the accepted theory. It was known as the *four element* or *four ache theory*. Although *Aristotle* died in 322 BC, his theory was strengthened by the work of *Empedocles*.

EXTRAORDINARY THINKERS

It is extraordinary that, even in those early times, element theories were being put forward. Many of the great names were associated to some degree with one element theory or another. Two of the most important ideas, which these extraordinary thinkers put forward are:

1 All matter is made up of small uncuttable pieces.
2 It is impossible to destroy matter.

Early *chemists* or *alchemists* devoted considerable time and energy to trying to change one metal into another. Of course gold was nearly always the desired result! Perhaps this was one of the reasons why there was so much early Greek interest in understanding the secrets of matter make-up.

Atomic theory

Aristotle's *four element* theory was the generally accepted theory until the middle of the seventeenth century, although Democritus' idea had been taught in the ninth century by *Razi*, who was a medical scientist.

Sir Robert Boyle

It was Robert Boyle, an Irishman born in Waterford and educated in England, who put paid to the four element theory. Boyle, known to many students through *Boyle's Law*, was a founder member of the Royal Society. He published 'The Skeptical Chymist' in 1661, when he was thirty-five years old. Boyle stated in his paper that *an element has only one kind of atom*. Boyle's work proved to be the foundation for others to work upon. *Isaac Newton* came up with the idea of attraction between particles, *Lavoiser* listed elements, *Dalton*, a Manchester teacher, produced the first evidence of the existence of atoms, *J. J. Thomson* discovered the electron and won the 1906 Nobel Prize for physics, *Milikan*, of the USA, measured the size of an electron, *Rutherford* produced a model of an atom which showed the atom to be mostly empty space – the latter produced the *Quantum Theory*, and the list goes on and on right up to the present.

Even today, the atom is not fully understood and research into subatomic particles goes on. It is ironic that, to study these minute particles, some of the largest machines on earth are used. These are large *accelerators* like the one in Geneva, which has an experimental path more than 6 kilometres long! Scientists hope that when they get all the answers they will be able to answer the age-old question: *what is the origin of the universe?* The Geneva Laboratory is called Cern and it is the European laboratory for particle physics. Another such institution is the Fermi National Laboratory, near Chicago in the United States. Both these laboratories are interested in the *quark theory*, which deals with

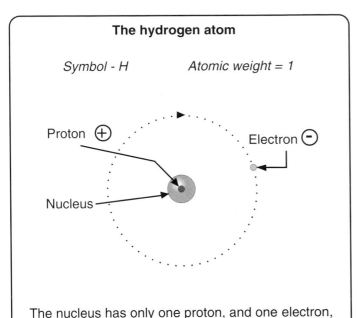

The hydrogen atom

Symbol - H   Atomic weight = 1

Proton ⊕   Electron ⊖

Nucleus

The nucleus has only one proton, and one electron, which spins around the nucleus. The atom is neutral because the positive proton cancels out the negative electron

FIGURE 3 *Hydrogen atom.*

mentioned, and neutrons. Protons have a positive electric charge and neutrons have no charge. Electrons, mentioned above, are negatively charged, and usually equal the number of protons in the nucleus. This means that there are equal numbers of positive and negative particles and so the atom remains neutral. The number of protons (or electrons), is known as the *atomic number* of the element concerned. It used to be thought that electrons orbited a nucleus in fixed paths (Rutherford 1911). However, the accepted idea in this present day is that the electrons whirl around at approximate radii in *cloud shells*. The shells give the probable position of the electrons.

Electrons are attracted to the nucleus by electrostatic force, in a similar way that a charged balloon is attracted to a dry wall. Just like in magnetism, electrostatic like charges *repel* and unlike charges *attract* one another.

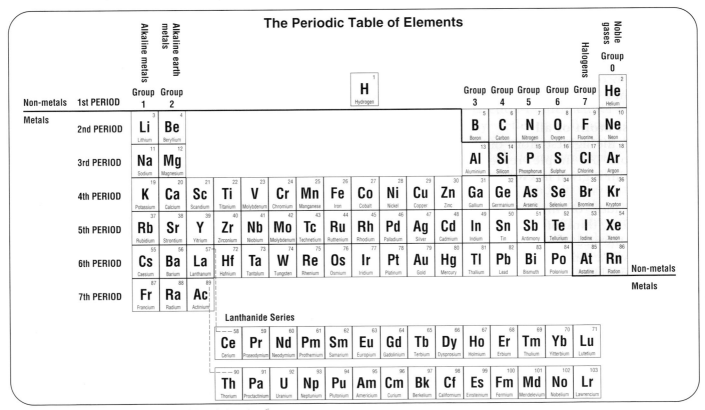

The Periodic Table of Elements

		Alkaline metals	Alkaline earth metals															Halogens	Noble gases
		Group 1	Group 2										Group 3	Group 4	Group 5	Group 6	Group 7		Group 0
Non-metals	1st PERIOD							1 **H** Hydrogen											2 **He** Helium
Metals	2nd PERIOD	3 **Li** Lithium	4 **Be** Beryllium											5 **B** Boron	6 **C** Carbon	7 **N** Nitrogen	8 **O** Oxygen	9 **F** Fluorine	10 **Ne** Neon
	3rd PERIOD	11 **Na** Sodium	12 **Mg** Magnesium											13 **Al** Aluminium	14 **Si** Silicon	15 **P** Phosphorus	16 **S** Sulphur	17 **Cl** Chlorine	18 **Ar** Argon
	4th PERIOD	19 **K** Potassium	20 **Ca** Calcium	21 **Sc** Scandium	22 **Ti** Titanium	23 **V** Molybdenum	24 **Cr** Chromium	25 **Mn** Manganese	26 **Fe** Iron	27 **Co** Cobalt	28 **Ni** Nickel	29 **Cu** Copper	30 **Zn** Zinc	31 **Ga** Gallium	32 **Ge** Germanium	33 **As** Arsenic	34 **Se** Selenium	35 **Br** Bromine	36 **Kr** Krypton
	5th PERIOD	37 **Rb** Rubidium	38 **Sr** Strontium	39 **Y** Yitrium	40 **Zr** Zirconium	41 **Nb** Niobium	42 **Mo** Molybdenum	43 **Tc** Technetium	44 **Ru** Ruthenium	45 **Rh** Rhodium	46 **Pd** Palladium	47 **Ag** Silver	48 **Cd** Cadmium	49 **In** Indium	50 **Sn** Tin	51 **Sb** Antimony	52 **Te** Tellurium	53 **I** Iodine	54 **Xe** Xenon
	6th PERIOD	55 **Cs** Caesium	56 **Ba** Barium	57 **La** Lanthanum	72 **Hf** Hafnium	73 **Ta** Tantalum	74 **W** Tungsten	75 **Re** Rhenium	76 **Os** Osmium	77 **Ir** Iridium	78 **Pt** Platinum	79 **Au** Gold	80 **Hg** Mercury	81 **Tl** Thallium	82 **Pb** Lead	83 **Bi** Bismuth	84 **Po** Polonium	85 **At** Astatine	86 **Rn** Radon
	7th PERIOD	87 **Fr** Francium	88 **Ra** Radium	89 **Ac** Actinium															

Non-metals

Metals

Lanthanide Series

58 **Ce** Cerium	59 **Pr** Praseodymium	60 **Nd** Neodymium	61 **Pm** Prothemium	62 **Sm** Samarium	63 **Eu** Europium	64 **Gd** Gadolinium	65 **Tb** Terbium	66 **Dy** Dysprosium	67 **Ho** Holmium	68 **Er** Erbium	69 **Tm** Thulium	70 **Yb** Ytterbium	71 **Lu** Lutetium
90 **Th** Thorium	91 **Pa** Proctactinium	92 **U** Uranium	93 **Np** Neptunium	94 **Pu** Plutonium	95 **Am** Americium	96 **Cm** Curium	97 **Bk** Berkelium	98 **Cf** Californium	99 **Es** Einsteinium	100 **Fm** Fermium	101 **Md** Mendelevium	102 **No** Nobelium	103 **Lr** Lawrencium

TABLE 1 *Periodic Table – Table of the elements.*

Electrons and shells

The atoms of all the different elements are different. We have seen that the hydrogen atom has only one proton. However, aluminium has 13, iron has 26, silver has 47, tin has 50, gold has 79, uranium has 92, etc. Atoms of different elements have different atomic structures. An atom may have up to seven shells, which may contain electrons. In an atom with more than two electrons, the first two electrons are contained in the first shell. Other electrons move into the second shell, and so on. A second shell can hold up to eight electrons. Therefore, the number of electrons in an atom determines its overall structure. In any atom, the first shell can hold two electrons, the second 8, and so on. *If n is the number of the shell, then $2n^2$ is the number of electrons it can hold.*

Electrons tend to fill up the shells nearest the nucleus first, and leave any *vacancies* (spaces for electrons) in the outer shells. It is the outer shell that is most responsible for the properties of an element.

ELEMENTS ARRANGED IN A TABLE

Information about the known elements is available in a special chart, which is known as the *periodic table of the elements*. As Boyle said, *each element has only one kind of atom.* Ninety-two of these elements are to be found in nature. The others have emerged as a result of work in the study of nuclear physics. These are known as *transuranic elements.* This is because of the association of nuclear physics with uranium. A periodic table of the elements is shown in **TABLE 1**.

This table provides us with a summary of information about each particular element, and also separates them into special groups. Elements are arranged according to their atomic numbers, thus demonstrating the *periodic law.* Dimitri Ivanovich Mendeleev, who was a professor of chemistry in the University of St Petersburg, published this law in 1869. Mendeleev stated that *the properties of the elements are in periodic dependence of their atomic weights.* It was he who arranged the elements in a table of the kind shown in **TABLE 1**. If you study the periodic table, you will see that elements with similar properties are grouped together, and therefore, from an element's position in the table, you can get a good idea of its properties. It is worth remembering that elements with the same numbers

of electrons in their outer shells tend to have similar chemical properties. The *valence* of an atom, or *how it combines with other atoms*, depends on the number of electrons in its outer shell. In periodic tables, vertical columns are called *groups*, and horizontal rows are known as *periods*. Elements in each vertical column, or group, have *similar properties* and have the *same number of electrons in their outer shells*. In general, elements in a periodic table are *less metallic* in groups nearer to the right hand side of the table.

HOW ATOMS COMBINE OR LINK UP WITH ONE ANOTHER

We have been discussing single atoms up to now, but, in fact, single atoms are exceptional in the make-up of matter. Helium, neon, argon, krypton, xenon and radon all belong to a chemical group known as the noble gases, which are inert in nature. The single atom is the building block, or structure, in each of these substances. We now briefly consider methods by which atoms combine, stick together, or *bond*, to form substances. We consider three types of bonding:

1 **Covalent bonding.**
2 **Ionic or electrovalent bonding.**
3 **Metallic bonding.**

Covalent bonding

This type of bonding, known as primary bonding, depends on the sharing of a pair of electrons by two or more atoms. Each of the two atoms supplies one of the electrons. Atoms within the molecule are held together by strong electrostatic forces. A good example of this type of bonding is demonstrated by the water molecule. In this case, two atoms of hydrogen combine with one atom of oxygen. As you can see in **FIGURE 4**, each hydrogen atom shares one of the oxygen atoms.

The molecule of water, as you can see, has a special shape. Another example of a covalently bonded substance is iron carbide (cementite) Fe_3C (three atoms of iron and one atom of carbon make one molecule of iron carbide). Cementite is discussed in Thermal Equilibrium Diagrams (page 39) and Heat Treatment (page 217). Covalent bonds are high strength bonds, broken only by high temperatures,

The covalent bond

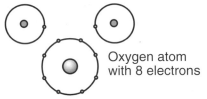

Hydrogen atom – 1 electron

Hydrogen atom – 1 electron

Oxygen atom with 8 electrons

Oxygen and hydrogen atoms before bonding

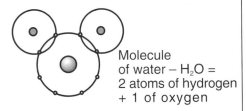

Molecule of water – H_2O = 2 atoms of hydrogen + 1 of oxygen

The water molecule formed by the atoms. Note how the electrons are *shared* to establish a covalent bond

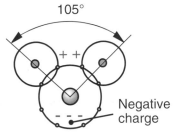

105°

+ +

Negative charge

The H_2O molecule has a fixed shape with a bond angle as shown. Because there are *unused* electrons at one end – this end has a negative charge, while the other end is positive

The positive ends attract the negative ends to join the molecules together

This electrostatic bond is weak and is known as *Van der Waal* bonding

and there are few electrons available to conduct electrical current or heat. Because this type of bond is so strong, atoms are not able to move when force is applied to a covalently bonded substance. This means that substances with covalent bonding are brittle like glass and have poor conductivity. However, the force which holds the molecules together is a weaker electrostatic force based on the weak attraction that molecules have towards one another. These weak electrostatic forces were first noted by the Dutch scientist Johannes Van der Waals when he was investigating the behaviour of gases. Van der Waals, who died in 1923, gave his name to the weak electrostatic forces between molecules or atoms, and others close by – hence the term *Van der Waals forces.*

The ionic or electrovalent bond

We have already seen that an atom can have the same number of electrons (negatively charged) and protons (positively charged), and that, in this state, the atom is electrically neutral. Some materials are made up of atoms which have electrons freely available, or weakly held. Such electrons can be easily knocked off or removed. Taking electrons from an atom upsets the balance, and causes the atom not to be neutral, but to *lose negativity* or become positive. The atom will now have more protons than electrons and is said to be *positively* charged – it has accepted electrons. On the other hand, if an electron is added to an atom, the atom will be *negatively* charged, because it has more electrons than protons – it has donated electrons. These *charged atoms* are called *ions*: the positive ones being *cations,* and the negative ones being *anions.*

In some chemical reactions electrons are transferred from one atom to another, producing cations (electrons missing), and anions (extra electrons). The formation of these charged ions is known as *ionisation.* When ionisation occurs, the cations and the anions are attracted and held together by the electrostatic forces between the positive cations and the negative anions. This is very similar to the first of the balloon experiments described earlier in this chapter. Atoms joined in this manner form an *ionic* bond, which is shown graphically in **FIGURE 5**.

FIGURE 4 *Covalent bond.*

The ionic bond

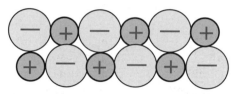

Anion

Cation

Electrostatic forces hold the ions together.
The large ions are negatively charged (Anions),
and the small ions are positively charged (Cations)

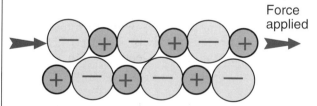

An ionic bonded lattice at rest – note how the
atoms are alternatively negative and positive,
because of electrostatic attraction

Force
applied

An ionic lattice with a *force applied* to try to
slide the top row in the direction of the arrows

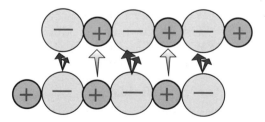

As the top row slides across, negative atoms
arrive on top of negative atoms and positive
atoms arrive on top of positive atoms.
The result is that the top row is *forced apart*
or *shattered* from the bottom row by
electrostatic repulsion

FIGURE 5 *Ionic bond.*

As you can see, the atoms in an ionic bond are
arranged in layers of alternate ions. The pattern
might be:

cation, anion, cation, anion, etc., on top of a layer of
anion, cation, anion, cation, etc.

The metallic bond

This type of bonding is most common in metallic
materials. **FIGURE 6** shows a simple representation
of the metallic bond, in which cations are bonded
together by electrons from the outer shells of other
atoms. This is made possible by the fact that metallic
materials lose electrons easily, to form cations. The
metallic bond, therefore, consists solely of cations
suspended in a mist, or cloud, of moving electrons.
Because these electrons are fairly mobile, they are
available to conduct heat, or electricity, and this, as a
general rule, makes metals good conductors of heat
and electricity.

Even if one layer of cations is forced to slip over the
layer below it, in a metallic bond, the bond will still
be maintained when the *slipped cations* take up their
new positions. This is a very important factor, in
that the bond is not destroyed, as might be expected.
A diagrammatic explanation is outlined in **FIGURE 7**.

THE PROPERTIES OF METALS AND NON-METALS

When we think of a metal, we usually think of a
solid, strong, heavy and sometimes shiny material.
However, this is not always true. For example, in the
periodic table, sodium is classified as a metal and it is
lighter than water. The chemical behaviour of a
metal tends to produce positive ions (cations) by
losing electrons from their atoms. Metals which
form cations most readily are said to be most
metallic. About three-quarters of the elements are
metals.

Properties of metals

The following is a list of some of the main
properties of metals. Metals are:

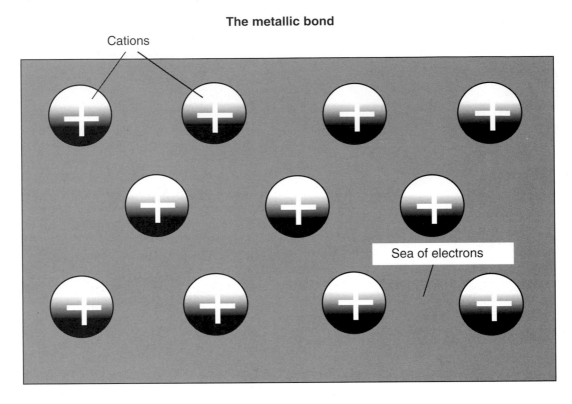

The metallic bond

Cations

Sea of electrons

The ions are positively charged (Cations) and are bonded together by a cloud, or sea of electrons, which are negatively charged

FIGURE 6 *Metallic bond.*

- **Good conductors of electricity and heat**
- **Malleable and ductile to some extent**
- **Electron donors which form oxides**
- **Capable of taking a shine**
- **Materials with high densities**
- **Materials with high tensile strength**
- **Solid except for mercury.**

As mentioned earlier, it is the large number of free-moving electrons in metals which enable them to conduct heat and electricity well.

Properties of non-metals

While metals produce positive ions (cations), non-metals produce negative ions (anions). Atoms of non-metals gain electrons, or are electron acceptors. Elements which attract electrons are electronegative.

Non-metals are normally:

- **Brittle**
- **Have no shine, i.e. have a dull surface**
- **Electron acceptors**
- **Bad conductors of heat and electricity. There are a few exceptions (e.g. carbon).**

Semi-metals or metalloids

These are elements which have some metallic properties, and some non-metallic properties. Some of them are *semiconductors*, e.g. silicon and germanium. These materials have been the foundation of the electronics industry. Silicon is used extensively for the production of many electronic components, including integrated circuits, which are generally known as *silicon chips*. **FIGURE 8** explains the

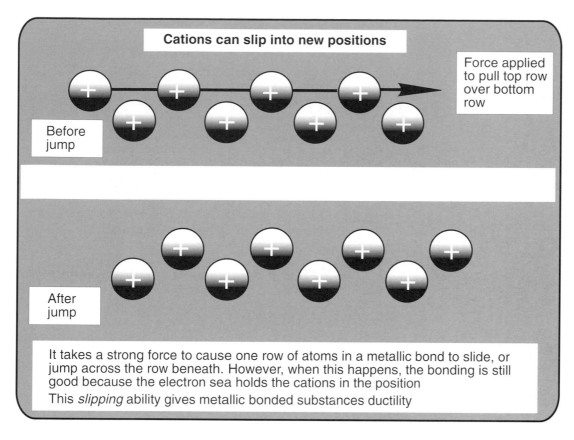

Cations can slip into new positions

Force applied to pull top row over bottom row

Before jump

After jump

It takes a strong force to cause one row of atoms in a metallic bond to slide, or jump across the row beneath. However, when this happens, the bonding is still good because the electron sea holds the cations in the position

This *slipping* ability gives metallic bonded substances ductility

FIGURE 7 *Slipped cations.*

difference between an N-type and a P-type semi-conductor. The two types joined together make up a PN-junction. This is the basis for the diode and the transistor. Electronics is a major industry in Ireland, but in California, where a major part of the industry developed, there was so much electronics work going on in one area, that it was named *Silicon Valley*. Much of the development in computing technology takes place in the United States, but component manufacture for computers seems to be centred in the East. Japan is recognised as a world leader in electronics products, while Taiwan, Hong Kong, and Korea are other strongholds. In Europe, Ireland holds a special place in the computer domain, with many specialist hardware and software companies having factories here.

THE STATES OF MATTER

Matter can exist in three forms which are solid, liquid and gas. The particular state that a substance is in at any time depends on its temperature and the pressure exerted on it. In general, substances are classified by the state they are in at ordinary ambient temperatures. For example, water is a liquid and lead is a solid. In a solid the atoms are held tightly together like bricks in a wall, and therefore solids have definite shapes. Liquids, on the other hand, have their atoms more loosely held together, and so, can change shape easily. Atoms in a gas have greater energy than the force holding the atoms together. Because of this, atoms in a gas move about at random. **FIGURE 9** is a representation of how atoms are arranged in solids, liquids and gases.

SOLIDIFYING METAL AND DENDRITIC GROWTH

In the study of metals, the change from solid to liquid, and vice-versa, is very important indeed. When a molten metal cools, a point is reached when the temperature approaches solidification temperature. At this time the metal starts to become solid.

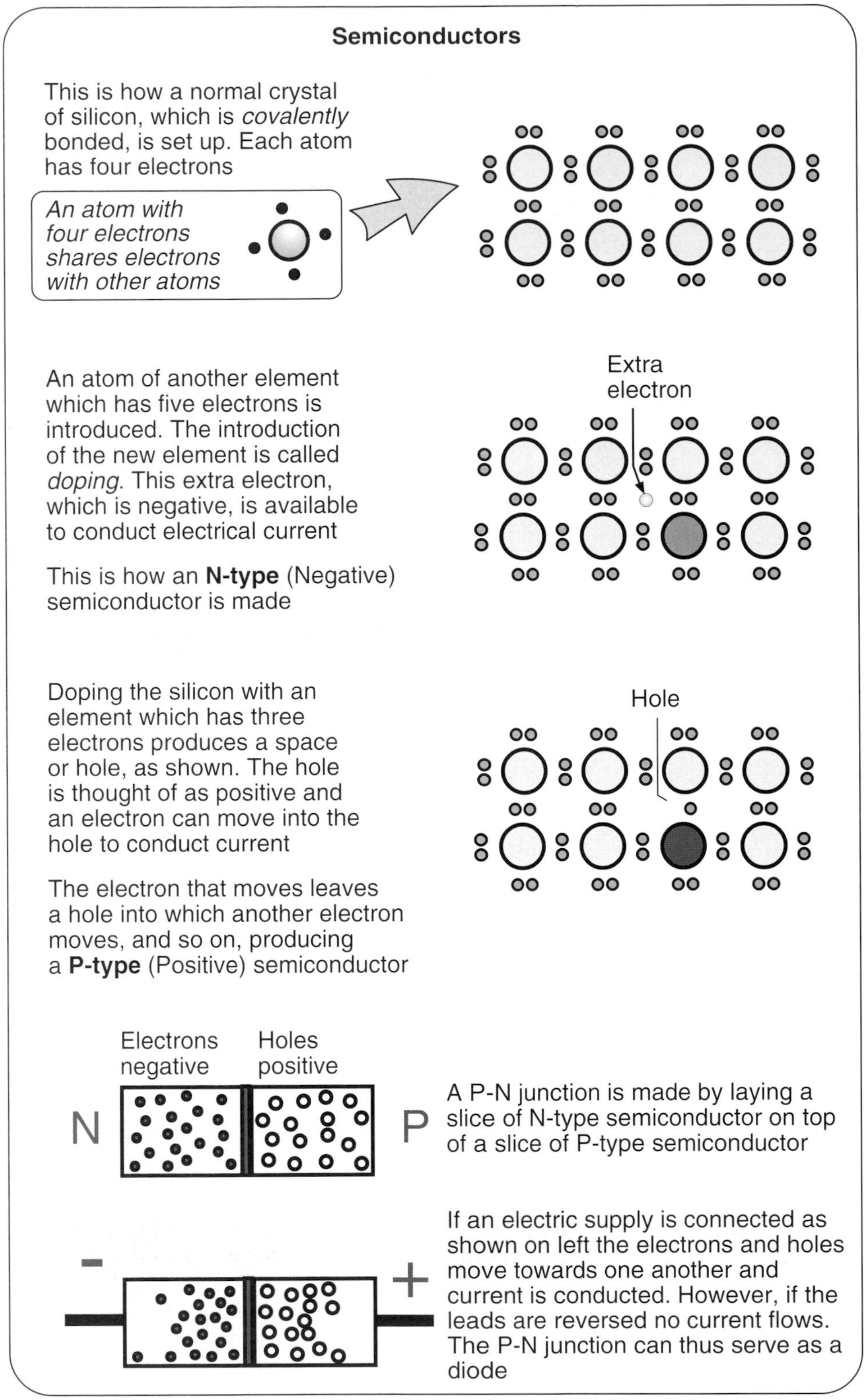

Semiconductors

This is how a normal crystal of silicon, which is *covalently* bonded, is set up. Each atom has four electrons

An atom with four electrons shares electrons with other atoms

An atom of another element which has five electrons is introduced. The introduction of the new element is called *doping*. This extra electron, which is negative, is available to conduct electrical current

This is how an **N-type** (Negative) semiconductor is made

Extra electron

Doping the silicon with an element which has three electrons produces a space or hole, as shown. The hole is thought of as positive and an electron can move into the hole to conduct current

The electron that moves leaves a hole into which another electron moves, and so on, producing a **P-type** (Positive) semiconductor

Hole

Electrons negative   Holes positive

N   P

A P-N junction is made by laying a slice of N-type semiconductor on top of a slice of P-type semiconductor

−   +

If an electric supply is connected as shown on left the electrons and holes move towards one another and current is conducted. However, if the leads are reversed no current flows. The P-N junction can thus serve as a diode

FIGURE 8   *Semiconductors.*

Small particles become solid first, and then these grow, as more metal solidifies around them. Solidification takes place in a kind of pattern, and separate grains, or crystals, are formed. The small solidifying particles grow branches, like trees, and eventually occupy a grain space. This type of growth is known as *dendritic growth*, and gets its name from the Greek for tree-like *dendrites* shown in **FIGURE 10**.

Crystal patterns and unit cells

In metals, atoms bond together in a pattern which is repeated over and over again, giving what is called a crystalline structure. Most metals crystallise with one of the following crystalline structures:

- **The body-centred cubic structure (BCC)**
- **The face-centred cubic structure (FCC)**
- **The close-packed hexagonal structure (CPH)**

The BCC structure has atoms arranged so that their centres are positioned on the corners of a cube, with one atom in the centre of the cube. In a metal with a BCC structure, the basic pattern repeats itself over and over again, to form a lattice, in a similar manner to the way in which bricks make up a wall. An important point to remember is that, while atomic models, or drawings of structures, are usually made of some type of balls, similar to **FIGURE 11** and **FIGURE 12**, this does not give a true

Structure of atoms in solids, liquids and gases

Definite shape

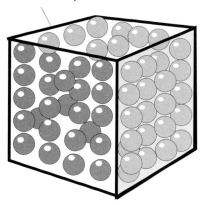 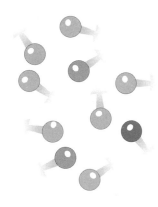

In solids, the atoms are bonded tightly into a particular shape and cannot move or vibrate very much. If the temperature of the solid is raised the particles can vibrate and move about more

In liquids, the atoms or molecules can move about easily, and can flow into a container and take up its shape

Gases have atoms or molecules that move about at random. As heat is applied particle speed increases and so does the volume of the gas concerned

FIGURE 9   Structure of atoms.

Dendritic growth

  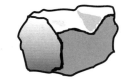

Solidification starts at one point and grows in a similar manner to a seed. As it grows, branches appear in the treelike structure. This process is known as dendritic growth, from the Greek word dendron for treelike

Branches reach out in all directions

Solid metal crystal formed as dendrite branches meet those from other crystals

FIGURE 10   Dendritic growth.

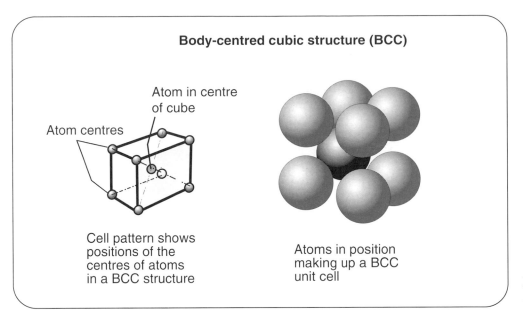

Body-centred cubic structure (BCC)

Atom in centre of cube

Atom centres

Cell pattern shows positions of the centres of atoms in a BCC structure

Atoms in position making up a BCC unit cell

FIGURE 11 *Body-centred cubic structure.*

representation of atoms. Remember that atoms are mostly empty space. However, the models help us to understand atomic structure and are very important.

The atom pattern which is repeated in a crystalline structure (e.g. BCC) is called a *unit cell*. Unit cells build up in all directions in a space lattice, within the crystal or grain. While grains in metals do not

have regular shapes, they are still *crystalline*. Every grain is made up in the same kind of pattern, which consists of a large number of unit cells.

Slip in BCC and FCC metals

If you study **FIGURE 11** and **FIGURE 12**, you should see that the atoms in an FCC unit cell are more tightly packed together than the atoms in a

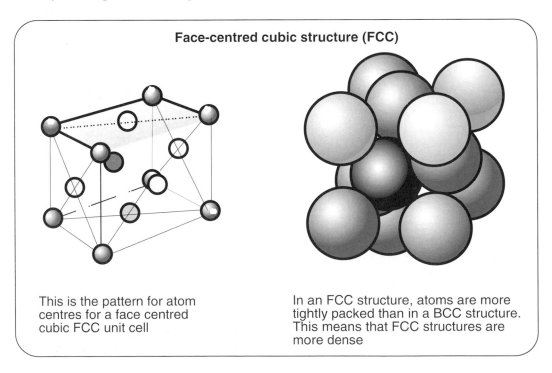

Face-centred cubic structure (FCC)

This is the pattern for atom centres for a face centred cubic FCC unit cell

In an FCC structure, atoms are more tightly packed than in a BCC structure. This means that FCC structures are more dense

FIGURE 12 *Face-centred cubic structure.*

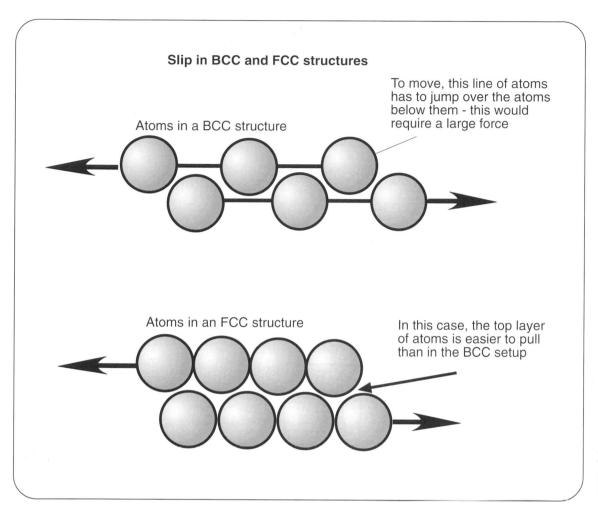

Slip in BCC and FCC structures

To move, this line of atoms has to jump over the atoms below them - this would require a large force

Atoms in a BCC structure

Atoms in an FCC structure

In this case, the top layer of atoms is easier to pull than in the BCC setup

FIGURE 13
Slip in BCC and FCC structures.

BCC unit cell. This fact can help to explain why different metals have different physical properties. When we discussed the metallic bond, reference was made to the slip. Slip means that part of a metal can slip over itself. Slip can take place in metals when they are subjected to certain shear-type forces. The occurrence of slip within BCC and FCC crystalline structures in metals is examined in **FIGURE 13**. If you study the diagrams, you should see that the chances of slip are much greater in an FCC-type metal. This is a very basic way of looking at slip, but it helps in the understanding of why FCC metals are ductile, while BCC metals are more brittle. The force required to overcome the metallic bond strength is greater than that often required to cause slip in crystals. We now examine why this is the case.

ATOMIC IMPERFECTIONS IN METALS

Crystalline structures in metals have many imperfections. Atoms are not always where they should be if the crystal structure was adhered to. In the perfect metal crystal, the atoms are arranged perfectly in all parts of the crystal. In actual fact, there may be missing atoms, too many atoms, atoms of an impurity in the structure, or perhaps distortions present within a crystal. Collectively, these faults or defects are known as *crystal defects*.

Line defects in crystals
If atoms are out of line in the grain body, or lattice, this is known as a line imperfection, or line defect. In the perfect set-up, the atoms might be in lines in the lattice. However, if half a line of atoms is

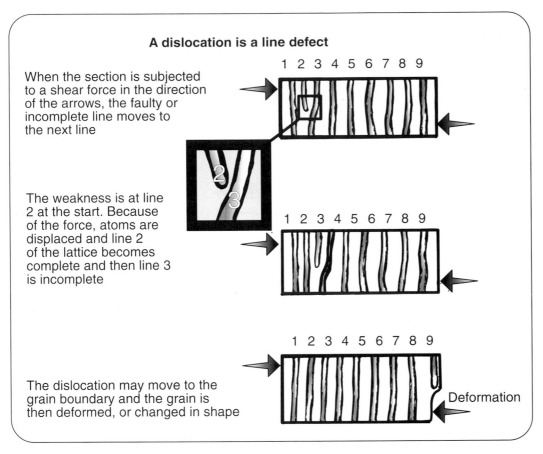

A dislocation is a line defect

When the section is subjected to a shear force in the direction of the arrows, the faulty or incomplete line moves to the next line

The weakness is at line 2 at the start. Because of the force, atoms are displaced and line 2 of the lattice becomes complete and then line 3 is incomplete

The dislocation may move to the grain boundary and the grain is then deformed, or changed in shape

Deformation

FIGURE 14 *Dislocation.*

misplaced, or missing altogether, then a line defect exists. Line defects are called *dislocations*, by virtue of the fact that lines or parts of lines of atoms are not where they should be, see **FIGURE 14**. Dislocations of this nature allow in effect grains to distort or slip under shear stress, as illustrated.

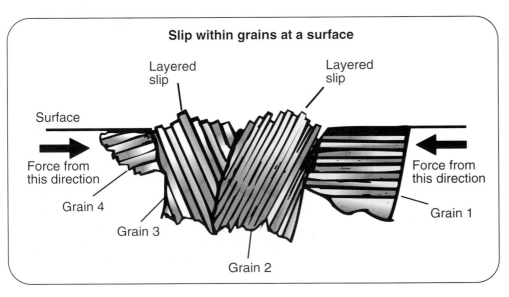

Slip within grains at a surface

Layered slip

Layered slip

Surface

Force from this direction

Force from this direction

Grain 4

Grain 1

Grain 3

Grain 2

FIGURE 15 *Slip within grains at a surface.*

Crystal point defects

In a perfectly formed crystal, the atoms are arranged in a pattern within the space lattice

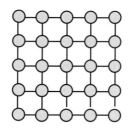

If there is an atom missing from the lattice, then the whole lattice is distorted as other atoms are forced into the vacant space

This is known as a *vacant site* defect

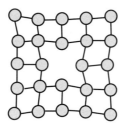

Substitute atom

In this case, a much larger atom has been substituted in the lattice and this distorts the structure

This is known as a *substitute defect*. Sometimes the substitute atom is smaller than the parent atoms

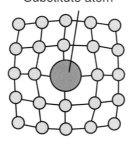

This diagram shows an interstitial crystal defect where a foreign atom has moved into a space between the atoms of the lattice

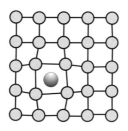

FIGURE 16 *Crystal point defects.*

The calculated theoretical strength of metals is seldom achieved. This is due to the fact that the crystal structures are not perfect because of defects. If a flat surface on a metal is finely polished, and then put under stress, as shown in **FIGURE 15**, slip occurs in some of the crystals in slightly different directions. This may be observed under a low powered microscope.

Slip in metals is largely due to the presence of dislocations, which may be of the type shown in **FIGURE 14**, or of a type known as *screw dislocation*. The distortion allowed by slip due to dislocations, lead to ductility in metals.

Point defects in metals

The top drawing in **FIGURE 16**, represents a perfect atomic pattern in a crystal of metal. This situation rarely exists. Sometimes an atom may be missing from a line or a row, and the lattice is placed under strain, as shown. When an atom is missing, a hole, or vacancy is left, which is why the defect is called a *vacant site defect.*

Another type of irregularity that occurs is when an atom of another element, which is not the same size as those in the lattice, is present. This substitute atom may be larger or smaller than the lattice atom. In either case, there is an amount of distortion. Known as a substitute defect, this defect is represented in the third drawing from the top, in **FIGURE 16**. In the case shown, a larger atom is in place.

If an atom from an impurity finds it way into a space, or interstice, in a lattice, the defect is called an *interstitial defect.*

Recrystallisation has been referred to on several occasions within this chapter. What is the importance of crystal size? If you look at **FIGURE 17**, you should see that large grains can lead to a weak material situation. In the top diagram, which has large grains, it is fairly obvious that the material is weak at the point indicated by the arrow. The structure with the small grains has more strength, and is nearly always desirable in components in service.

Crystal size and strength

In this section the grains or crystals are large and may result in a weak structure

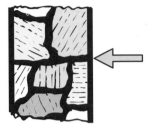

There is a line of weakness where the arrow points. Failure may occur along this line

The crystal size is much smaller in this sample which results in a more satisfactory structure

FIGURE 17 *Crystal size and strength.*

SUMMARY

An element has only one kind of atom.

It is impossible to destroy matter.

An atom has a nucleus, which is positively charged, and negatively charged electrons spinning around the nucleus.

Electrostatic force holds the nucleus and electrons together.

Hydrogen is the lightest of all atoms, and has only one proton and one electron.

There are three kinds of atomic bonds: the covalent bond, the ionic bond and the metallic bond.

In the covalent bond, electrons are shared by different atoms to form molecules.

Cations, which are positively charged, and anions, which are negatively charged, are attracted to one another, in the ionic bond.

The metallic bond consists of cations suspended in a mist of electrons.

Metals are electron donors, and form oxides.

Non-metals are normally electron acceptors.

Solidifying metals form dendrites which grow into crystals, or grains.

BCC structured metals are more brittle, and less ductile than FCC structured metals.

Metals should, theoretically, be stronger than they actually are in practice. This is because of defects within the crystalline structure.

There are two basic crystal defects in metals. These are line defects, and point defects.

Materials and their Properties

INTRODUCTION

A wide range of materials is put to use in the field of engineering technology in order to solve the problems that engineers have. There are many reasons why a particular material may be chosen for a particular application. Sometimes it is quite easy to understand why a certain choice is made but, on the other hand, it is not always so easy. Everyone comes into contact with a range of materials in everyday life. Most students are familiar with materials such as wood, concrete, metals, rubber, polymers (usually called plastics), fabrics, ceramics (e.g. most tea sets are ceramic), leather and stone.

FIGURE 1   *Wind machine. (Courtesy: the authors)*

A kitchen sink, hot food containers in a cafe, or a milk container in a dairy, may be manufactured from a stainless steel. Obvious reasons for the choice of this material for these applications are:

- **Stainless steel is easy to keep clean**
- **The metal has excellent resistance to corrosion.**

There may be other reasons for such a choice and we will consider these later in this chapter.

In the continuing development of machines which convert wind energy into electricity many different materials have been used to make the turbines. The turbine is the part with blades which is turned by the wind and is often mistakenly called a propeller. Surprisingly, laminated wood is an excellent material for making the blades, **FIGURE 1**. The reason may not be obvious. Any wind turbine has to withstand a great variety of forces from gentle winds to severe gusts. The blades of a wind machine in service naturally rotate, but also twist and bend when under strain. So the chosen material must be able to stand up to this type of action for many millions of times. Laminated timber is very good in this situation whereas metals tend to crack due to fatigue, a factor dealt with under 'material properties' below.

It would be expected that a polymer (plastic) material or a metal such as aluminium, would be more suitable for wind turbine blades. In fact, it has taken many years to develop a composite material that outperforms laminated wood for this application. The major disadvantage of wood is that it does not weather well.

WHAT ARE ENGINEERING MATERIALS?

Engineering materials are those materials which are used by all kinds of people in an ever-widening technological world. We can divide materials into two distinct sections. These are:

- **Metallic**
- **Non-metallic.**

The terms are fairly self-explanatory. Metallic materials include both ferrous metals and alloys, and non-ferrous metals and alloys. The new metallic composites and non-crystallised metals are also included here. Ferrous metals are those which contain iron. The important non-metallic materials are: polymers (plastic materials), ceramics, composites reinforced or strengthened materials, e.g. glass reinforced plastics (GRP) and carbon-carbon. Some of the further divisions into which materials fall are:

- **Metals and alloys**
- **Polymers or plastic materials**
- **Ceramics**
- **Composites.**

What influences the choice of material?

The obvious answer to this question is that the choice depends on the properties that a material possesses, as in the case of the kitchen sink or the turbine blade. However, there are other factors, such as cost and availability, which must also be taken into consideration.

MATERIAL PROPERTIES

In industry, there is a long list of material properties which are used to define the characteristics of a material. For simple, straightforward applications, a material may only have to fulfil a small number of requirements. However, for very complex applications, such as those in the aircraft and aerospace industries, the material properties required are many, and thus the choice of materials is reduced.

Some of the commonly used named properties and terms are:

- **Tensile strength**
- **Compressive strength**
- **Shear strength**
- **Torsional strength**
- **Fatigue strength**

- **Creep**
- **Hardness**
- **Toughness**
- **Ductility**
- **Density**
- **Elasticity**
- **Proof stress**
- **Electrical conductivity**
- **Thermal conductivity**
- **Thermal expansion**
- **Magnetic characteristics**
- **Resistance to corrosion**
- **Colour**
- **Suitability for a manufacturing process**
- **Comparative price per kg**
- **Machinability**
- **Melting point.**

Some specialised industries have developed their own material property specifications.

Some properties and terms defined

Tensile strength. This is the maximum stretching force that a material can withstand before it breaks. Various strengths and stresses are expressed in newtons per mm^2, **FIGURE 2**.

Shear strength is the strength that a material has, up to the point when one part, or layer, of material is forced to slide over the next part, or layer.

Hardness allows a metal to resist scratching and indentation. The hardness of a metal is determined by a hardness test. The hardness of a metal depends on the state in which it is, e.g. annealed or hardened.

Toughness is the ability of a metal to withstand a shock load or impact. Brittle metals have poor toughness, e.g. cast iron. Impact or notched bar testing is used to determine toughness. Tough materials do not break easily when twisted or bent.

Ductility is the property which allows a metal to be drawn out by a tensile force without fracturing. Ductility is essential in metals used for drawing and pressing. Ductility is determined by a tensile test.

Malleability is the property which allows a metal to be hammered or rolled into a thin sheet without fracturing. Malleability increases in most metals

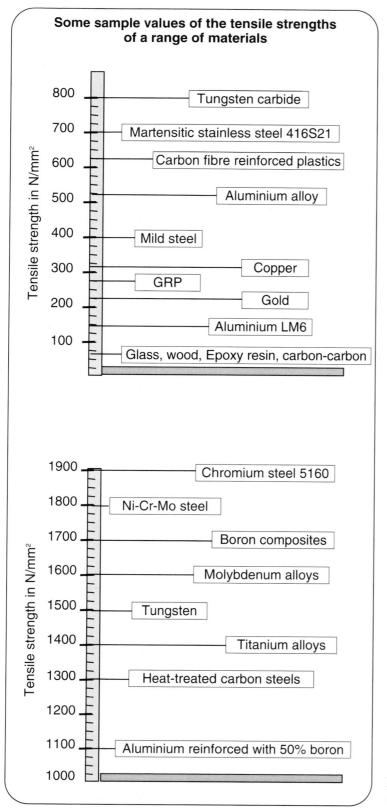

Some sample values of the tensile strengths of a range of materials

when they are heated. This is why steel is hot rolled.

Density is the mass per unit volume, e.g. how many kilograms does a cubic metre of the material weigh?

Fatigue strength. If a material is subjected to a changing load, as the wings of an aircraft are when the aircraft is flying, eventually, the material will break after a certain number of *loadings*. Fatigue strength is the actual force acting in the loading, and the number of times, or cycles, the material can withstand the changing load situation before it breaks. (See fatigue testing).

Creep. When a material is subjected to a constant load or force over a period of time it may stretch particularly at high temperatures.

Elasticity is the tendency of a material to return to its original shape after it has been deformed. Some materials have great elasticity (e.g. rubber), but some have little (e.g. concrete).

Electrical conductivity is a measure of how well electricity will flow through the material. For a material to have good electrical conductivity it must have low resistance. Electrical resistance is measured in ohms. Some materials are poor conductors and so have a high resistance – these are called insulators (e.g. polythene, rubber, ceramics). Current research indicates that it is possible to make certain polymers with good electrical conductivity. For this purpose, short chain molecules are required as opposed to the normal long chain molecules associated with polymers.

Thermal conductivity is a measure of how well heat will flow though a material. The letter k was used to denote this property but this has been changed recently. Now it is represented by λ, which is the Greek letter *lambda*.

FIGURE 2 *Chart of different tensile strengths of some materials.*

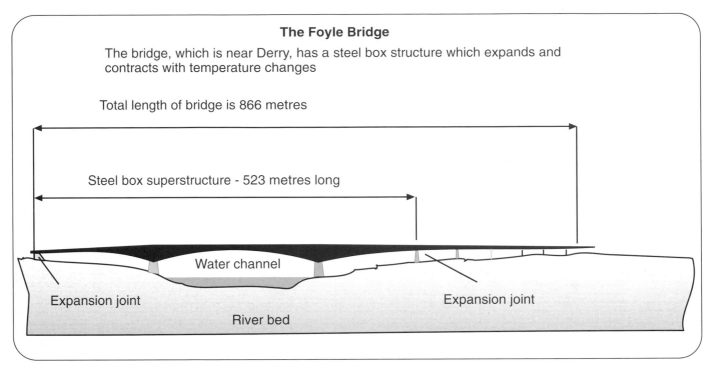

The Foyle Bridge

The bridge, which is near Derry, has a steel box structure which expands and contracts with temperature changes

Total length of bridge is 866 metres

Steel box superstructure - 523 metres long

Water channel

Expansion joint

Expansion joint

River bed

FIGURE 3 *Foyle Bridge.*

Copper and aluminium are examples of materials with good thermal conductivity. These are used to make saucepans, in which it is important that the heat is conducted quickly. Materials which do not conduct heat well, are called *thermal insulators*. Thermal insulation is used to slow down heat loss in homes (e.g. fibre glass in roof spaces, plastic foams in cavity walls). Heat always flows from hot to cold.

Thermal expansion occurs when heat causes materials to expand. Components in internal combustion engines, such as spark ignition (petrol/gas, etc.) and compression ignition (diesel) engines are subjected to temperature changes which cause expansion. Engineers calculate the amount that each component will expand under normal running conditions and make suitable allowances for the expansion. The fractional change in length per unit rise in temperature, is called the *coefficient of linear expansion*.

Look at the information about the Foyle Bridge, in **FIGURE 3** and **FIGURE 4**. You should see that the steel box superstructure is 523 metres long. Think

about the temperature range within which the bridge has to work. In winter, temperature may fall to −4°C, and in the summer, the temperature may rise to 26°C. These figures would give a working range of 30°C. However, the road surface of the bridge, as well as other surfaces, absorb energy from the sun's rays. On a hot summer's day, the amount of energy available for absorption, may be in the region of 200 W/m², which may raise the bridge temperature to 50 or 60°C. The design engineer must work out all these factors before a bridge is designed, and if a mistake is made, the bridge in question may fail.

Allowing for a safety temperature margin, we can suppose that the temperature range of the steel is 100°C. How much combined room for expansion should have been left in the expansion joints?

The coefficient of expansion of the steel is 13.3 x 10^{-6}/°C. This means that one metre of steel expands by 13.3 x 10^{-6} metres for each rise in temperature of 1°C. If the temperature falls, steel contracts by the same amount.

FIGURE 4 *The Foyle Bridge. Insert photograph shows the expansion joint. As the bridge expands the gaps close. (Courtesy: the authors)*

Solution:

Length of steel section	= 523 metres
Change in temperature	= 100°C
Change in length (expansion)	= 13.3 x 10⁻⁶ x 523 x 100 m
	= 695590/1000000 m
	= **0.696 m or 696 mm**

Allowances must be made for thermal expansion in cases such as:

- **Steel bridge structures**
- **Joints in railway lines**
- **Concrete walls and paths**
- **Valve clearances in IC engines.**

Specific heat capacity. This is the amount of heat in joules that is needed to raise one kilogram of the material by 1°C. Copper has specific heat capacity of 0.39 kJ/kg/°C, while for water, the value is 4.2 kJ/kg/°C. (Note: specific refers to *1 unit* of mass raised by *1 unit* of temperature).

SUMMARY

Materials are broadly divided into: metallic materials and non-metallic materials.

The choice of a material for a particular application depends on its properties and on other factors such as price and availability.

The strength of the material, is one of the main considerations involved in the selection process. Tensile, compressive and shear are some of the types of stresses which materials experience in service.

Thermal expansion can be a major problem in large structures, and an allowance for such expansion must be incorporated in the basic design.

Metallurgy

INTRODUCTION

Metallurgy is generally taken to mean: *the extraction of metals from their various ores, the heat treatment of metals and the production of alloys.*

This chapter examines the methods of mining and extraction that are used in the present day to produce the metals required by industry, technology and science. Heat Treatment (page 217) is a separate chapter, and the formation of alloys is considered in the chapter on Thermal Equilibrium Diagrams. (page 39)

There was a time when lumps of metals such as copper, silver and gold could be found more or less lying on the ground for the picking up. Metals found in this way are known as *native metals.* It was during the Neolithic or New Stone Age that the transition from the use of stone, bone, horn, wood, etc., to the use of metals took place. Ireland had at that time (around 2000 BC) established an export trade in special porcellanite axes, with various parts of Europe. Later, during Ireland's 'El Dorado' period, traders came to buy golden objects because Ireland was probably the richest source of gold and gold artefacts in the western hemisphere.

METAL NUGGETS

In the past, native metals were found in lumps, or nuggets, and then hammered roughly into shape for use as crude tools. Gold and silver were not of much use, because of their softness, which left them unsuitable for cutting tools. However, early experimenters soon found out that when copper is hammered, it becomes harder, and so copper became the first really useful metal. As far as we can tell, it was about 5500 years ago, that a very hard form of copper was discovered. It was smelted from a copper ore, which contained some tin and, of course, was what we now call *bronze.*

The Irish contribution

Even in those early times, Ireland was a land with highly skilled metalworkers, who were also artists. These skilled smiths were the custodians of the Celtic art which flourished in Ireland and Britain for centuries. Ireland, as far as we can tell, was not invaded by the Romans, and continued to develop its own metalworking techniques and styles. These included enamelling and repoussé work of the highest standards. Many articles made by gifted Irish metalworkers can be seen in museums all over Europe. Others have been lost forever, as was reported in Wakeman's survey of 1889, when he wrote: "tons of early bronzes, consisting of arms, implements, and objects of personal decoration, dug up from our bogs, or dredged from river courses or lochs, in all parts of Ireland, were consigned to the furnaces of native or British brass-founders, where they were simply melted down as old metal – their real value not being recognised".

Irish metalwork has not been given the publicity it deserves. The authors, like many others, have often heard Ireland described as a land of saints and scholars, but seldom as a land of metalworkers. We wonder why the Irish people are slow to acclaim the tremendous contribution to both Irish and European development made by their ancestral smiths. Fortunately, many beautiful pieces of Irish metalwork are preserved in the National Museum, in Dublin, and in other museums around the world. In fact, pride of place is given to gold, silver and bronze artefacts in the Irish National Museum.

The attraction of gold

No metal has attracted humans as much as gold, which, as stated earlier, can be found as gold nuggets. It was the finding of such nuggets by a man called George Carmack, in 1896, that started the Klondyke gold rush in Alaska, now part of the United States of

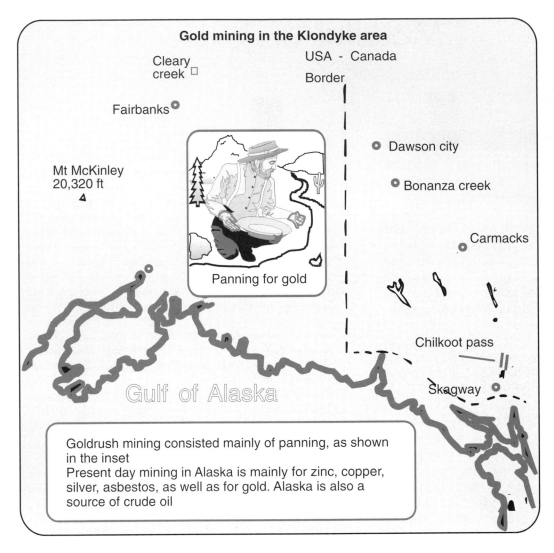

Gold mining in the Klondyke area

Cleary creek □

USA - Canada Border

Fairbanks ○

Dawson city ○

Mt McKinley 20,320 ft ▲

Bonanza creek ○

Panning for gold

Carmacks ○

Chilkoot pass

Gulf of Alaska

Skagway

Goldrush mining consisted mainly of panning, as shown in the inset
Present day mining in Alaska is mainly for zinc, copper, silver, asbestos, as well as for gold. Alaska is also a source of crude oil

FIGURE 1 *Gold mining in Alaska.*

America. The Russians had already found gold in those parts around about twenty years earlier, but the stampede of around 30,000 people only began after Carmack lodged his claim. Many men left Ireland and Britain to make their fortune in Nome, Fairbanks, or Cleary Creek. Some did, but some perished on the way over Chilkoot Pass, and many others found only disappointment (**FIGURE 1**).

SIMPLE MINING METHODS

Mining for gold in the goldrush days was simple. Gold dust was *panned* from streams and rivers in a frying-pan-like metal dish. Miners were sometimes referred to as *panhandlers*. Sluices were used along river banks to wash out the gold. Shaking sluices, were the next development to improve the separation process. Many of the crude systems, which were developed by these miners, who came from many countries of the world, later became standard mining methods. It was during the modification of a water-driven jolting box, that an Englishman named Lester Pelton, accidentally invented the now famous *pelton turbine* (**FIGURE 2**). Different forms of mining, using water to separate the metal, or ore, from the soil, were tried. *Hydraulic mining* had its beginnings at this time, when miners

FIGURE 2 *A 260,000 kW Pelton turbine. Jets of water at high pressure strike the specially shaped buckets, and the rotating turbine drives a generator. (Courtesy: Sulzer Escher Wyss, Switzerland)*

started pumping water through hoses directed at gravel banks, to make it easier to find the gold.

METALLIC MINERALS

Generally speaking, an ore is a solid, naturally-occurring mineral from which at least one metal can be extracted. Of course the extraction must be economic. In other words, somebody must be able to make a profit from the whole business! Before we consider the mining of the ores, and the extraction

of the metals from them, we will take a brief look at solid *metallic minerals*.

Metallic minerals come from the rocks in the earth's surface and are solid substances. The composition of a mineral is expressed using a chemical formula, because a mineral is a *chemical compound*. Haematite (or hematite) is an example of a mineral. Its chemical formula is Fe_2O_3 and it is the most important ore of iron. It is a compound of iron and oxygen. Compounds always form in a ratio, which is set by the chemical nature of the elements. Fe_2O_3 has two atoms of Fe (iron), and three atoms of O (oxygen).

The two parts of a compound

There are two parts in a chemical compound. The first part which is usually metal, for example, Fe_2 in Fe_2O_3, is positively charged (cation). The second part is negatively charged (anion). Because the charges balance one another, the compound remains neutral. Cations and anions are dealt with in detail under Structure of Materials (page 3). *(Remember that a cation is positive – the t has a plus on top.)*

MINING AND MINING METHODS

Ores are mined using five basic types of mining, which are considered in this section.

Open cast mining

This system is used to gather ores where they lie near to the surface. Usually the ore is in fairly horizontal layers, and top soil can be removed by giant excavating machinery. Sometimes, jets of water are used to wash away other deposits in order to uncover beds of ore. This is a modern version of the early goldminers' method. It is known as 'hydraulic mining' (**FIGURE 3**).

Underground mining

Underground mining, **FIGURE 5**, is well-known because of its association with coal mining. The methods used for metal ore mining are similar to those used in coal mining. Where the minerals are deep beneath the surface, vertical shafts are sunk, and tunnels are used to reach the ores. In many cases, the ore is crushed after blasting, before it is brought to the surface.

Underground mining is the most expensive method of mining. Huge expense is incurred in any underground mining operation, and therefore, the

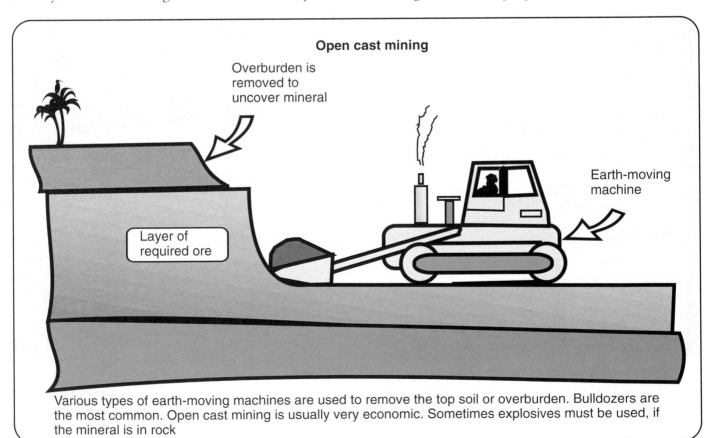

Open cast mining

Overburden is removed to uncover mineral

Layer of required ore

Earth-moving machine

Various types of earth-moving machines are used to remove the top soil or overburden. Bulldozers are the most common. Open cast mining is usually very economic. Sometimes explosives must be used, if the mineral is in rock

FIGURE 3   *Open cast mining.*

FIGURE 4 *The largest stacker in the world operating in an open cast mine. Weighing 5,300 tonnes, the stacker is 180 metres long, 65 metres high and is capable of moving 240,000 cubic metres of material each day – this is the equivalent of the volume of almost 1,000 single-storey houses.*
(Courtesy: Asea Brown Boveri)

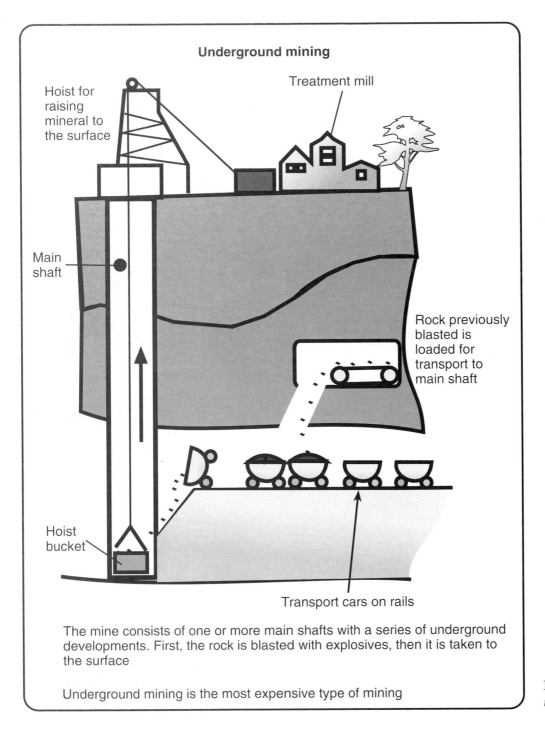

Underground mining

Hoist for raising mineral to the surface

Treatment mill

Main shaft

Rock previously blasted is loaded for transport to main shaft

Hoist bucket

Transport cars on rails

The mine consists of one or more main shafts with a series of underground developments. First, the rock is blasted with explosives, then it is taken to the surface

Underground mining is the most expensive type of mining

FIGURE 5 *Underground mining.*

mining company must be certain that what it is looking for is to be found in sufficient quantities to make it worthwhile. Ore-bearing rock is first blasted by explosives, brought to the shaft, and then hauled to the surface for treatment.

Open pit mining
Used where an ore-bearing rock is deep and wide. An advantage here is that a lot of mechanisation is possible. The ore-bearing rock is drilled and blasted, then carried away by huge lorries (**FIGURE 6**).

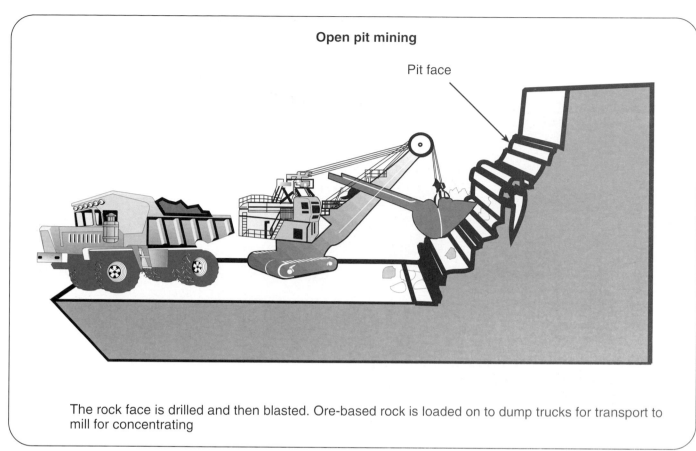

Open pit mining

Pit face

The rock face is drilled and then blasted. Ore-based rock is loaded on to dump trucks for transport to mill for concentrating

FIGURE 6   *Open pit mining.*

Open pit mining is similar to *quarrying*. Copper is mined in Peru by open pit mining. One such mine is near Lima, at Cuajone. You can see an open pit mine in **FIGURE 7**.

The ore at Cuajone contains 1% copper which is very high for this type of deposit, and modern mining techniques make mining in such a remote region an economic proposition. The copper is refined by Empresa Minera del Peru in its electrolytic refinery.

Dredging in shallow water

Dredging is the method used when the ore deposits lie under water (**FIGURE 8**). The dredge is a purpose-built ship, which has a chain and bucket elevator. A dredger can be seen in **FIGURE 9**. The over burden (layer above ore) is first stripped, and then the ore is brought on board the dredge. Ore and waste are separated on board, and the waste is deposited in a previously mined area. Dredgers are served by small to medium sized carriers, which bring the ore ashore for further processing.

Solution mining

This method is used to recover minerals such as magnesium salts, or any mineral which will dissolve freely in water. Oil-drilling rigs are used to drill into the mineral-bearing area (**FIGURE 10**). Water, which is pumped down one pipe, dissolves the mineral involved, and the solution is taken up a second pipe to the surface for treatment. The installation of the treatment works on the surface is obviously expensive, and only large deposits of minerals make this type of mining feasible.

Ore concentration or ore dressing

Before sending ores for extraction processing, it is

FIGURE 7 *This picture shows how the pit is created. Each track is wide enough for a large dump truck. The mine is in Peru, near Lima, and produces copper. Only 1% copper is contained in the rock, but this is considered a very high content for an open pit mine. (Courtesy: Shell UK)*

necessary to remove as much waste as possible. In this way, the *concentration* of the desired mineral is increased (the percentage of useful mineral in each tonne will be higher). The economics here are fairly simple. Mined ore has to be transported to wherever the treatment plant is. This may mean a journey of hundreds, or even thousands of kilometres. Transport costs depend on the number of tonnes carried, and the distance involved. It is silly and uneconomic, to transport *waste*. This is why the mining companies try to remove as much waste as possible at the point of mining.

To remove the waste, the ore is:

1 Crushed.
2 Ground.
3 Concentrated.

Gravity or wet mill concentration

Some ores are much heavier than the waste and this fact is used in separation. A type of *jolting box* is used, in which the particles are kept wet. The shaking motion causes the minerals of different specific gravities, to separate into layers. Generally, this process is used before flotation.

Flotation

This method is often used to separate two ores contained in a mixture (**FIGURE 11**). Lead ore, known as *galena* (PbS), is nearly always mined with zinc ore, called *zinc blende* (ZnS), and these two can be separated by flotation. The ore mixture, which consists of extremely fine particles, is swirled around in large tanks. Air is blown through the ore and chemical flotation agents are added which produce a froth. One result of all this, is that the galena sinks to the bottom, while the zinc blende, which sticks to the froth, floats to the surface, where it is skimmed off with a skimmer. Special selective collecting agents can be added to flotation baths, which give

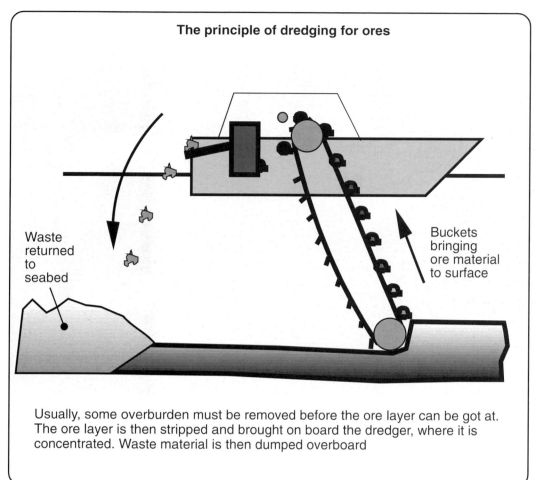

The principle of dredging for ores

Waste returned to seabed

Buckets bringing ore material to surface

Usually, some overburden must be removed before the ore layer can be got at. The ore layer is then stripped and brought on board the dredger, where it is concentrated. Waste material is then dumped overboard

FIGURE 8 *Dredging.*

particular ores a surface treatment that allows the ore particles to stick to the froth bubbles.

Magnetic separation
If the ore is magnetic, then it can be separated from the waste by this method (**FIGURE 12**). Finely-ground crude ore is passed over a rotating drum, which has a magnet inside it. The ore is held on the drum until after the waste has fallen off and then it is released or scraped off by a scraper.

Amalgamation
Mention has been made earlier in the chapter of gold mining in Alaska. Amalgamation is a modern process, used extensively in the recovery of gold from gold-bearing rock or sand. Although early attempts at this process, such as the *MacArthur-Forrest*

process, used solutions of potassium cyanide, the modern approach is to use mercury. It is interesting to note that the process was developed to recover gold and silver from *tailings*. (Tailings is the name given to the heaps of mining waste left at mines.)

First, the rock or sand is crushed. The resulting fine particles are mixed with a little mercury, which sticks to the surface of the gold, and not to the waste. Copper plates in the container *collect* all the coated particles because the mercury sticks onto copper readily. The waste is then removed by washing with water. The mercury is recovered by distilling and the gold is purified.

Metal extraction
We have discussed the mining of ores and the various methods of concentrating them. Now, we

FIGURE 9 *This dredger dredges for tin ore off the coast of Indonesia. Chutes are to be seen fore and aft, which are used to convey concentrated ore to ore carriers, and to return the waste to the sea. (Courtesy: Shell UK)*

come to the part where we look at how the metals are extracted from the concentrates.

The main headings under which metal extraction can be examined are:

- **Pyrometallurgical methods**
- **Thermoelectrolytic or electrometallurgy methods**
- **Hydrometallurgical method.**

Pyrometallurgy

Pyrometallurgical methods, as the name implies, involves heat. It is used mainly where the metal ore occurs as an oxide, such as is the case with iron or tin. The general set-up is that the ore is mixed with a reducing agent (in the case of iron, coke is used), and a flux. When the mixture is heated in a furnace, molten metal, slag and gas are produced. Production of metal by pyrometallurgy can be represented by:

Ore + reducing agent + flux = metal + slag + waste

Hydrometallurgy

In this method of metal extraction, ore is dissolved in a solvent, to make a solution, in a process known as *leaching*. Leaching is done in special tanks, which are fitted with agitators or stirrers, to help to form the solution. Solutions are treated by electrolysis, which results in the separation of the metal. There are several forms of electrolysis which may be used.

Thermo-electrometallurgy

This method is used to extract metals from fused mineral mixtures, or from salt mixtures. Aluminium is produced by this method, as is magnesium. A metal which has a special use in spacecraft, beryllium, is also produced in this way. Beryllium is used to get rid of the heat of re-entry, through the atmosphere, by spacecraft. These metals cannot be produced by pyrometallurgy or by hydrometallurgy. A major disadvantage of the electrolytic processes, is that huge amounts of electricity are required. It is, therefore, normal to find this production method

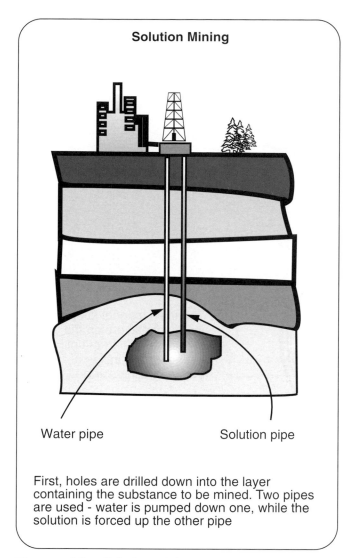

Solution Mining

Water pipe

Solution pipe

First, holes are drilled down into the layer containing the substance to be mined. Two pipes are used - water is pumped down one, while the solution is forced up the other pipe

FIGURE 10 *Solution mining.*

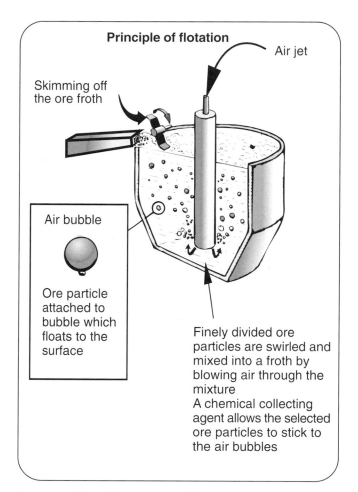

Principle of flotation

Air jet

Skimming off the ore froth

Air bubble

Ore particle attached to bubble which floats to the surface

Finely divided ore particles are swirled and mixed into a froth by blowing air through the mixture
A chemical collecting agent allows the selected ore particles to stick to the air bubbles

FIGURE 11 *The principle of flotation.*

very near to a cheap supply of electricity. The cheapest form of usable electricity, in these times, is hydroelectricity, generated by damming suitable water supplies, and arranging the flow of water, so that turbines are turned which drive generators. Most electrolytic refineries are, in fact, situated near to large hydro stations.

The electrolysis process is similar to electroplating, which is dealt with under Corrosion (page 229). In the case of aluminium, the *electrolyte* is molten *alumina* (Al_2O_3) mixed with cryolite.

Carbon rods are made the *anodes*, and the walls and bottom of the container are made the *cathode* (see Non-Ferrous Metals, page 99). Due to the Direct Current (DC) electricity passing through the electrolyte, the oxygen from the Al_2O_3 (i.e. the O_3 part) is deposited at the anodes and the aluminium collects at the cathode.

Blister copper is refined (made purer) by electrolysis. In this case, the blister copper is the anode and pure copper is deposited at the cathode (see production of copper). During the electrolysis, the cathode is attached to the negative, and the anode is attached to the positive of the DC supply of current. At the cathode, positive metal ions accept electrons, and therefore deposit metal. Ions at the anode lose

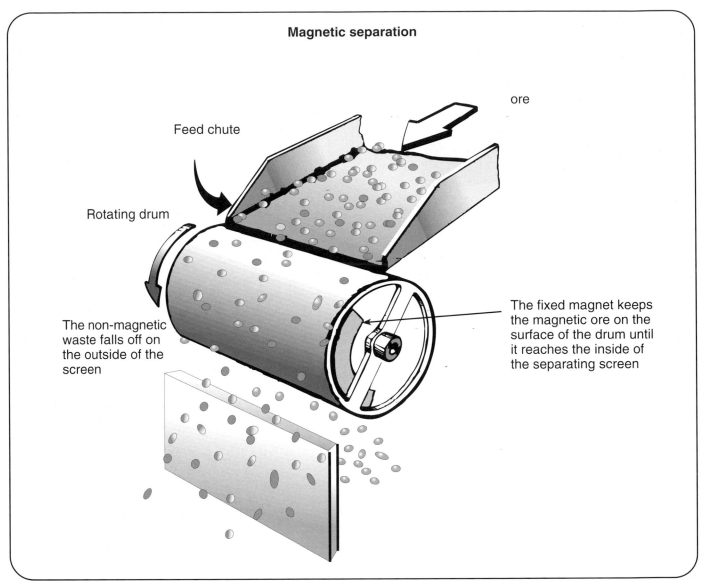

Magnetic separation

ore

Feed chute

Rotating drum

The non-magnetic waste falls off on the outside of the screen

The fixed magnet keeps the magnetic ore on the surface of the drum until it reaches the inside of the separating screen

FIGURE 12   *Magnetic separation.*

electrons and become gas. Cations move towards the cathode. The gaining of electrons by ions at the cathode is reduction, while the losing of electrons by ions at the anode is oxidation. In batteries the anode supplies the electrons to the circuit, and is marked as the negative terminal.

SMELTING AND REFINING

The ore of a metal, which, as we have seen, is a two-part chemical compound, must be processed to isolate the metal. Most ores are chemically linked to oxygen or sulphur. Different methods of processing ores are used, depending on the metal being extracted. An outline of the methods has already been given.

Reduction
Many metals are extracted from their ores by *reduction*. (Reduction and oxidation were mentioned briefly under electrometallurgy.) Reduction is the effective removal of oxygen from a chemical compound. In the case of iron, the ore, *haematite,*

which has the chemical formula, Fe_2O_3 is reduced to iron as follows:

$$Fe_2O_3 + 3C = 2Fe + 3CO$$

What this very simple representation shows, is that the oxygen (O_3) part of the ore (Fe_2O_3), combined with the reducing agent, coke (C), to produce carbon monoxide. Basically, this has the effect of isolating the iron. In actual fact, the reduction of iron is much more complicated, but this simple version tends to demonstrate the removal of oxygen. The oxygen from the iron ore (Fe_2O_3), is the O_3 part. Carbon, in the form of coke, is called the *reducing agent*, because it takes the oxygen from the ore.

Oxidation, on the other hand, can be thought of as the gaining of oxygen, as in the case of rusting of iron, where oxygen combines with the iron to form rust. Chemically, a substance is *reduced* if it gains electrons, and is *oxidised* if it loses electrons. In this sense, iron is oxidised if it combines with any substance, that will accept its electrons.

Reduction–oxidation

Look again at the reduction of iron, and you will notice that, while the iron was reduced (lost oxygen – gained electrons), the carbon was oxidised (lost electrons – became carbon monoxide). The tendency of any *element* to *reduce* or *oxidise* can be measured, and set out in a table almost like the electrochemical series referred to in Corrosion (page 229).

In the reduction, or the oxidation case, the *potential* is called the *redox potential*, and it is also measured in volts. The word *redox* is formed from the first three letters of the word *reduction*, and the first two letters of the word *oxidation*. Redox reactions occur in electrolysis.

SUMMARY

Metallurgy is the extraction of metals from ores, the heat treatment of metals, and knowledge about alloys.
Panning is a simple form of mining, using a basin, or pan, to wash gravel to isolate metal nuggets. Panning was used extensively by miners in the various early gold rushes.

Metallic minerals are mainly two-part compounds. Fe_2O_3 is an example.
Open cast mining is used to mine for ores near the surface. Excavators are used to remove the soil, in order to get at the ore.
Underground mining is very expensive. Sufficient quantities of the ore must be present in the mine to make mining worthwhile.
Open pit mining. Similar to quarrying, open pit mining is used to mine copper ore. For this type of mining, the ore-bearing rock is wide and deep, and starts near the surface.
Dredging is a mining process used to recover ores beneath shallow waters. A special ship, with buckets on a large chain lifts the material from the bottom, and brings it on board for treatment.
Solution mining involves the pumping of water down a pipe into water soluble mineral-bearing rock, and extracting the element from the recovered solution.
Ore concentration is the removal of as much of the waste as possible by crushing and separating. The idea is to prevent large amounts of waste being transported. Transport costs are high.
Flotation is a separation process, which uses chemical flotation agents to make a froth that brings metal particles to the surface of a bath, where the froth is skimmed off.
Magnetic separation is suitable when the metal bearing ore can be attracted by a magnet.
Amalgamation makes use of mercury to gather together particles of metal, usually gold. The mercury is recovered by distillation.
Pyrometallurgy is the extraction of metals from ores using heat, such as in the blast-furnace.
Hydrometallurgy. Ore is dissolved in a solvent in leaching tanks to make a solution. The solution is treated by electrolysis to separate the metal.
Thermo-electrometallurgy requires large supplies of electricity to separate metals by electrolysis. The container is made the cathode, and the metal collects on the container surface.
Reduction refers to the effective removal of the oxygen part of a chemical compound, by smelting, as is the case with Fe_2O_3 in the production of iron.

Thermal Equilibrium Diagrams

INTRODUCTION

Thermal equilibrium diagrams are special diagrams which contain information about changes that take place in alloys. The temperature at which a particular alloy changes from liquid to solid is an example of the type of thermal information contained in a *thermal equilibrium diagram*.

The word *alloy* is derived from the French word 'aloier', which means 'to combine'. An alloy, then, is a combination of two or more elements. At least one of these elements must be a metal. In the case of plain carbon steel, the main constituents are iron and carbon. While iron is a metal, carbon is not. It is common to have alloys of two metals. These are known as binary alloys and include brasses, bronzes and solder.

ALLOY TECHNOLOGY

The production of alloys is extremely complex and exacting, and really is a whole branch of knowledge in its own right. In this book we take a very simplified look at some of the main features of alloys and associated technology.

By making alloys, we can improve on the properties of pure metals. Strength can be increased, as can hardness, corrosion resistance, etc. Therefore it is easy to understand why alloys are so very widely used in engineering applications.

Most pure metals are soft and not very useful in the pure state. There are, of course, exceptions, which is the case in the use of copper and aluminium for conducting electricity. Both of these metals are excellent electrical conductors in the pure state.

Forming an alloy

During the *solidification* which takes place on cooling, the elements of an alloy combine in some particular way. The type of combination which occurs depends on the elements contained in the alloy in question.

To help us to understand what actually happens, close attention is given to the relationship between the composition of the alloy and the temperatures at which major changes take place. For example, we look first at what happens when a pure metal cools from liquid to solid. The information is shown on a graph in FIGURE 1. You will see that temperature is on the vertical scale and time is on the horizontal scale. At 1500°C, the pure metal is fully liquid. As

THE SUMERIANS AND THE IRISH

Between the rivers Euphrates and Tigris, in Mesopotamia, lived people called the Sumerians. They are said to be the first people to make use of the wheel. They were also great metalworkers and were able to work gold and copper very skillfully. Bronze, which is an alloy of copper and tin, is said to have been invented by them (probably from a copper ore which contained some tin in its natural state). This metal gave them better tools because bronze is harder than copper and possesses better durability.

It is worth remembering that the Irish metal-workers who worked in bronze, silver and gold, achieved an extremely high level of expertise which was exported to other parts of Europe, including England. There was, at the time, a brisk barter trade between the people of Cornwall and the Irish metalworkers. This trade was founded on the Irish need for tin, which they used to alloy with native copper, to produce high quality bronze. These Cornish traders brought tin and traded for bronze tools and implements. Ireland and Cornwall had been settled by Celts and, therefore, the peoples shared much in common, including the language. The Cornish language, which survives today, is very similar to the Irish language.

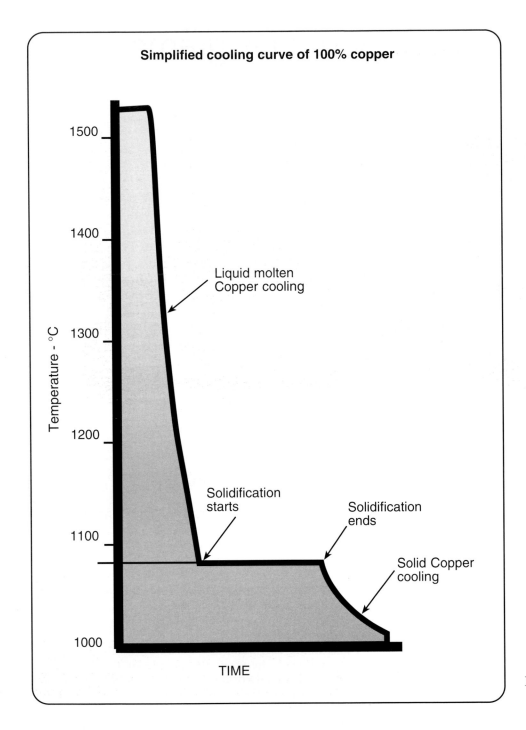

Simplified cooling curve of 100% copper

Liquid molten
Copper cooling

Solidification
starts

Solidification
ends

Solid Copper
cooling

Temperature - °C

TIME

FIGURE 1 *Cooling curve of 100% copper.*

time passes, the temperature of the metal falls (the metal cools), until a temperature is reached where a change begins to take place. At this temperature, 1083°C for copper, the liquid metal begins to change into solid.

The change does not happen instantly, but takes a little time. When this time has passed, the solidification ends, and all the metal has changed to solid. Again, more cooling takes place, until the solid metal reaches ambient temperature. If the metal is

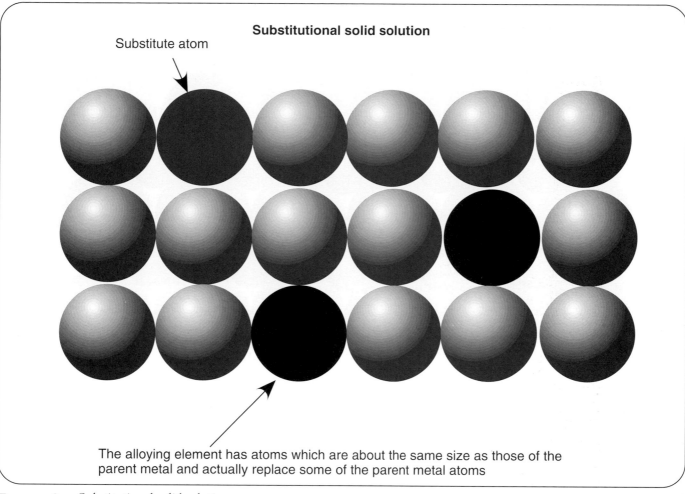

FIGURE 2 *Substitutional solid solution.*

absolutely pure and contains no traces of other elements, then there will be some under-cooling before crystallisation gets properly started. In under-cooling, the temperature of the cooling metal drops slightly below the liquid-to-solid change temperature for a short period. However, for our simplified approach, no under-cooling has been shown on the cooling curve.

Constant temperature change

An extremely important feature to notice from the graph is that while the liquid-to-solid change is taking place, the temperature does not change, but remains constant. It is shown in **FIGURE 1** as the horizontal line which stretches from where solidification starts to where solidification ends.

This situation is similar to that when water changes to ice, which we call freezing. In metallurgy, the term *freeze point* is also used.

If a solid pure metal is heated and the temperature is monitored, it will be seen that the metal will melt (change into liquid) at constant temperature. We refer to this temperature as the melting point temperature.

To help understand the constant temperature change point, it is worth thinking about the boiling of water. If you heat water and watch the temperature changes using a thermometer, the temperature of the water will rise until it boils. Then, if you continue to heat the water, you will notice that the

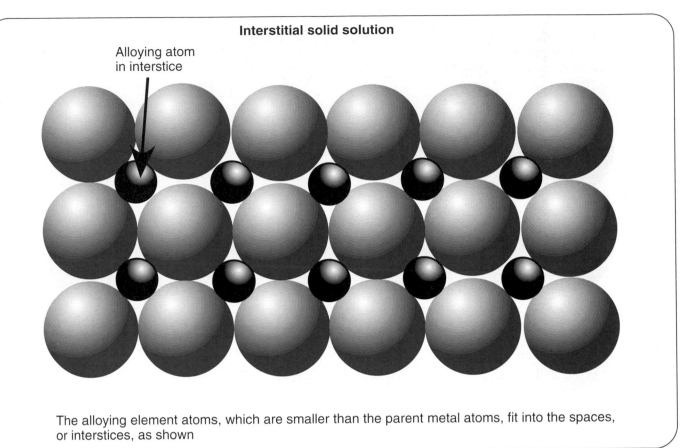

Interstitial solid solution

Alloying atom
in interstice

The alloying element atoms, which are smaller than the parent metal atoms, fit into the spaces, or interstices, as shown

FIGURE 3 *Interstital solid solution.*

temperature does not rise any further, but that the water changes into steam. (If you have never carried out this simple experiment, then you should try and do it as soon as you can.) The heat that changes the liquid into steam is known as hidden or *latent heat*.

The amount of heat required to cause a change from solid to liquid or from liquid to gas is stated in Joules per kilogram. When steam changes back into water, most of the latent heat can be recovered using a condenser.

Temperature remains constant when a pure metal changes from liquid to solid, because the *latent heat of fusion* (when the metal was changed into liquid) is given up. It is the giving out of this heat that keeps the metal at a steady temperature while the change takes place.

SOLID SOLUTION ALLOYS

The first type of combination we will look at is when the two metals are *completely soluble* in one another. Metals which combine in this way are said to form solid solutions. When this type of alloy solidifies, only one type of crystal is formed and, if viewed under a suitable microscope, a solid solution looks just like a pure metal. Solid solution alloys normally have similar properties to pure metals, but have greater strength. However, they have poorer electrical conductivity than pure metals, are harder than pure metals, but are not as elastic as pure metals.

The usual forms of solid solution are:

(a) *Substitutional solid solution* in which atoms of the parent metal (or solvent metal) are replaced, or substituted by atoms of the second, or alloying metal (solute metal). In this case, the atoms of the two metals in the alloy, are of similar size and direct substitution takes place. This is represented in **FIGURE 2**.

(b) *Interstitial solid solution* where the atoms of the parent or solvent metal are bigger than the atoms of the alloying or solute metal. In this case, the smaller atoms fit into the interstices (spaces) between the larger atoms. **FIGURE 3** illustrates this structure.

In both substitutional and interstitial solid solutions, the overall atomic structure set-up is virtually unchanged. When a substitutional alloy is formed, the atoms of the solute metal take the place of atoms of the solvent metal. For this type of alloy to form then, the two sets of atoms must be about the same size. The substitutions are normally at random, and usually there is no pattern to be seen. Sometimes, however, when conditions are right, the substitutions happen in an ordered way. Ordered structures are also called *superlattices*, and have slightly different properties than the disordered, or random structured alloys. Also, in the interstitial case, the smaller atoms of the alloying element fit in between the large original atoms.

Copper-nickel, copper-gold, gold-silver, and nickel-platinum are some examples of solid solution alloys, which have a face-centred cubic (FCC) structure. Molybdenum-tungsten, and iron-chromium, form solid solutions with body-centred cubic (BCC) structures.

The particular pair of metals we will look at, is copper and nickel. Copper and nickel form a solid solution of the substitutional kind. There are two metals in the alloy and alloys made from two metals are known as *binary alloys.*

Composition of alloys

Two metals may be alloyed in many different compositions. The composition is the amount of each metal in the alloy. For example, you could have 80% A and 20% B, for the two metals A and B. It is usual to state the composition in percentages, by weight.

When a study of how two metals form an alloy is being made, a large number of different compositions are considered. For example, for copper and nickel, the first composition studied might be 95% copper and 5% nickel. The next might be 90% copper and 10% nickel, and so on. Cooling curves are prepared for all the different compositions used, and a *thermal analysis* is made. This means that the temperatures of different change points are written down and a special chart is prepared. We will now see how this is done.

Study of copper-nickel alloys

As you might expect, the characteristics of the different alloy compositions are different. The temperature at which they become solid changes with a change in composition.

FIGURE 4 shows six cooling curves (graphs), for different copper-nickel alloys. The graph for pure copper is shown at top left, and you can see the graph for pure nickel at bottom right.

The solidification temperatures are, for pure copper, 1083°C, and for pure nickel, 1455°C.

You will notice that when some nickel is present, the alloy does not solidify at constant temperature, but does so between an upper and a lower reading.

If you look at the cooling curve for 60% Cu (copper), and 40% Ni (nickel), you will see that it starts to solidify at 1280°C and that it is fully solid at 1210°C. Between 1280°C and 1210°C, the alloy is a mixture of solid and liquid, similar to paste.

When all the cooling curves have been studied, a thermal analysis diagram is made, which is called a *thermal equilibrium diagram.* Information about the temperatures at which solidification starts and ends is taken from the various cooling curves, collected together and presented on the thermal equilibrium diagram, **FIGURE 5**.

Study **FIGURE 5** and note how the information from the six graphs is used in its preparation. The temperature at which copper changes from liquid to solid is shown on the left-hand vertical axis. Each of the four alloys considered is represented by a vertical

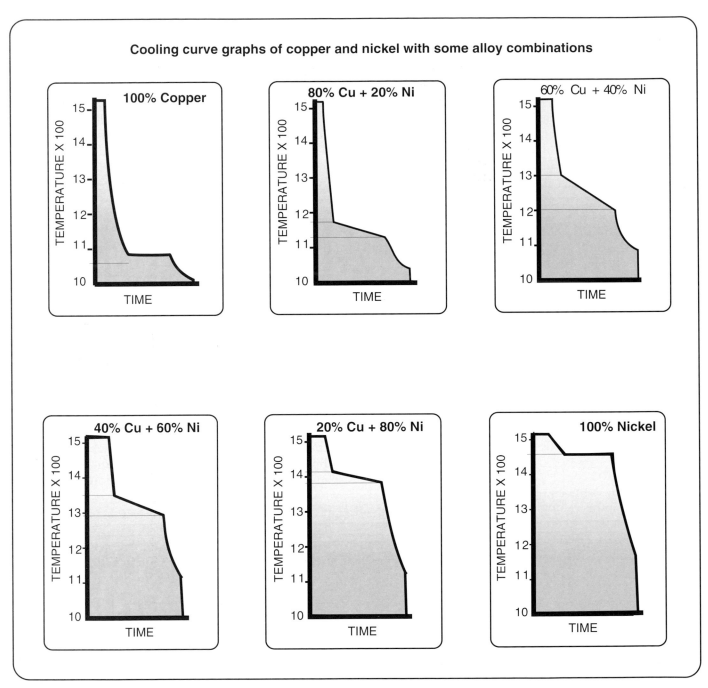

FIGURE 4   *Cooling curve graph.*

line. You can see that for 80% Cu + 20% Ni, two temperature points are marked on the vertical line (alloy line). These two points are obtained from **FIGURE 4**. When all the points are marked on the sheet, the lines are drawn. The line joining all the liquid-to-solid starting points is called the *liquidus line*. All the points at which the alloys have completely changed to solid are joined by the *solidus line*. These lines are shown in the diagram. Consider the alloy lines in the diagram. Above the liquidus

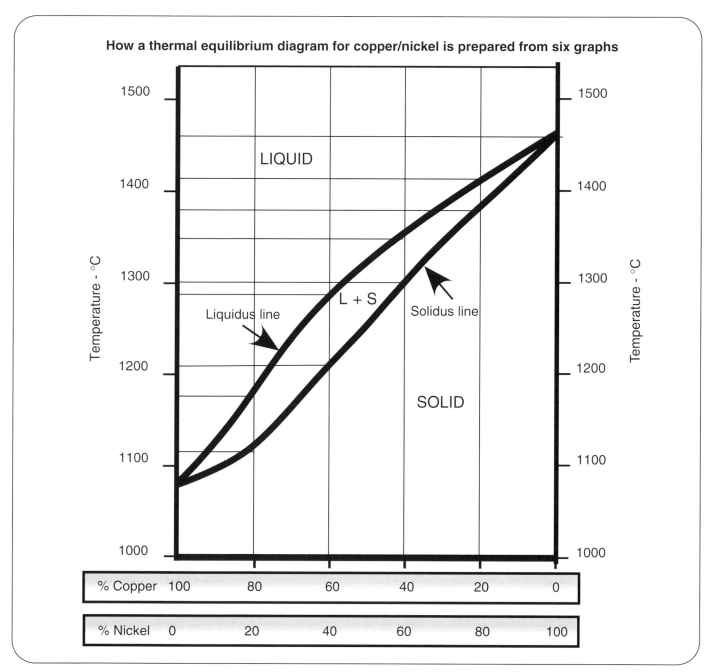

How a thermal equilibrium diagram for copper/nickel is prepared from six graphs

FIGURE 5 *Thermal equilibrium diagram.*

line, each alloy is liquid, and below the solidus line, it is fully solid. However, between the liquidus and the solidus lines, the alloys are a mixture of liquid and solid. The nearer to the solidus line the temperature is, the more will be the solid content.

UNDERSTANDING THERMAL EQUILIBRIUM DIAGRAMS

You now know how a thermal equilibrium diagram is made up. To help you to understand the one just

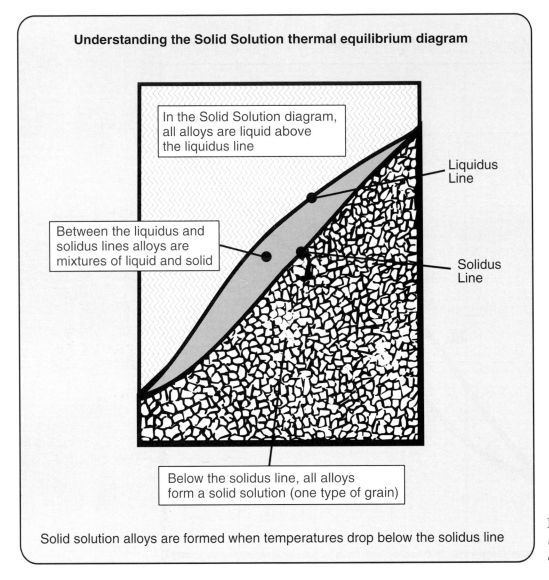

Understanding the Solid Solution thermal equilibrium diagram

In the Solid Solution diagram, all alloys are liquid above the liquidus line

Liquidus Line

Between the liquidus and solidus lines alloys are mixtures of liquid and solid

Solidus Line

Below the solidus line, all alloys form a solid solution (one type of grain)

Solid solution alloys are formed when temperatures drop below the solidus line

FIGURE 6 *Understanding the Solid Solution thermal equilibrium diagram.*

described, we have summarised the information in **FIGURE 6**.

There are three zones in the diagram. Above the liquidus line there is the *liquid phase* zone. Between the liquidus and solidus lines there is the *liquid/solid* (two phase) zone, and finally, below the solidus line is the *solid phase* zone. Once an alloy of this type cools below solidus line temperature, the solid solution formed will have grains similar to a pure metal. So what use can be made of such diagrams? Although our study of this topic is a simplified one,

some idea of what can be learned from a thermal equilibrium diagram can be seen in **FIGURE 7**.

In this figure, a 60% Cu + 40% Ni alloy, represented by the dotted line, is examined. From the diagram the temperature at which solidification begins is easily read by drawing a horizontal line to the temperature axis. The temperature is 1291°C. The alloy is fully solid at about 1214°C. It is easy to get this information from the diagram.

Suppose we want to know the state of the same alloy

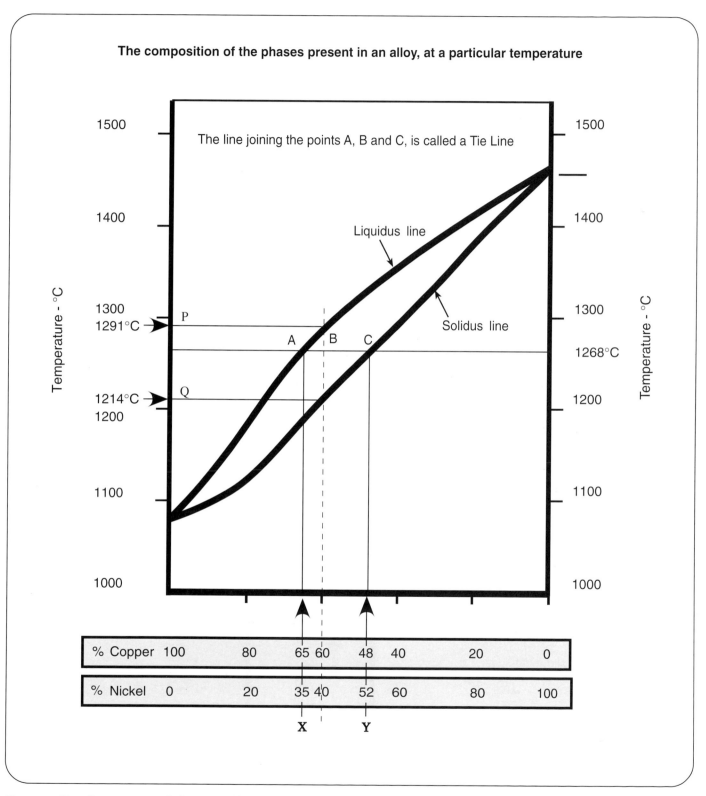

FIGURE 7 *Composition of phases in alloys.*

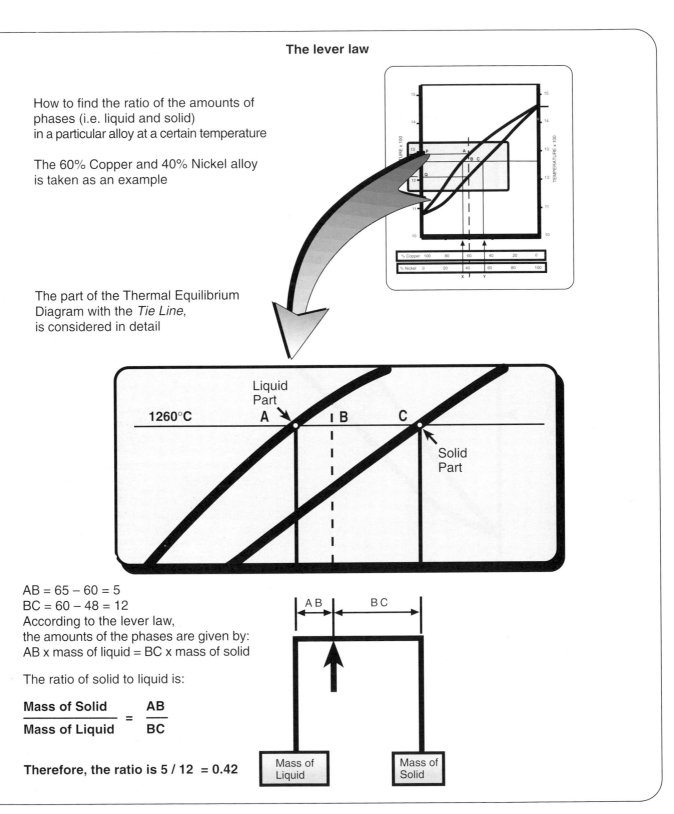

The lever law

How to find the ratio of the amounts of phases (i.e. liquid and solid) in a particular alloy at a certain temperature

The 60% Copper and 40% Nickel alloy is taken as an example

The part of the Thermal Equilibrium Diagram with the *Tie Line*, is considered in detail

AB = 65 − 60 = 5
BC = 60 − 48 = 12
According to the lever law,
the amounts of the phases are given by:
AB x mass of liquid = BC x mass of solid

The ratio of solid to liquid is:

$$\frac{\textbf{Mass of Solid}}{\textbf{Mass of Liquid}} = \frac{\textbf{AB}}{\textbf{BC}}$$

Therefore, the ratio is 5 / 12 = 0.42

FIGURE 8 *Ratio of phases using lever law.*

48

when the temperature is 1268°C. A line is drawn across the diagram, and crosses the liquidus line at A, the alloy line at B, and the solidus line at C.

The part of the line which joins the points A, B and C is called a *tie line*. It can be seen that our point of consideration is at B. The alloy at this point consists of *two phases*, liquid and solid. The composition of the liquid is obtained by drawing a vertical line down from point A. In this case, the liquid has a composition of 65% copper and 35% nickel. Similarly, the composition of the solid is obtained from point C. The solid has a composition of 48% copper and 52% nickel.

So far, we have seen that quite a bit of information is available from a thermal equilibrium diagram, but there is still more. **FIGURE 8** examines the same alloy composition as **FIGURE 7**, but this time the ratio of the amounts of the phases (liquid and solid) is found using the *lever law*, with the tie line ABC.

The name lever law is taken from basic physics. Moments are taken for a balanced lever, by multiplying each force by its distance from the fulcrum, and equating the *sides* of the lever. For the tie line above, the point B is the equivalent of the fulcrum.

What is the meaning of equilibrium?

In technology and science, *equilibrium* refers to a balance existing in a system. In metallurgy, equilibrium means, in effect, that the cooling of a metal, or an alloy, is so slow that all the changes that might take place get the chance to do so. This is practically impossible, so equilibrium is taken to mean *cooling very slowly*.

To achieve equilibrium, it would be necessary, at every stage of cooling, to give the alloy elements time to *diffuse* (mix through one another), which would lead to a state that each grain of metal would have the same composition throughout.

Complete diffusion seldom takes place in a casting situation, because the cooling is not slow enough. Solidification generally takes place before diffusion is complete. When this happens, grains of the alloy do not have a uniform composition. In a binary alloy,

such as copper-nickel, the centre of a grain will be *richer* in one metal, and the outer part of the grain or crystal will be richer in the second metal, although the average composition throughout the grain would be constant.

This is known as *coring*. Where coring is severe, the alloy does not have the properties it should have. It may well be weaker than a similar alloy which solidified in an equilibrium situation.

Solid solution alloys, such as the one above, have a particular composition which will give maximum *tensile strength*. In the case of copper-nickel, the maximum tensile strength occurs when the alloy contains about 60% nickel. This particular alloy is known as *monel*. The copper increases its strength by *solid solution strengthening*. Atoms of nickel replace atoms of copper in the solid solution formed – a substitutional solid solution, and because nickel has greater strength than copper, the 'copper' is strengthened.

EUTECTIC COMBINATIONS OR EUTECTIC ALLOYS

The second type of combination we look at is called a *eutectic* alloy. Eutectic comes from the Greek word, *eutektos*, which translates as easily melted, and we see why this name was given to this type of alloy. In a eutectic alloy, the two metals are completely soluble in the liquid or melted state, but are *insoluble* in the solid state. When cooling is finished, crystals or grains are formed which are made up of the two separate metals. The eutectic grain may be thought of as a mixture of the two metals, which might have a layer of one metal on top of a layer of the second metal, and so on. This situation is completely different to the solid solution case, where the cooled solid grains look just like one metal, when a prepared sample is viewed under a suitable microscope.

The cadmium/bismuth eutectic mixture

Cadmium and bismuth are completely soluble in the liquid state, but are completely insoluble in the solid state. Cadmium (Cd), is a fairly soft, white silvery metal, which has a melting point of about 320°C. It is usually mined along with zinc. Its main uses are

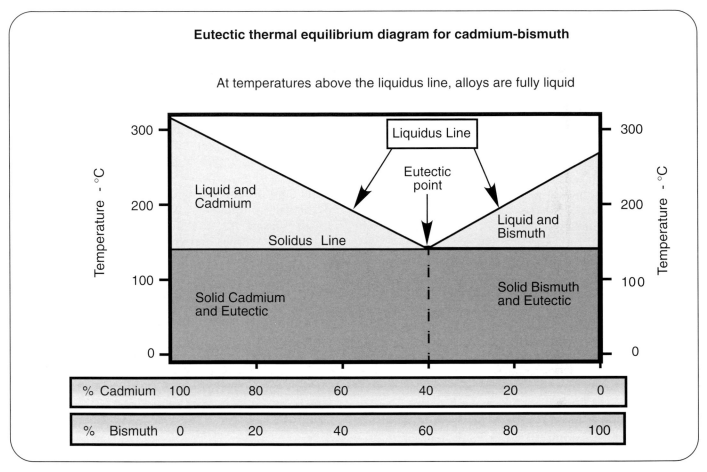

FIGURE 9 *Eutectic thermal equilibrium diagram for cadmium-bismuth.*

for electroplating nuts and bolts, for making welding alloys and, because it is a very good absorber of neutrons, it can be used to control nuclear reactions. Bismuth (Bi), is a white, brittle metal, with a melting point of 271°C. It is used extensively in the preparation of alloys. One such alloy, which is interesting, is known as *Wood's metal*. This interestingly named alloy consists of 50% bismuth, 25% lead, 12.5% tin and 12.5% cadmium, and has the extremely low melting point of 71°C.

A thermal equilibrium diagram for cadmium-bismuth is shown in **FIGURE 9**. It should be remembered that this diagram is built up in the same way as the solid solution equilibrium diagram, although you will notice that they are very different from each other. There is one point on the diagram

where the liquid alloy changes to solid, without going through a liquid-solid, or pasty stage. This is called the *eutectic point*, and it is the lowest melting point of any composition for the alloy. It is significant, and seems almost magical that when cadmium, which melts at 320°C, and bismuth, which melts at 271°C, are alloyed, an alloy can be made that melts at 140°C. This fact has obvious advantages in the welding of metals. Another important feature of the diagram is that all the alloys become solid at this temperature (140°C), which is called the *eutectic temperature*. The zones are indicated on the diagram. A pictorial-type version of the cadmium/bismuth equilibrium diagram is featured in **FIGURE 10**.

The various zones are easier to identify in this sketch. In the solid cadmium and liquid zone, it is seen that

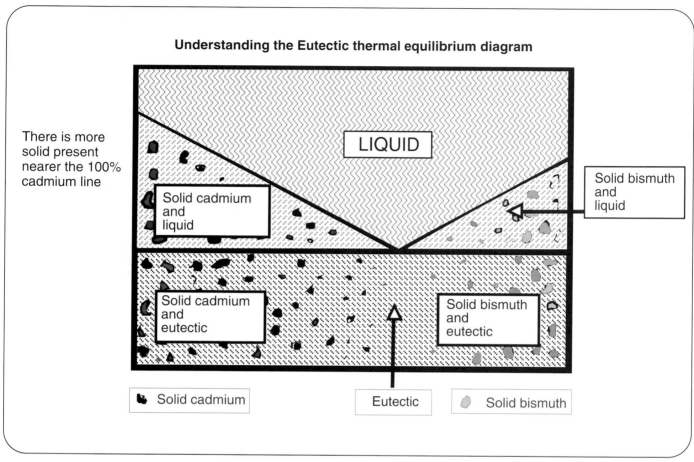

FIGURE 10   *Understanding the Eutectic thermal equilibrium diagram.*

there is a large amount of solid cadmium present near the 100% cadmium axis, and this decreases in alloys formed nearer to the eutectic point. In the solid bismuth and liquid zone, a similar situation exists, but in this case, the solid is bismuth. Below the horizontal solidus line, all alloys are solid and cooling.

In the eutectic point region, there is only the eutectic composition alloy formed, and neither solid cadmium nor solid bismuth are present. You can see that, as the composition of the alloy moves away from the eutectic composition, grains of either cadmium or bismuth appear in the *eutectic matrix*.

In alloys which contain larger amounts of cadmium, solid cadmium appears. Alloys with more than 60% bismuth present contain some solid bismuth grains.

PARTIAL SOLUBILITY

Lead and tin only dissolve in each other to a limited extent, and the resulting thermal equilibrium diagram is more complex than either the solid solution diagram or the eutectic diagram, which we have already considered. The lead/tin alloys are known as *partial solubility alloys*, and the thermal equilibrium diagram for this type of alloy is termed a *partial solubility* thermal equilibrium diagram.

The lead/tin thermal equilibrium diagram is a combination of both the solid solution and the eutectic diagrams and, consequently, is more difficult to understand. Consider **FIGURE 11**. The heavy curved line starting at the bottom left-hand corner and curving upwards to the right, ends near the 80%

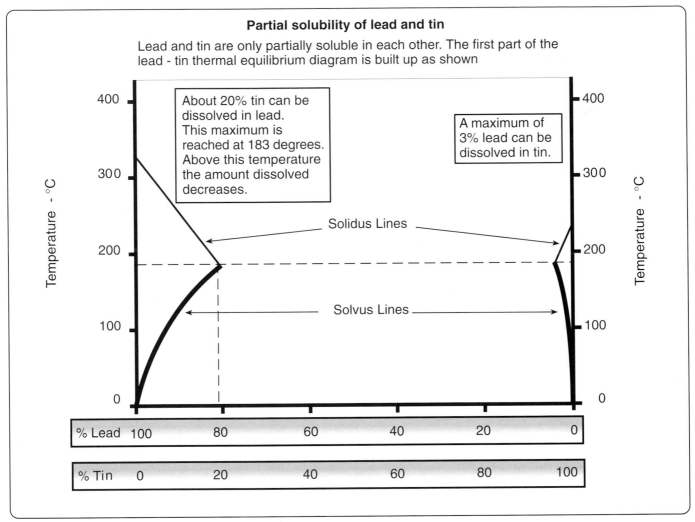

Partial solubility of lead and tin

Lead and tin are only partially soluble in each other. The first part of the lead - tin thermal equilibrium diagram is built up as shown

About 20% tin can be dissolved in lead. This maximum is reached at 183 degrees. Above this temperature the amount dissolved decreases.

A maximum of 3% lead can be dissolved in tin.

Solidus Lines

Solvus Lines

Temperature - °C

Temperature - °C

% Lead 100   80   60   40   20   0

% Tin 0   20   40   60   80   100

FIGURE 11   *Partial solubility of lead and tin.*

lead (Pb) + 20% tin (Sn) alloy, on the 183°C temperature line. This heavy black line is a *solvus line,* and it plots the amount of tin that dissolves in lead as the temperature is increased to 183°C, when the maximum amount of tin (about 20% by weight) is dissolved. For example, at a temperature of 100°C, about 7% tin can be dissolved in lead. A similar line on the right shows that the maximum amount of lead that can dissolve in tin is 3%, by weight.

Now we will look at the partly completed partial solubility equilibrium diagram for lead/tin alloys shown in **FIGURE 12**. The liquidus and solidus lines are clearly marked. Also, you can see that two solid solutions are formed. An *alpha* (α) solid solution of

lead with tin is formed at the left-hand side, between the solidus line and the solvus line, while a *beta* (β) solid solution of tin with lead forms on the right-hand side.

Consider the 90% lead + 10% tin alloy as it cools. At about 315°C, the liquidus is crossed, and the alloy begins to solidify. When the temperature drops to 280°C, solidification is complete and the solidus line is crossed. The alloy is now a solid solution of lead and tin. But when the temperature falls to 120°C, the solid solution changes to a eutectic mixture of the two solid solutions, a + b. Each time one of the equilibrium lines on a thermal equilibrium diagram, is crossed, there is at least one phase change.

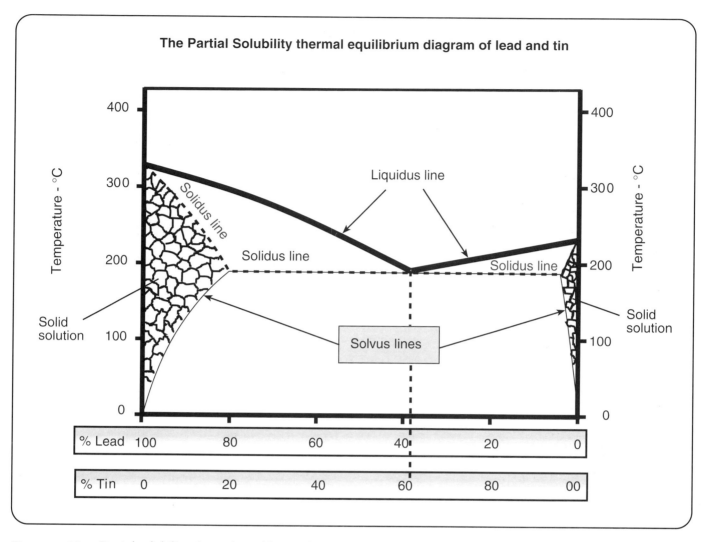

FIGURE 12 *Partial solubility thermal equilibrium diagram of lead and tin.*

A completed partial solubility thermal equilibrium diagram for lead and tin is presented in **FIGURE 13**. You can see the similarity it has to the eutectic equilibrium diagram. There is a eutectic point at 183°C, when the composition is about 62% tin and 38% lead and the *eutectic mixture* forms. Alloys of other compositions contain some solid solution also. This is very similar to what happens in the eutectic situation, except that in this case, the solid is a solid solution alloy of lead and tin. The liquidus lines are similar to the eutectic diagram, while the solidus line is different, but there are still pasty stages.

Soft solders are based on lead/tin alloys, and two important solder compositions are shown. The eutectic alloy, known as *tinman's solder*, is used extensively for soft soldering, in the electronics and communications industries.

A soft-soldered joint must solidify very quickly, and so does the eutectic alloy, because it goes from liquid to solid without going through a pasty stage.

Another important composition is 70% lead and 30% tin, and it is called *plumbers' solder*. This is the alloy which made it possible to join lead water and gas pipes in the not too distant past. However, the main use for this alloy today is in the jointing of

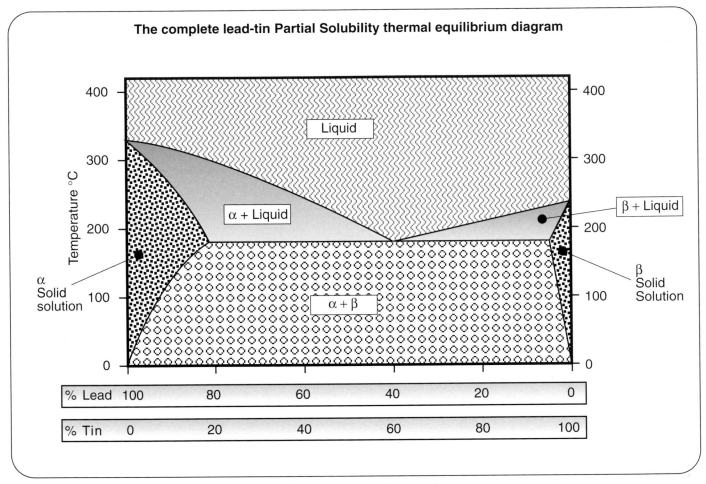

The complete lead-tin Partial Solubility thermal equilibrium diagram

FIGURE 13   *The complete lead-tin Partial Solubility thermal equilibrium diagram.*

underground lead-sheathed electrical and telecommunications cables. The long pasty stage gives the jointer time to shape the joint, using a special glove, or former.

INTERMETALLIC COMPOUNDS

An *intermetallic compound* is a type of combination in binary alloys, formed when a chemical compound results. These are also known as *intermediate compounds* or *intermediate phases*.

There are two types which are often encountered in metallurgy:

1 Electron compounds.
2 Interstitial compounds.

Electron compounds are very similar in structure to solid solutions, and have *metallic bonding*. They take their name from the fact that compounds form according the valency electron ratio between the metals concerned. Compounds of this type tend to form between metals with similar *electrochemical* properties. CuZn is an example of an electron compound which has a 3:2 valency electron ratio.

Interstitial compounds, as the name suggests, form between metals, or metals and non-metallic elements, with atom sizes similar to those that form interstitial solid solutions. One set of atoms fit into the spaces, or interstices, between the other larger atoms. *Iron carbide* (Fe_3C), or cementite, which is important in the study of iron/carbon diagrams, is an interstitial compound that has a complex structure.

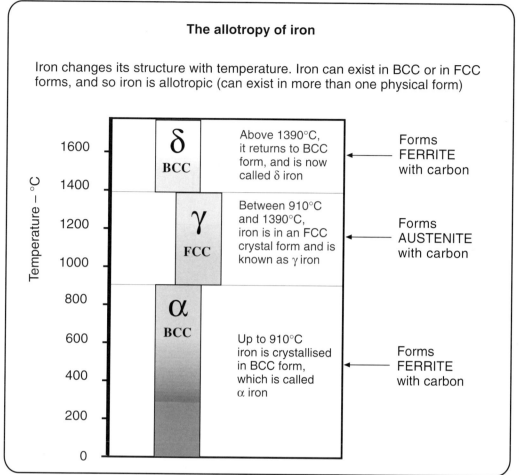

The allotropy of iron

Iron changes its structure with temperature. Iron can exist in BCC or in FCC forms, and so iron is allotropic (can exist in more than one physical form)

δ

BCC

Above 1390°C, it returns to BCC form, and is now called δ iron

Forms FERRITE with carbon

γ

FCC

Between 910°C and 1390°C, iron is in an FCC crystal form and is known as γ iron

Forms AUSTENITE with carbon

α

BCC

Up to 910°C iron is crystallised in BCC form, which is called α iron

Forms FERRITE with carbon

Temperature – °C

FIGURE 14 *The allotropy of iron.*

In general, intermetallic compounds are very hard and brittle. Fe_3C is what gives the hardness in high carbon steel. Iron carbide is really an intermediate compound, because only one of the elements is a metal. Generally, though, it is described as an intermetallic compound. $CuAl_2$ is another example which is significant in *age hardening* aluminium alloys.

Intermetallic compounds are usually very hard and brittle. Their melting points are higher than the melting points of either of the elements in the compound.

IRON IS ALLOTROPIC

An extremely important piece of information about iron is outlined in **FIGURE 14**. Iron, when cooling from a high temperature, displays two special points,

known as *arrest points* or *critical points*. We have already discussed the boiling of water, latent heat, heat of fusion and change points in cooling curves earlier in the chapter.

The change points occur at 1390°C and 910°C, and show that iron changes its crystal structure at these temperatures. Above 1390°C, iron exists with a body-centred cubic (BCC) lattice, but between 1390°C and 910°C, it exists with a face-centred cubic (FCC) lattice. Iron is, therefore, *allotropic*, which means that it can exist in different forms.

The forms in which iron exist are, as noted above, temperature dependent. Iron above 1390°C is known as *delta iron*. It is denoted by the Greek letter (δ), called delta, which is the equivalent of d, in English. (D is the capital delta).

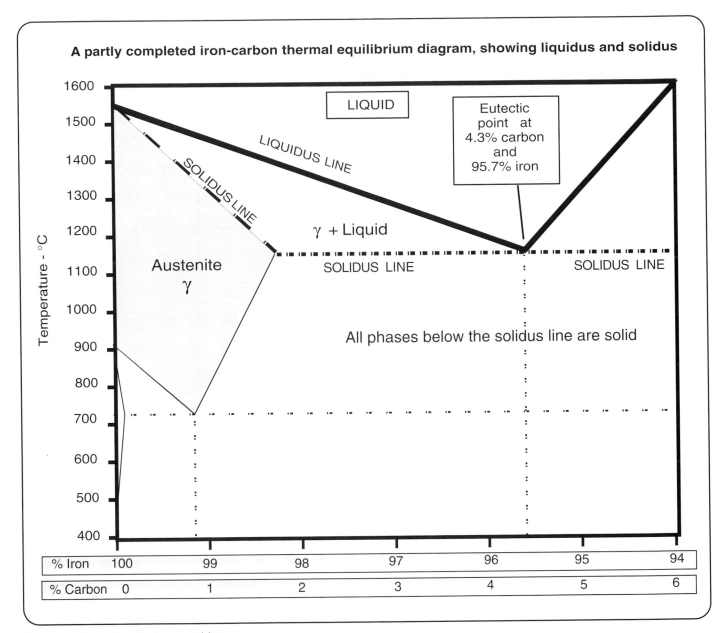

A partly completed iron-carbon thermal equilibrium diagram, showing liquidus and solidus

LIQUID

Eutectic point at 4.3% carbon and 95.7% iron

LIQUIDUS LINE

SOLIDUS LINE

γ + Liquid

SOLIDUS LINE

SOLIDUS LINE

Austenite γ

All phases below the solidus line are solid

Temperature - °C

% Iron	100	99	98	97	96	95	94
% Carbon	0	1	2	3	4	5	6

FIGURE 15   *Iron/carbon equilibrium.*

Between 1390°C and 910°C, iron is known as *gamma iron*, and is denoted by γ (the Greek version of g). Gamma iron combines with carbon to produce *austenite*. Below 910°C, iron is known as alpha iron, denoted by α (the Greek a).

The change from a BCC, to an FCC structure is accompanied by a slight *shrinkage in volume*, while the reverse change causes an expansion in volume. The reason for these changes in volume, is that an FCC structure has the atoms packed in closer together than a BCC structure.

Iron–carbon equilibrium diagram
When carbon is added to iron, it has a similar effect to that when nickel is added to copper. Pure copper

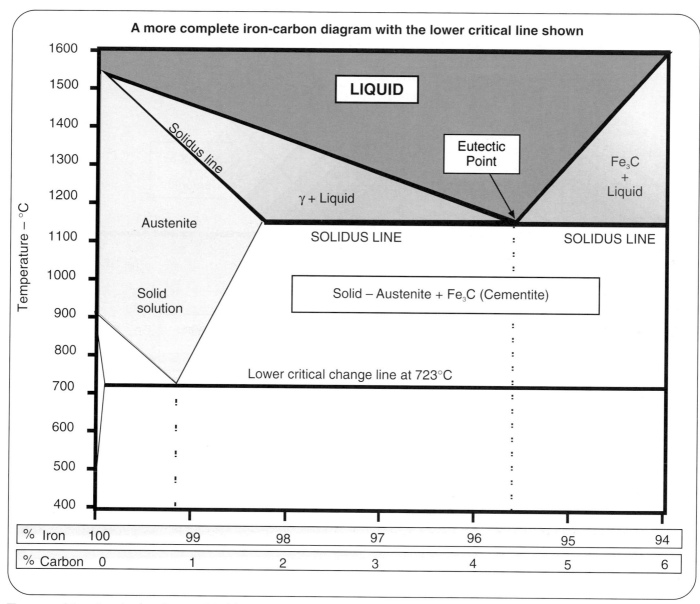

A more complete iron-carbon diagram with the lower critical line shown

FIGURE 16   *Iron/carbon lower critical line.*

has one critical point, but alloys of copper and nickel have two, an upper and a lower.

First, we look at a partly completed equilibrium diagram for iron/carbon, with up to 6% carbon added, **FIGURE 15**. The liquidus and solidus lines are easily identified. You can see that the lowest temperature at which an iron/carbon alloy can remain liquid is 1140°C. This eutectic point occurs when 4.3% carbon is contained in the alloy.

Note the effect that adding more carbon has on the temperature at which iron/carbon alloys begin to solidify. Follow the liquidus line from the top left of **FIGURE 15**, and you can see that the *critical temperature* falls, as the carbon content increases up to 4.3%. When the carbon content rises above 4.3%, the critical temperature also rises. Under the sloped part of the solidus line, up to about 2% carbon, a solid solution called *austenite*, already mentioned, is present. Austenite, because of its FCC structure, can

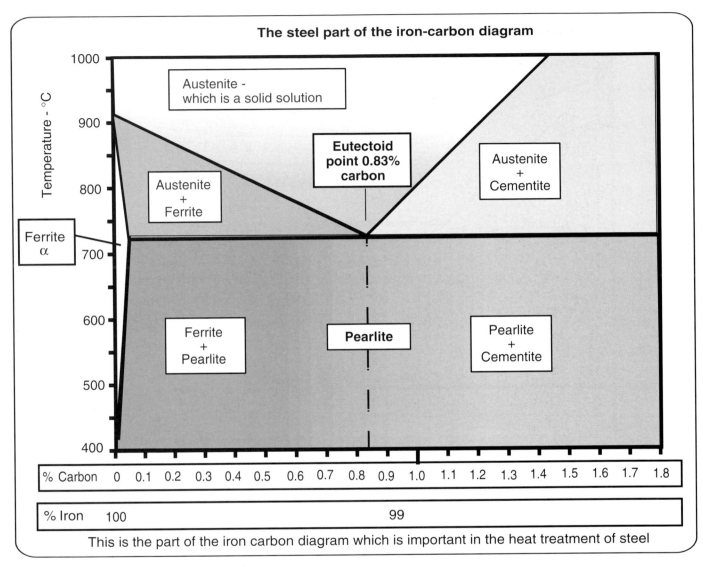

FIGURE 17 *Steel part of iron/carbon diagram.*

hold up to 2% carbon in solid solution, and it is worth noting that *ferrite*, which has a BCC structure, can only accept a very small amount of carbon, about 0.02%.

At the bottom of the austenite zone, there is what looks like another eutectic point, but, as you can see, there is only solid in that area. (This point is at about 700°C, well below the solidus line.)

Now, we move on to **FIGURE 16**, which is a more complete diagram. The zones shown are similar to those we have studied earlier. The austenite zone is seen to extend downwards to the *lower critical line*, to a point where the alloy contains 0.83% carbon and 99.17% iron. This point is known as a *eutectoid point*, and it is very easy to confuse it with a eutectic point. One way of remembering the difference, is that the word *eutectoid*, ends in *id*, as does the word *solid*. At a eutectoid point, the change is from *solid to solid*, while at a eutectic point, the change is from *liquid to solid*.

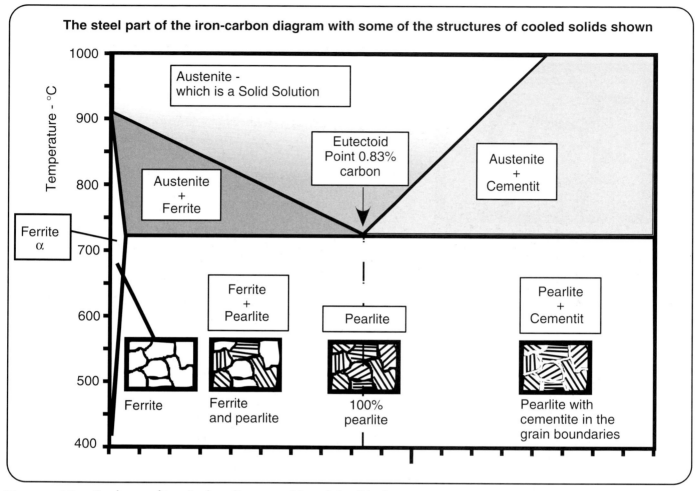

The steel part of the iron-carbon diagram with some of the structures of cooled solids shown

FIGURE 18   *Steel part of iron/carbon diagrams with cooled solids shown.*

The steel part of the iron–carbon diagram

Generally speaking, the iron carbon alloys, with a carbon content of up to 2%, are known as steel. Alloys with carbon contents from 2% upwards are identified as cast iron. One major difference between the two, is that carbon can be present in cast iron as flakes of graphite, but in steels, the carbon is present as iron carbide.

The steel part of the iron carbon diagram, with carbon contents up to 1.8%, is given in **FIGURE 17**, in which all the phases are solid. At the eutectoid point, 0.83% carbon, solid austenite changes into *two solid phases*, ferrite and cementite. These two solids combine to produce a mixture called *pearlite*, which consists of alternate layers of ferrite and cementite.

Pearlite is mostly ferrite, and gives off a sheen similar to *mother of pearl*, hence the name. At the left of this diagram, it is seen that alpha iron can only dissolve a small amount of carbon.

Representations of various structures are shown in **FIGURE 18**. Ferrite is represented as white, pearlite as black and white layers, while cementite is also shown as white.

The eutectoid mixture is all pearlite, which is more realistically represented in **FIGURE 19**.

Heat treatment of steels is dealt with under Manufacturing, (page 181) where further reference is made to the iron/carbon solid structures.

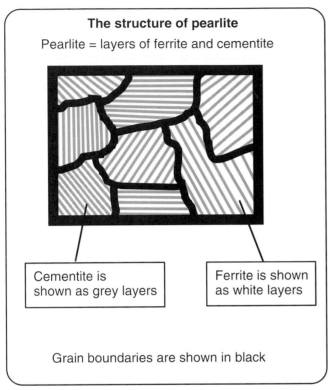

The structure of pearlite

Pearlite = layers of ferrite and cementite

Cementite is shown as grey layers

Ferrite is shown as white layers

Grain boundaries are shown in black

FIGURE 19   *The structure of pearlite.*

SUMMARY

An *alloy* is a combination of two or more elements, one of which is a metal. Usually the elements are metals. Carbon steel is an alloy of iron and carbon. Carbon is not a metal.

Alloys normally have more desirable properties than pure metals. Alloys have greater strength than the parent, or solvent metal.

Thermal equilibrium diagrams show the temperatures at which phase changes take place in alloys of different compositions. The vertical axis represents temperature, and the horizontal axis represents percentage composition of alloys.

A *solid solution alloy* results if the atoms of one metal either substitute for atoms of the solvent metal (*substitutional solid solution*), or fit in to spaces between atoms of the solvent metal (*interstitial solid solution*).

A thermal equilibrium diagram for a solid solution alloy is torpedo-shaped, with a point at each end.

Equilibrium, in alloying, means cooling very slowly so that the alloy elements have time to diffuse through one another.

A *binary alloy* is one formed from two elements, usually two metals.

Coring results when diffusion is not complete. The centre of the crystals of the alloy are richer in one metal, and the outer part of the crystal is richer in the second metal.

A *eutectic* combination results in an alloy with a low melting point, known as a eutectic point. At this point, the liquid phase changes to the solid phase without going through a liquid + solid phase.

The *eutectic alloy*, in a binary system, melts at a temperature below that of both the alloying metals. This is clearly seen on a eutectic thermal equilibrium diagram, which is very different from a solid solution thermal equilibrium diagram.

Because lead and tin only *partially dissolve* in one another, a more complicated thermal equilibrium diagrams emerges. It is a combination of a solid solution diagram and a eutectic diagram. The *partial solubility thermal diagram* for lead and tin shows a eutectic point.

An *intermetallic compound* is a chemical compound formed between at least two elements. Iron carbide, for example, is a compound of iron and carbon.

Iron is *allotropic* because it can exist as a BCC or an FCC structure.

Austenite is an FCC solid solution structure, which can contain up to 2% carbon.

Cementite is a compound of iron and carbon. It is also known as *iron carbide*.

Ferrite is almost pure iron but contains about 0.002% carbon.

Pearlite is a layered structure of ferrite and cementite. It has a sheen that compares to that of mother of pearl.

A *eutectoid point* occurs in an iron-carbon thermal equilibrium diagram. At the eutectoid point, solid austenite changes into solid pearlite.

ENGINEERING TECHNOLOGY

Steels and Iron

INTRODUCTION

Steel can be thought of as the general purpose metal, but in fact, there are many different steels, as we shall see later. The variety of uses for steels is enormous indeed. Steel of one kind or another is used to manufacture cars, bridges, machine tools, machines of all kinds, cutlery, springs, nails, fencing wire, factory and barn roofs, tractors and farm implements, ships, computer cases, cookers, central heating radiators, advertising signs, beverage cans, cement mixers, staplers, spades and other gardening tools, filing cabinets, railings, lamposts, surgical instruments, kitchen sinks, paper clips, etc. The list could go on and on.

Mankind has progressed from the Stone Age, the Bronze Age and the Iron Age to, as indicated from the list above, what is now commonly called the Steel Age. It is with the production of iron, from which steel is made, that we will start.

IRON

Before going on to iron ores proper, it is worth spending a little time on *meteorites*. A meteorite is a solid mass, which comes from space, and lands on the earth. Most meteorites contain iron in the form of nickel-iron alloys. There is little by way of records, to show how many meteorites have fallen to earth. In fact, the largest recorded meteorite, which fell in Africa in prehistoric times, consisted mainly of a nickel-iron alloy, and weighed 60 tonnes. Astronomers have a keen interest in meteorites, as there is always the chance that a large mass might strike the earth.

However, our interest is from a metallurgical point of view. It is likely that, at some time during the Iron Age, or later, meteoric alloy was made into tools or weapons.

Iron ores

Although iron is very common throughout the

Colonel Jim Bowie, the early American frontiersman, whose forefathers are reputed to have come from County Clare, had a special knife. This knife, it is said, was forged from a meteorite, and was superior to any other hunting knife of the time. The blade of the Bowie knife, was 380 mm long, and had an edge on one side only. (Bowie died at the Alamo in 1836 along with the equally famous Davy Crockett, who also had Irish connections – his people came from Derry.) Even today, Bowie style hunting knives are sold in their thousands. Other stories exist in various cultures, of weapons made from 'metal of the Gods', which were much superior to iron weapons. Perhaps it was from the use of meteorites, that ideas for alloy steels came!

earth's crust, economic ores exist in two main forms. These are *Haematite* (or Hematite), and *Magnetite*.

Haematite, (Fe_2O_3), takes its name from the Greek word for blood, because it usually has a blood red streak in it. Haematite can range in colour from steel grey to coal black, but can always be distinguished by the 'red streaks'.

Magnetite (Fe_3O_4), contains the greatest concentration of iron, at about 72%. This is a black, shining ore, with a metallic lustre. Because of its strong magnetic properties, it has attracted attention since early days. Sometimes magnetite has polarity (has a north pole and a south pole – like a magnet), and is known as *Lodestone*. Lode comes from an Old English word meaning *course*. Lodestone suspended by a thread, helped keep early fishermen an course during fog. This was the first directional compass. As already stated, haematite and magnetite are the two main ores of iron, but there are others of importance.

Limonite (also known as Brown Haematite); this ore compound has a yellow-brown streak.

Siderite is coloured from a greyish brown to a yellowish brown, with large granular or fibrous appearance.

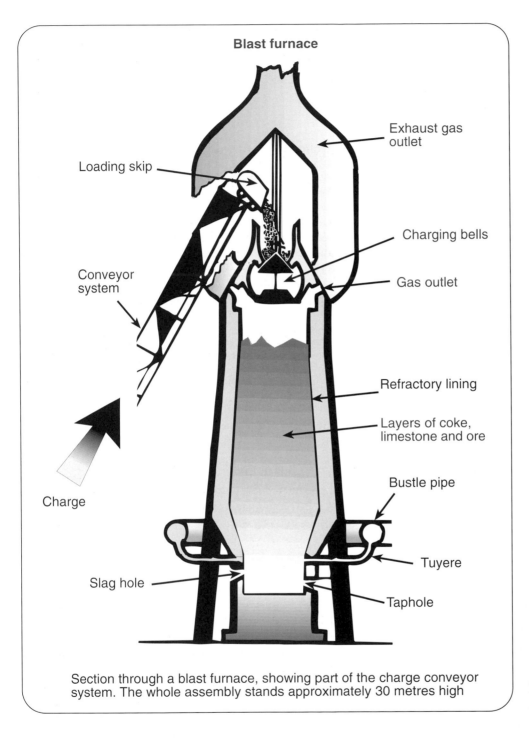

Blast furnace

Exhaust gas outlet

Loading skip

Charging bells

Conveyor system

Gas outlet

Refractory lining

Layers of coke, limestone and ore

Bustle pipe

Charge

Tuyere

Slag hole

Taphole

Section through a blast furnace, showing part of the charge conveyor system. The whole assembly stands approximately 30 metres high

Figure 1 *Diagram of Blast Furnace.*

THE PRODUCTION OF IRON

High quality iron ore is available from America, Australia, North Africa, Commonwealth of Independent States (formerly Russia), and Scandinavia. First, the ore is graded and crushed, and the fine particles are sintered. Sintering, is a method of converting powder, or fine particles, into a continuous mass. It is done by first compacting the ore powder, and then heating it to a temperature

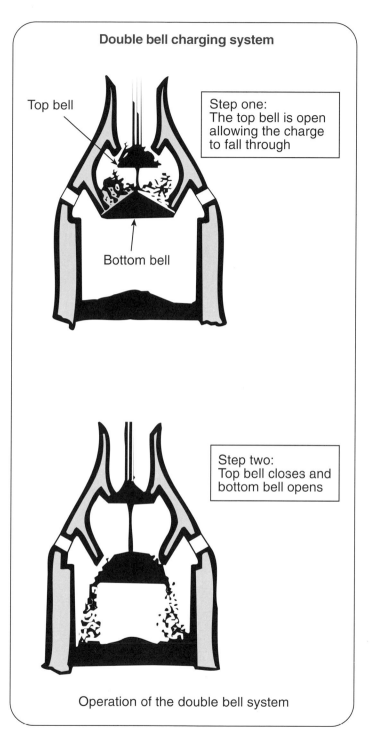

Double bell charging system

Top bell

Bottom bell

Step one:
The top bell is open allowing the charge to fall through

Step two:
Top bell closes and bottom bell opens

Operation of the double bell system

FIGURE 2   *Double bell system.*

particles of iron ore being gathered into ball-shaped masses or *agglomerates*. The collecting together process is termed agglomeration. Before sintering the iron ore, it is mixed with coke, and usually limestone. Conveyor buckets take the sinter with more iron ore, coke and limestone, up to the top of a furnace, which is called a blast furnace, **FIGURE 1**. Once inside the furnace, the whole mixture is 'fired'. Blasts of hot air are blown up through the furnace, which brings it to a white hot temperature. Smelted iron runs to the bottom of the furnace, where it is tapped off, now and then. The limestone combines with impurities in the furnace, and forms a slag, which is lighter than the iron, and hence floats on top of it. The slag, too, is tapped off about every two hours. A blast furnace can run continuously for about two years, before the refractory lining has to be renewed.

A special *gas-trap* system with a *double bell*, or bell and cone, arrangement, allows the furnace to be charged without too much heat loss, **FIGURE 2**. It is important that the temperature of the furnace be kept fairly constant.

Pig iron

Most of the molten iron goes directly to the steel mills, although some is cast into *pigs* (buckets). Iron in the pigs is known as pig iron, and is used to make cast iron. The molten iron is up to 95% pure, but may contain sulphur, phosphorous, silicon and carbon, as impurities.

Primitive iron-making methods

In at least one part of Africa, iron is still being made today by the same methods which have been used since 500 BC. A double bellows system is used to blow air into a stone/clay furnace. This is necessary to get the high temperature needed for smelting. When smelting has taken place, the furnace is allowed to cool down. Then the *lump* of iron is removed. Pieces of iron are broken off and hammered when red hot, to get rid of the impurities. Arrowheads, etc., are made from these *purified* pieces by the blacksmith. Among the tribes who still make iron in this way, the blacksmith is treated with great respect and is thought to get his power from heaven, or some mystical body!

well below the melting point of the metal in the ore. This results in the waste being removed, and the fine

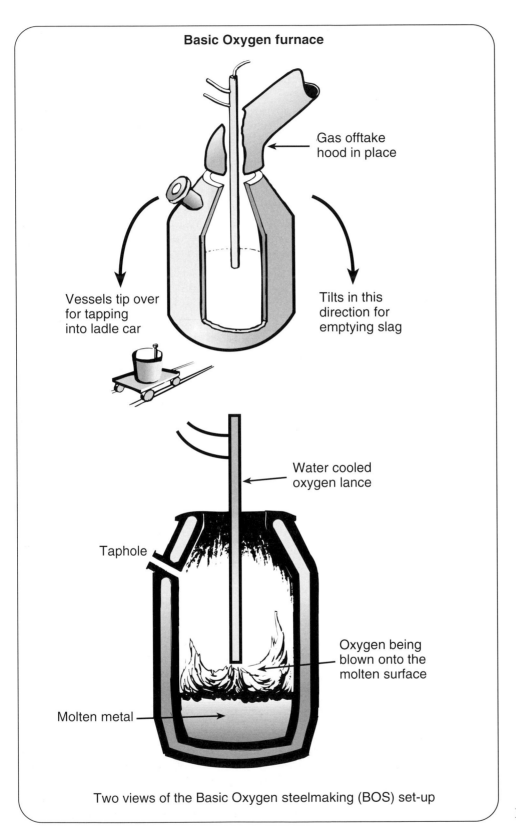

Basic Oxygen furnace

Gas offtake hood in place

Vessels tip over for tapping into ladle car

Tilts in this direction for emptying slag

Water cooled oxygen lance

Taphole

Oxygen being blown onto the molten surface

Molten metal

Two views of the Basic Oxygen steelmaking (BOS) set-up

FIGURE 3 *Basic oxygen process.*

HOW STEEL IS PRODUCED

There are *two* stages in the production of steel:

1 The extraction of iron from the iron ore, which we have already considered.
2 The refining of iron in special furnaces.

Iron from the blast furnace contains around 4% carbon, and sometimes up to 3-4% sulphur, phosphorus, manganese and silicon. Refining, then, is basically a process which removes most of these unwanted elements. They are removed by heating and bringing them into contact with oxygen. The impurities combine with oxygen to form oxides which form a slag.

The processes used to produce steel

The *three* main processes used in the production of steel are, in order of tonnes produced:

1 The basic oxygen process.
2 The electric arc process.
3 The open hearth process.

THE BASIC OXYGEN PROCESS

This is a modern development of the old Bessemer process. The main difference is that, while the Bessemer process used compressed air, (blown up through the bottom of the vessel), the basic oxygen process, often referred to as basic oxygen steel-making (BOS), uses oxygen. The oxygen is brought on to the surface of the metal by a water-cooled lance. Roughly 20% of air is oxygen, so that about 80% of the compressed air used in the Bessemer took no part in getting rid of impurities, but, in fact, had the effect of cooling the furnace. As well as changing from air to oxygen, there have been many other improvements, with the result that a basic oxygen furnace can produce about 400 tonnes of steel in about an hour, see **FIGURE 3**.

Basic oxygen process

The vessel used is made from steel, and is lined with a non-acid *basic* refractory lining. This basic lining is made of dolomite, which is a mineral ($CaCO_3$, $MgCO_3$) named after a French man called Dolomieu. Early Bessemer converters were lined with *Ganister* (acid lining), which could only be used with irons, which were low in phosphorus and sulphur contents.

However, in 1878, Gilchrist introduced dolomite as a furnace lining material. Because it could withstand very high temperatures, and was 'non acid', this *basic lining* meant that the phosphorus could be burned off along with most of the sulphur, to form slag. Basic slag is a good fertiliser because it contains phosphoric acid. Some of the phosphorus and the sulphur are absorbed by the basic lining.

Scrap charging

Scrap iron and steel, which form up to 30% of the charge, are first tipped into the tilted vessel, which has been preheated. Molten iron from the blast furnace, which is carried in torpedo cars, is now fed in to make up the rest of the charge. This leaves the furnace ready for the blow.

The blow

A special hood for collecting fumes fits onto the top of the vessel. The water-cooled pipe, which carries the oxygen down to the surface of the hot metal, is lowered down through the hood until it is 600 mm above the molten metal. For 15 minutes, a large volume, almost 900 m^3 of oxygen, at high pressure, is blown onto the hot metal surface. This causes a rise in temperature, which melts any scrap not already melted. The oxygen *burns off* the impurities. Samples are taken to check the composition of the steel.

Pouring

Once the chemical analysis indicates that the metal composition is what is required, the oxygen lance is lifted up, and the hood is removed. Now, the molten steel is poured out through a spout-like *taphole*, by turning the vessel on one side. The steel is then cast into ingots, or is processed by continuous castings.

Slagging

When all the steel has been poured out, the vessel is turned upside down, in the opposite direction to that for pouring, for slag removal.

THE ELECTRIC ARC PROCESS

Cold scrap metal makes up the charge in this furnace although some *hot metal* was used in the past. Heat for this furnace is by an electric arc, similar to that used in electric arc welding. The process is used to produce steels of high quality, because it is fairly easy to control the composition. As you can see in

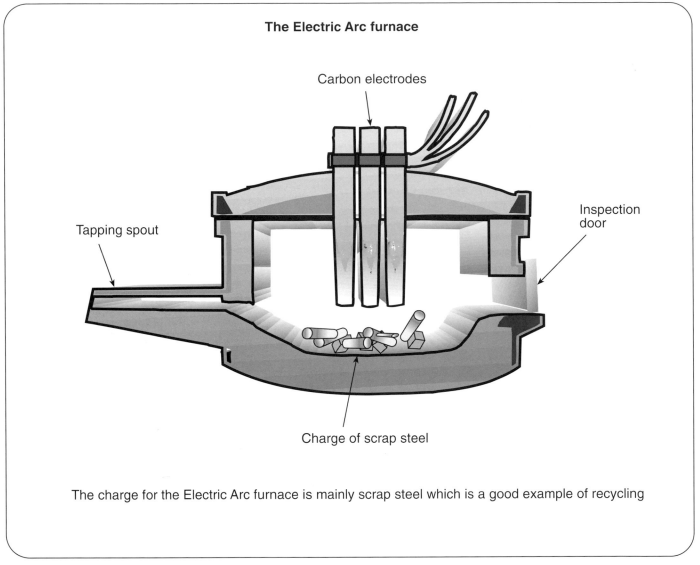

The Electric Arc furnace

Carbon electrodes

Tapping spout

Inspection door

Charge of scrap steel

The charge for the Electric Arc furnace is mainly scrap steel which is a good example of recycling

FIGURE 4   *Electric arc furnace.*

FIGURE 4, there are three electrodes. These are connected so that electric current flows from one electrode through the metal to the next electrode, heating and melting the scrap metal charge. The electric power required is very high. For example, a 90 tonne electric arc furnace might need up to 31 Megawatts (MW) to completely melt the charge, enough electricity to supply 15,000 houses.

Electric arc furnace
The furnace is a circular vessel that sits on a system of *rollers*, which allows it to tip over for slagging and tapping. To allow the furnace to be charged, a swivelling roof moves to one side, complete with raised carbon electrodes. A 90 tonne electric arc furnace is around 6 metres in diameter, and the carbon electrodes have a diameter of 560 millimetres.

Charging
The charge consists solely of scrap. Scrap is loaded into a *clamshell furnace charging bucket*, and then from

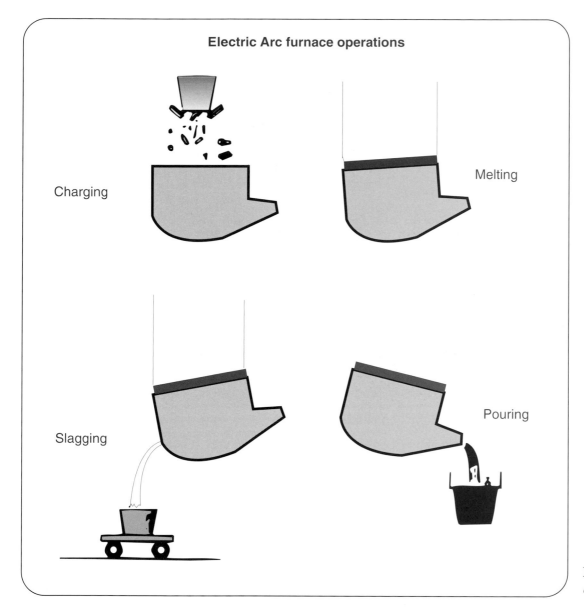

Electric Arc furnace operations

Charging

Melting

Slagging

Pouring

FIGURE 5 *Electric arc furnace operations.*

this into the furnace. Now, the roof-electrode assembly is swung back into place, and the electrodes are lowered. Electric current is switched on and the arc is started, by raising the electrodes a little above the surface of the scrap.

Refining
Heat from the arc melts the scrap. To get rid of impurities, and to control the composition of the steel, iron oxide, lime, and fluorspar are added as needed. The iron oxide gives off its oxygen for

oxidising the impurities. Lime and fluorspar are both fluxes (fluorspar takes its name from the Latin word *fluere*, which means *to flow*). During the process, samples are taken and analysed, and adjustments are made if necessary, see **FIGURE 5**

Slagging and tapping
Slag is first either raked off, or poured off, into *slag ladles*. Tapping follows by tilting the furnace so that the molten steel pours out the spout into the teeming pouring ladle.

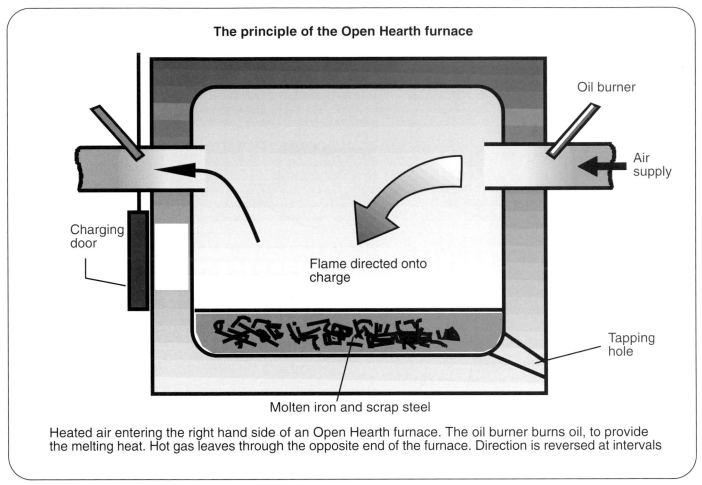

The principle of the Open Hearth furnace

Oil burner

Air supply

Charging door

Flame directed onto charge

Tapping hole

Molten iron and scrap steel

Heated air entering the right hand side of an Open Hearth furnace. The oil burner burns oil, to provide the melting heat. Hot gas leaves through the opposite end of the furnace. Direction is reversed at intervals

FIGURE 6   *Open hearth furnace.*

THE OPEN HEARTH PROCESS

This is an old process, having been used for about one hundred years, **FIGURE 6**. First, scrap is fed into the shallow basin-like hearth. A flame from either a gas or oil nozzle jet heats the space above the scrap and most of the scrap melts. Now, the molten iron part of the charge is added. In recent years, oxygen lancing has been used to remove unwanted carbon and other impurities. Another method of supplying oxygen is by enriching the combustion air with oxygen. These improvements have meant that the rate of output has been increased dramatically. However, it still takes 10 hours to convert 350 tonnes of steel by this method, making it very slow indeed, compared to the basic oxygen process. For this reason, it is likely that the use of the open hearth process will fade out in the near future.

CAST IRONS AND THEIR APPLICATIONS

It has already been mentioned that pig iron from the blast-furnace is used to make *cast iron*. Cast iron is not just one single metal. It is the name given to a 'family' of irons, which are extremely suitable for casting into moulds. Iron casting takes place in an iron foundry, and it is here that the cast iron is made in a furnace, which is small by comparison with any of the furnaces discussed so far. Traditionally a cupola furnace, shown in **FIGURE 7**, has been used. This is like a smaller version of the blast furnace. However, the standard furnace in the cast iron

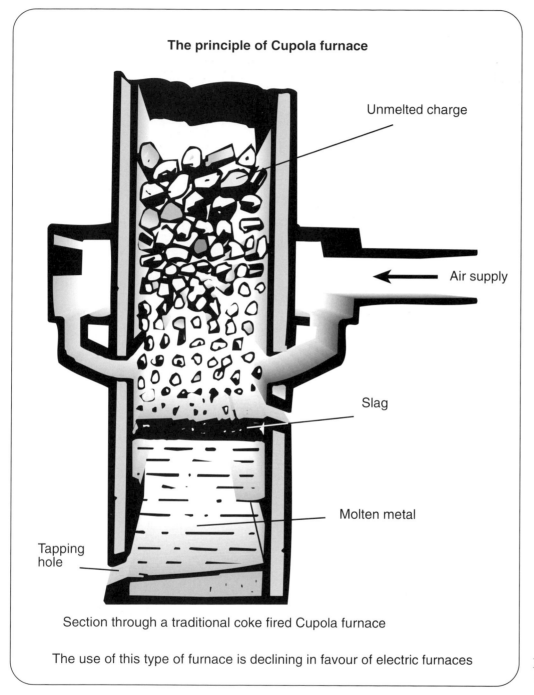

The principle of Cupola furnace

Unmelted charge

Air supply

Slag

Molten metal

Tapping
hole

Section through a traditional coke fired Cupola furnace

The use of this type of furnace is declining in favour of electric furnaces

FIGURE 7 *The principle of Cupola furnace.*

industry at present is an electric furnace. One of the main reasons for using electric furnaces is that they can be very closely controlled. Modern electric furnaces are controlled by computers.

Principle of Cupola furnace
Pig iron and scrap are the raw materials, together with other special elements. Steel scrap can be used, but it is mainly scrap cast iron which finds its way to

FIGURE 8   *This is a channel-type induction furnace, with a capacity of 65 tonnes. It is used for holding and heating cast iron. (Courtesy: Asea Brown Boveri)*

the foundry. The traditional furnace shown here is coke-fired. As in the blast furnace, limestone is used as a flux to *trap* the impurities into a slag. The molten iron is tapped from the bottom of the cupola into a ladle, which is then used to fill the moulds, as required. However, the metal is not always needed immediately, and if this is the case, it is stored in a holding furnace. This furnace 'holds' the molten iron at a temperature of 1450°C, until it is needed on the moulding line.

Electric induction furnaces are much smaller in size, and are easier to manage seen in **FIGURE 8**. Most foundries tend to have more than one casting furnace, and at least one holding furnace. Holding furnaces are usually of the twin inductor mains frequency type.

CAST IRON MOULDING METHODS

The traditional moulding method is by hand, using greens and moulding techniques, where the *moulding*

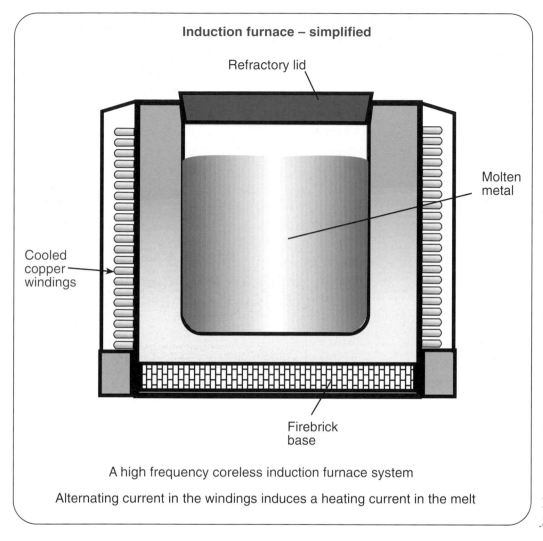

Induction furnace – simplified

Refractory lid

Molten
metal

Cooled
copper
windings

Firebrick
base

A high frequency coreless induction furnace system

Alternating current in the windings induces a heating current in the melt

FIGURE 9 *The Induction furnace.*

sand (clay) sticks together to form the mould. Other methods have now been adapted for use with cast iron. Cast irons can be die-cast. Die-casting has always been associated with low-temperature zinc-based alloys, or aluminium alloys. However, it is also in common use for cast iron. Steel moulds are used, and, as these are expensive to make, this type of moulding is only used when large numbers of castings are required.

Shell moulding

This method makes use of polymer resins to mix with sand, which is laid onto a heated metal pattern. A thin skin, or shell mould, which is baked hard, is produced. Molten cast iron is then poured into the mould. Shell moulding is also used for alloy steels.

The process can be seen in **FIGURES 10** and **11**.

Centrifugal casting

The name gives a good clue to how this is done. Molten metal is fed into a rotating mould. Centrifugal force, acting on the metal, forces it into the mould. The iron cools and solidifies, giving a hollow casting. Cast iron ornaments and pipes are manufactured by this method. Centrifugal casting is widely used in the polymer (plastics) industry. The method is shown in **FIGURE 12**

Cooling rate

The cooling rate affects the structure of cast iron, see **FIGURE 13**. If the iron is cooled slowly, graphite appears as flakes, or rosettes. This causes weakness in

Figure 10   *Shell moulding. The operator is to be seen dumping a sand/resin mixture onto a heated metal pattern within the box in front of him. Patterns are normally made from either steel or aluminium. Heat from the pattern partially cures the mould mixture. Curing is completed by heating by oven or special heater. In the background of this photograph, you can see a mould being heated. (Courtesy: Deloro Stellite GmbH)*

the iron. Fast cooling, on the other hand, causes cementite to form, which, as you know, is hard. If a casting has a thin section, then this section will cool quickly, and become hard. The illustration shows how cooling rate and thickness affect cast iron. When castings in grey iron are required with certain hard surfaces, then the fast cooling, mentioned above, is employed. Normally, the selective cooling is achieved by inserting large pieces of metal in the mould, near to the surface to be hardened. Slideways on machines such as lathes and milling machines are treated in this way. Cooling may also be slowed down to prevent hardening.

COMPOSITION OF CAST IRONS

Cast irons contain between 2% and 4% carbon, which is much more than is present in steel. In cast iron, the carbon can be present as:

FIGURE 11 *Close-up of moulds/patterns, after curing by heating. When cooling takes place, the patterns are removed and the moulds are ready for use. Deloro pour their own specially developed alloys. (Courtesy: Deloro Stellite GmbH)*

- **Graphite flakes** – it is from graphite that the centre of a pencil is made. Flakes of graphite have the effect of weakening the structure
- **Cementite**, or iron carbide (Fe_3C), which is discussed elsewhere in the text.
- **Other elements** influence the form, in which the carbon will exist in the cast iron. Silicon has the effect of making the carbon appear as graphite.

CLASSIFICATION OF CAST IRONS

Cast irons can be divided into the following groups:

- **Grey cast irons**
- **Malleable cast irons**
- **Spheroidal graphite, or nodular irons**
- **Special purpose irons.**

Grey cast iron

This is an alloy of iron, carbon, and silicon, with other elements added to modify properties, **FIGURE 14**. Grey cast iron is so called because it has a grey colour if it is broken. Graphite causes the grey colour. Most of the grey irons have a pearlitic matrix (crystalline phase), which gives good strength qualities. Where machinability is important, a ferrite matrix is best. There are seven main standardised grades of grey cast irons in use, together with many non-standard grades.

The seven standard grades designated by the British Standards Institution (BSI), are: 150, 180, 220, 260,

FIGURE 12 *Centrifugal casting is in progress in this photograph. Molten metal has been poured into a spinning cylindrical die-mould, which is made from steel or graphite, and excess metal is being poured out of the die. A range of cylindrical components up to 750 mm in diameter, and 325 kg, can be produced by this process, which gives excellent quality. (Courtesy: Deloro Stellite GmbH)*

300, 350, and 400. The numbers give the minimum tensile strengths in N/mm^2.

The main advantages of grey cast iron are:

- **It can be cast into very intricate shapes, for example cylinder heads for engines**
- **It has good resistance to sliding wear because of the graphite flakes**
- **Overall machinability is very good, especially with the ferrite matrix**
- **It can be surface-hardened, with the use of chilling pieces**
- **Grey cast iron moulding is an economic method of manufacture.**

Malleable cast irons

Malleable cast iron can be thought of as a metal which has some of the properties of grey cast iron, and some of the properties of mild steel. It is tougher than grey iron, less ductile than mild steel, is fairly soft, and machines very well. If this iron is cooled quickly, no graphite is formed, and the iron will be white if it is broken. It is the cementite which causes the white colour, and these irons are known as *white irons*.

There are *three* kinds of malleable cast iron:

- **Whiteheart**
- **Blackheart**
- **Pearlitic iron.**

The names of all three are related to the appearance of fractures of the irons, when sections are broken.

Whiteheart

In the *as cast* state, the metal has a high carbon content, consists of pearlite and cementite, and is hard and brittle. Whiteheart malleable is easy to cast in thin sections which have a tough core. Whiteheart is produced by placing the castings in steel boxes containing haematite. The boxes are heated in a malleablising furnace to about 1000°C, and kept at this temperature for up to 12 hours. Controlled cooling completes the process. The result is a structure of high tensile pearlite, surrounded by soft ductile ferrite. Whiteheart cast iron is made in Europe for non-critical application, but it is not made in the United States. It has a tensile strength of about 400 N/mm^2 depending on the heat treatment received and the actual composition of the iron. (The tensile strength of mild steel is 400 N/mm^2.) The structure of Whiteheart malleable cast iron is shown in **FIGURE 15**.

Blackheart

The production of Blackheart cast iron is similar to that for Whiteheart. It is held at a temperature of 950°C for twelve hours, and then allowed to cool very slowly. Cooling is at around 4°C per hour. The final structure has graphite in *nodules* (little round knotty lumps), in ferrite, over the whole section (unlike Whiteheart). The presence of the graphite causes the material to machine easily. The tensile strength of Blackheart malleable is about 300–330N/mm^2.

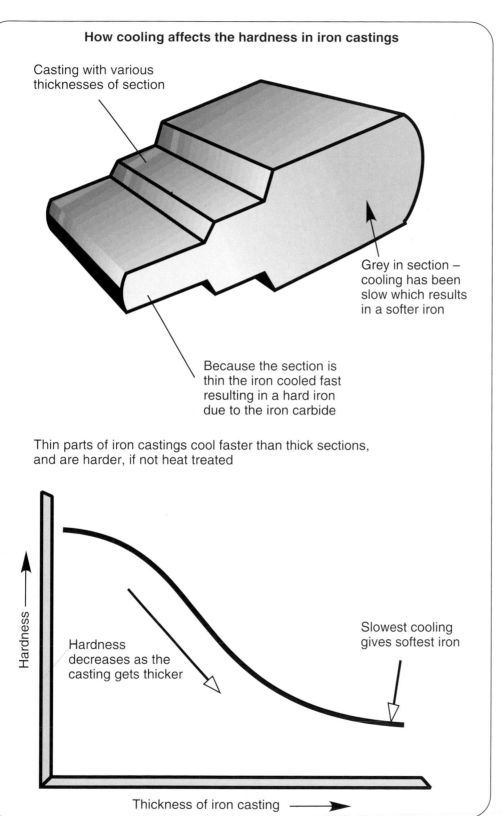

How cooling affects the hardness in iron castings

Casting with various thicknesses of section

Grey in section –
cooling has been
slow which results
in a softer iron

Because the section is
thin the iron cooled fast
resulting in a hard iron
due to the iron carbide

Thin parts of iron castings cool faster than thick sections,
and are harder, if not heat treated

Hardness

Hardness
decreases as the
casting gets thicker

Slowest cooling
gives softest iron

Thickness of iron casting ⟶

FIGURE 13 *Cooling effects.*

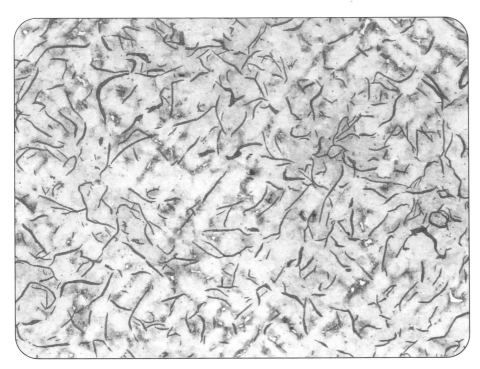

FIGURE 14 *This a photomicrograph of grey cast iron. The structure is magnified 100 times. Long flakes of graphite (dark grey) can easily be identified — they look like worms. (Courtesy: BCRIA Birmingham)*

Pearlitic iron

This type of malleable iron is made from the same white iron (2%–3% carbon), as Blackheart. Heat treatment of pearlitic is usually carried out in *two* stages. The first stage is similar to the Blackheart process, after which the castings are quenched in oil. The second stage is the tempering to the required hardness.

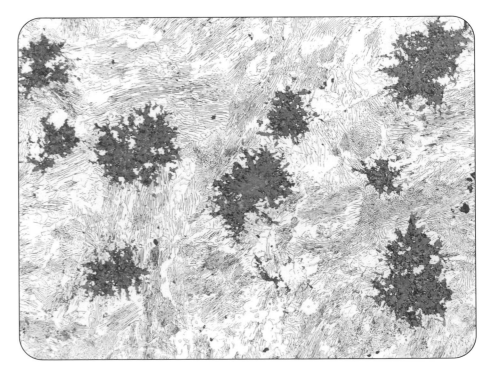

FIGURE 15 *In this photomicrograph of Whiteheart malleable cast iron, the carbon is gathered into clusters, or rosettes. If you examine the structure closely, you can see that the matrix which contains the rosettes of carbon is pearlitic (layers of grey cementite and layers of white ferrite). (Courtesy: BCRIA, Birmingham)*

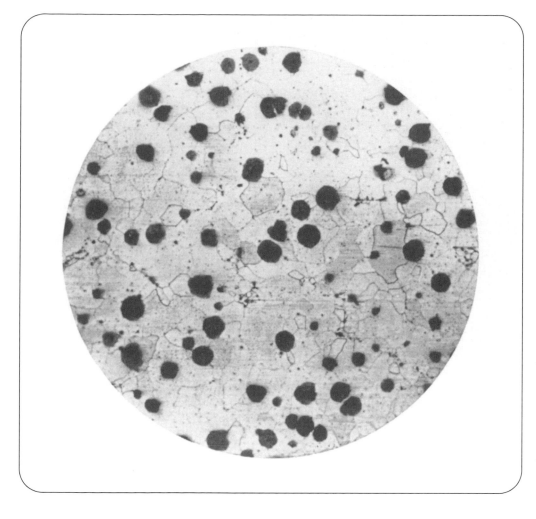

FIGURE 16 *This is SG iron in the annealed state, magnified 100 times. The round black parts are actually balls, or spheres of carbon, which give both ductility and strength.*
(Courtesy: Blackmoor Foundry Co Ltd)

Pearlitic malleable iron can have a tensile strength up to 700 N/mm². British Standards designate malleable cast irons as follows: type/tensile strength/ % elongation. The letter B is for Blackheart iron, P is for pearlitic iron, and A is for Whiteheart iron.

Example is a pearlitic malleable iron, with a tensile strength of 570 N/mm² and a percentage elongation of 3%.

BS list two grades for Whiteheart, three for Blackheart, and five for pearlitic malleable cast irons.

Spheroidal graphite (SG) or nodular irons, see **FIGURE 16**. It was discovered, towards the end of the 1940's, that certain irons treated with magnesium had graphite in nodules, or spheroids, rather than in flakes. This iron was named spheroidal graphite iron,

often referred to as SG iron. The production of SG iron is usually carried out in a special electric furnace. Just before it is to be cast, it is inoculated with magnesium alloy. This can cause a violent reaction, if not carefully controlled. Low sulphur base iron must be used because the magnesium would combine with sulphur to form magnesium sulphide.

If this happened, the magnesium would not nodularise the carbon. The properties of SG iron are better than those of malleable iron. SG irons have a high degree of ductility, which can be increased by suitable heat treatment. Because of this ductility, SG iron is often called *ductile iron*. High tensile strength, combined with ductility, have meant that SG irons are now being used in applications which had been

FIGURE 17 *When SG iron is austempered, the result is the structure shown here. Carbon masses are now shaped like two cones joined base-to-base, and have an umbrella-like appearance in the photomicrograph. During the austempering, the austenite does not get time to diffuse to pearlite, and the needle-like structure that is formed is known as **bainite**. (Courtesy – BCRIA, Birmingham)*

reserved for steel forgings. The tensile strength of SG iron can be as high as 800 N/mm², with 2% elongation – this is the 800/2 grade. There are six BS grades of SG iron. (The 800/2 grade has the highest tensile strength).

SPECIAL PURPOSE IRONS

Austempered ductile iron

These are a comparatively new family of SG irons, which are given a special new heat treatment called austempering heat treatment, see **FIGURE 17**. They have excellent combinations of *toughness*, *strength*, and *ductility*, coupled with good wear resistance. Castings are easily machined before being given the special heat treatment. Best results are obtained from first-class, defect-free SG castings. First, the castings are 'soaked' at the austempering temperature between 850°C and 950°C. Then, they are put into a liquid at 235–250°C, and kept there for about four hours. It is during these hours that the austempering occurs, when the iron is transformed into a structure called bainite. When the castings are cooled, they are ready for service.

Two important points should be noted:

1 An extremely high tensile strength of up to 1600 N/mm² can be obtained. Consider that the tensile strength of SG iron in the *as cast* condition is usually less than half this value.
2 High ductility can be combined with high strength, e.g. 14% elongation at 1000 N/mm². Compare this with the 800/2 grade of SG iron.

A popular application of austempered ductile irons (ADI's) is for gear manufacture. Up to very recently, gears were made, in most cases, from hardened steel forgings, which are very expensive to produce. ADI's prove to be much less expensive.

Other special irons

There is quite a number of special cast irons, which have limited application. Most of these rely on the introduction of an alloying metal to impart special properties such as hardness, corrosion resistance or strength.

Austenitic irons

These contain nickel and have special properties

such as corrosion resistance, and are called the *Ni-Resist* group of irons. The Ni-Resist group offers outstanding resistance to corrosion, erosion and high temperatures.

SUMMARY

The two common iron ores are *haematite*, which has red streaks, and *magnetite*, which is magnetic.

Iron is produced in a blast furnace, which is charged with *iron ore, coke and limestone*. The limestone acts as a flux.

Pig iron is the name given to the iron directly produced by a blast-furnace.

Steel is an *alloy* of iron and carbon. Carbon is not a metal but has some metallic properties: it can conduct electricity.

The two steps to produce steel are: *extracting* the iron from the ore, and the *refining* of the iron by controlling the amount of carbon etc.

The *Basic Oxygen* process uses oxygen to help produce steel. It is a very fast method, and a furnace may produce 400 tonnes of steel in an hour.

Scrap steel is the main ingredient to produce steel by the *Electric Arc* steel-making process.

Cast iron is the name given to a range of irons which contain a high percentage of carbon and are good for casting into moulds.

Cupola furnaces were traditionally used in cast iron production, but *electric induction* furnaces are smaller and easier to use.

Many items made from cast iron are cast into sand moulds. The sand used is like a sticky clay, and this method of production is known as *sandcasting*.

Grey cast iron, so called because of its colour when a section is broken, has a very wide range of uses.

Spheroidal graphite (SG) iron has carbon present in little nodules or spheres. This makes the iron stronger than if the carbon is present as flakes, as in grey cast iron.

Classification of Carbon and Alloy Steels

INTRODUCTION

Plain carbon steel is an alloy of iron and carbon. Iron itself is fairly soft and tough, and does not have a very desirable range of properties. However, when iron and carbon are alloyed, the result is a range of very useful carbon steels. Up to 1.7% by weight, of carbon, can be present in the alloy. However, 1.3% by weight, is the usual maximum. Small amounts of other elements such as sulphur, silicon, phosphorus and manganese, are also contained in carbon steel. It is very important that both the sulphur and the phosphorous contents should be kept very low because their presence tends to cause cracking in carbon steels.

PROPERTIES OF CARBON STEELS

The properties of carbon steels can be altered over a wide range by:

Varying the percentage of carbon present in the steel.
Choice and use of heat treatment.

Since heat treatment of steels is discussed under Heat Treatment, we will concentrate here on the effect of varying the percentage of carbon present in the steel. On the thermal equilibrium diagram for iron-carbon (carbon steel), the *eutectoid point* occurs when 0.83% carbon is present in the steel. This fact is used in the classification of carbon steels. Steels with less than the eutectoid content, which is 0.83%, are known as *hypo-eutectoid* carbon steels, while those with a carbon content above the eutectoid content, are called *hyper-eutectoid* carbon steels.

Hypo is a prefix which generally means *under* – hence, we have *hypodermic* injection, which is an *under the skin* injection. Hyper means over, and we often hear a child being described as hyper-active (overactive). Hypersonic is used to denote speeds over Mach 5 (Mach 1 is the speed of sound, which is 331 m/s). The term mach number, is named after Ernst Mach 1838-1916.

Carbon steels are more generally divided into the divisions:

- **Mild steels, which contain up to 0.25% carbon (also known as low carbon steels)**
- **Medium carbon steels, which fall between 0.26% and 0.5% carbon**
- **High carbon steels containing over 0.6% carbon.**

Coding and compositions

All steel alloys are coded according to their compositions and properties. Three coding systems are in common use. These are: the British Standards (BS), DIN and the AISI-SAE (American Iron and Steel Institute, Society of Automotive Engineers). In Europe, it is the BS and DIN systems, which are most common, although all systems are reasonably well linked. In the BS system, each steel is designated by a code made up as follows: three digits, a letter, two more digits. The type of steel is given by the first three digits. From 000 up to 199, denotes a carbon steel, which may contain manganese. The percentage of manganese is found by dividing by 100, for example, a steel code with 150 as the first three digits, denotes a carbon steel which contains 1.5% manganese. When there is no manganese in the steel, the first three digits are 000, which means that the steel is carbon steel.

The letter following the first three digits gives an indication of the properties of the steel, and, finally, the last two digits tell us the percentage of carbon present in the steel, if the digits are divided by 100.

Properties of carbon steel

Because ferrite is almost pure iron, it is soft, ductile and not very strong. Therefore, steel with a large percentage of ferrite will have almost the same properties as ferrite. *Iron carbide*, or *cementite* is extremely hard, but also very brittle. So, a steel containing mostly cementite will be hard and brittle.

FIGURE 1 *Here, you can see the Esso/Shell Brent A oil rig, which operates in the North Sea. It is manufactured mainly from carbon steels. The actual drilling mechanism is on the top. (Courtesy: Shell UK)*

Steel with a lot of pearlite will have high strength, but will also be tough.

Alloy steels

The plain carbon steels are not strictly *plain* because, as already mentioned, they contain small amounts of other elements such as manganese. Carbon steels can be made to have a wide variety of mechanical properties. These properties depend on the carbon content, and on the heat treatment received. It has been found that the addition of certain other metals to steel, can influence structure and properties. These are alloy steels, and there are many, but each one has its own particular application. It suits a particular job because it has one or several special properties. There are general divisions into which alloy steels are divided:

- **Structural**
- **Tool and die**
- **Stainless and heat resisting**
- **Magnetic.**

Structural steels

These are the alloys used to make the *hard-working* parts of engines and machines. Axles, crankshafts, connecting rods, are some of the highly-stressed parts in question. These components are subjected to shock loads (e.g. the stub axle on a car has to withstand the *shock load* when the car wheel drops into a pothole). The alloying materials are mainly nickel, manganese, chromium and molybdenum, which are used to make high strength shock-resistant structural, or constructional alloy steels. Special steels known as *maraging steels*, may also be included here. These are high-strength high alloy steels. Normally, they contain large amounts of nickel, typically 18% to 22%, and smaller amounts of molybdenum, cobalt and titanium. Maraging steels may be heat treated by heating them to 840°C, and then allowing them to cool in air. The result is an extremely high-strength and hard *martensitic* steel, the strength increasing by a factor of three (from 700 N/mm² 00 to 2100 N/mm²), due to the heat-treatment. The name *maraging* is a combination of martensite and ageing or age hardening: mar – ageing. The preferred spelling is *maraging*.

Tool and die alloy steels

As the name suggests, all sorts of tools and dies are made from this type of alloy. Carbon steels may be used to produce some tools, but, because of the fact that it is brittle when hard, its applications are limited. For this reason, industry has developed alloy

Steel type classification in the BS system	
First 3 digit range	**Type of steel denoted by the first 3 digits**
000 - 199	Carbon or carbon-manganese steels
200 - 240	Free cutting steels
250	Spring steels - silicon and manganese added
300 - 499	The stainless steels including heat-resisting steels
500 - 999	Special alloy steels

British Standard (BS) coding system for 000 to 999 steels		
First 3 digits	**The letter**	**The last two digits**
Denote type of steel. Gives the amount of manganese in the alloy. The number is 100 x the manganese content. If, for example, these digits are 025, then the percentage of manganese is: (025 / 100)% = 0.25%	**A** - means that the steel has had its composition checked by chemical analysis **H** - means that the steel is suitable for a certain range of hardnesses **M** - means that the steel has certain mechanical properties **S** - means that the steel is a stainless steel	These are the digits that tell us the carbon content of the steel. If, for example, the last two digits are 12, then the percentage of carbon in the steel is: (12 / 100)% = 0.12%

Example of how coding works - If a steel is coded as 080M40, it is decoded as follows:-

It is a carbon or carbon-manganese steel
It contains 0.80% manganese and 0.40% carbon

It has certain specified mechanical properties

FIGURE 2 *Steel type classification in the BS system.*

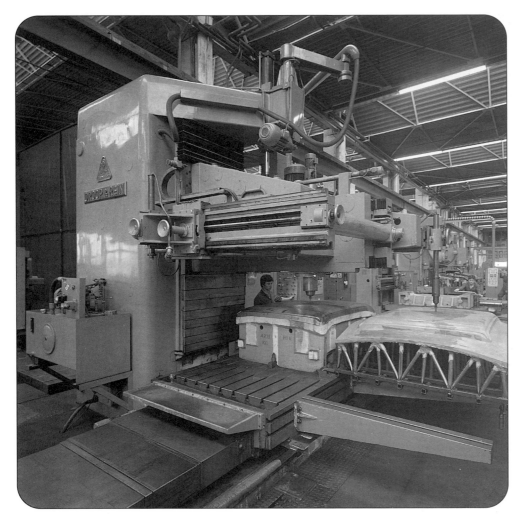

FIGURE 3 *The machine shown here is used to produce press tools by copying a pattern of what is required. On the right, you can see what looks like the spindle and chuck of a drilling machine. This is the part that moves over the pattern or model, and relays information to the cutting tool, which machines the die (seen here on the bed of the machine) to shape. The pattern is normally made larger than the actual unit required, and the pantograph (the copying part combined with the cutting part) can be set so that the unit is made to the exact required size. This method helps to eliminate inaccuracies in the pattern. (Courtesy: Lapple)*

tool steels, which possess the necessary properties for this type of application. The range of application is very wide indeed. Chisels, ball bearings, shear blades, master gauges, extrusion dies, cutting tools, press punches and dies, are some of the items constructed from this particular kind of alloy steel.

Many combinations of alloying elements are used depending on what kind of job the alloy has to do. Usually, the alloy has to be very hard, have high wear resistance, and not soften when heated.

The main metals used for alloying are: tungsten, chromium, molybdenum and vanadium.

Vanadium has the effect of making the grain fine, which is necessary in order to have good toughness and to be able to withstand shock loads. The addition of chromium and tungsten give steels high speed cutting properties allowing them to cut well at high temperatures, while molybdenum imparts high temperature strength, as well as improving creep resistance.

Steels which are extremely important in the machining of components, are the *free cutting* steels, which have sulphur and/or lead added. Both of these elements impart very good *machinability* to steels. Because of the sulphur addition, the steels are also known as *resulphurised* steels.

Stainless steels

In 1913, Brearley discovered that if steel contains some chromium, its corrosion resistance is increased.

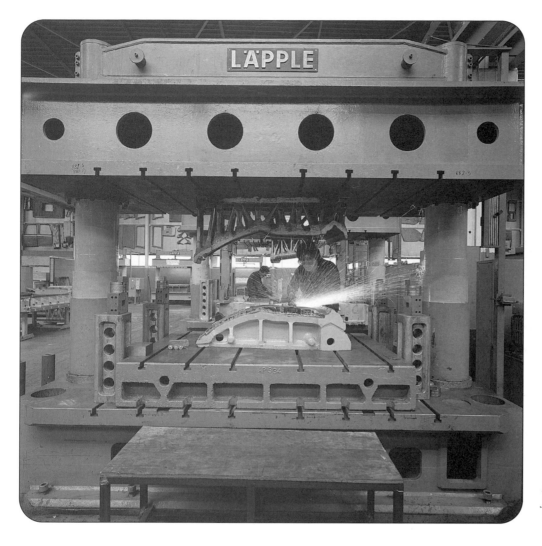

FIGURE 4 *In this photograph, the toolmaker is finishing the die using a hand-held grinder.*

This resistance to corrosion led to the name stainless steel.

There are different kinds of stainless steel:

- **Austenitic**
- **Ferritic**
- **Martensitic.**

Austenitic stainless steels contain up to 26% chromium (a minimum of 12%), and sometimes some molybdenum. Because these steels are fully austenitic at all temperatures, they always have a face centred cubic (FCC) structure, which gives them good ductility. A common type of austenitic stainless steel is known as 18/8 steel, which contains 18% chromium and 8% nickel. This is the steel which was traditionally used to make kitchen ware (e.g. sinks etc.). In recent years, it has been replaced for this application, by the 12/12 alloy (12% chromium and 12% nickel). Austenitic stainless steels are suitable for forming by presswork (the 12/12 being more ductile than the 18/8). They have good corrosion resistance, and are non-magnetic. Austenitic stainless steels are the easiest to weld of all the stainless steels, but can only be hardened by work hardening.

Ferritic stainless steels contain between 12% and 30% chromium, but no nickel. They have bodycentred (BCC) structures and, consequently, poor ductility. This type of alloy can be welded and is used mainly

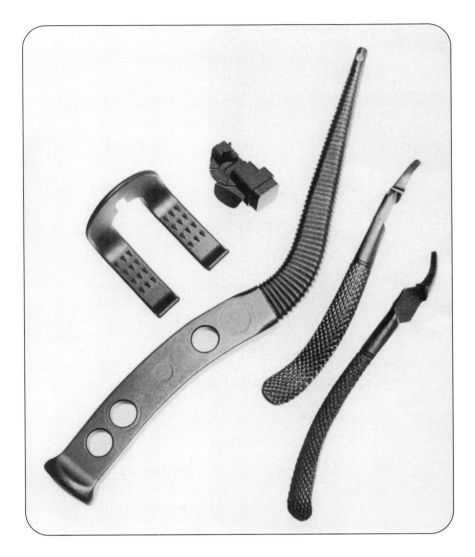

FIGURE 5 *The surgical instruments shown here are made from a range of stainless steels, including 18/8 stainless steel. Manufactured by the investment, or lost wax casting process, these instruments, can be easily sterilised in service. (Courtesy: Roscommon Precision Castings Ltd.)*

for chemical plant parts, because of its excellent resistance to corrosion and its comparatively lower cost. Car exhausts and wheel trims are other uses for this material.

Martensitic stainless steels, as the name implies, can be hardened by heat treatment. About 14%-17% chromium is present with 0.3% carbon. When the alloy is heated to about 1240°C, austenite is formed, which, when quenched in oil or air, changes to martensite, producing a very hard structure. Suitable tempering can produce a range of *hardness-high strength* combinations. Corrosion resistance is not as good as either austenitic or ferritic stainless steels. The main uses are for: table knives, valve and pump parts, ball and roller bearings, as well as turbine parts.

Heat-resisting alloys have a particular composition in the stainless steel range. These must not oxidise or lose strength at high temperatures. They can contain up to 30% chromium, but a typical alloy would be 20% chromium, 25% nickel, and 0.15% carbon.

Magnetic alloys

There are two kinds of magnetic alloys:

1 Alloys used for making permanent magnets.
2 Alloys used to concentrate magnetism in transformers or induction coils.

FIGURE 6 *This close-up photograph shows the components of a miniature stepper motor, which is of the type used in computer hard drives or hard disks. Notice the windings on the field coil (the part with the wires coming from it), there are ten poles on this model. The cores material is made from magnetically soft steel. (Courtesy: the authors)*

1 Permanent magnetic, or *magnetically hard* alloys
These are used for loudspeakers, electric motors, magnetic chucks, etc. Cobalt is the main alloying metal, and an example is alcomax lll, which contains 24.5% cobalt, 8% aluminium, 13.5% nickel, 3% copper, plus a little niobium. An alloy which is used to make permanent magnets is said to be *magnetically hard*. The magnetism is retained.

2 Temporary magnetic, or *magnetically soft* alloys
Magnetically soft, is the term used to describe alloys which give us 'electro magnets' and transformer cores. In such applications, the alloy is wound with polyester insulated wire of small diameter, e.g. 0.7 mm, and current is passed through the usually large number of windings. The alloy stays magnetic as long as the electrical current flows. However, once the current is switched off, the magnetism collapses. These alloys contain mostly iron with about 4% silicon.

SUMMARY

Plain carbon steels are alloys of iron and carbon, but also contain small amounts of silicon, sulphur, phosphorous and manganese.
The properties of plain carbon steels may be changed by heat treatment. The carbon content of low carbon steels can be increased.
Mild steels, also known as low carbon steels, contain up to 0.25% carbon.
Medium carbon steels contain between 0.26% and 0.50% carbon.
High carbon steels are those which contain more than 0.60% carbon.
Alloy steels have other elements added such as tungsten, chromium, molybdenum and vanadium, which give these steels special properties.
Stainless steels are special alloys which have high resistance to corrosion, and may contain chromium, and/or nickel.
Magnetic alloys are used in the manufacture of magnets, either permanent or temporary.

Rolling Steel into Shape

INTRODUCTION

We have already dealt with the production of steel by the various methods. The steelmaking furnaces produce steel in the form of *ingots*, which are large rough chunks of metal, and may weigh anything from 2 to 40 tonnes. Ingots may have different shapes, but it is not hard to understand that these large pieces of steel are not in a usable form. In other words, before the steel is sold to the user, it must be made into bars, rods, sheets, pipes, and the other sections for which there is a demand.

Here, we look at the traditional method of shaping the raw steel by rolling. In the section on manufacturing, continuous casting of steel is discussed briefly. The advantages of that process is evident when you consider that it eliminates many of the stages which we are now going to deal with.

PRIMARY ROLLING

Primary rolling is the first stage in changing the shape of the ingots. As can be seen from **FIGURE 1**, the ingots are first heated to about 1200°C, before being rolled. When steel is heated, it becomes malleable, and it is more easily shaped. This is why it is rolled when it is very hot. The first rolling, or primary rolling, produces blooms, billets, and slabs, as shown. One rolling of a piece of steel through a particular set of rollers is called a *pass*. It takes many passes through the rolls to produce a bloom, a billet, or a slab, and the power required is immense.

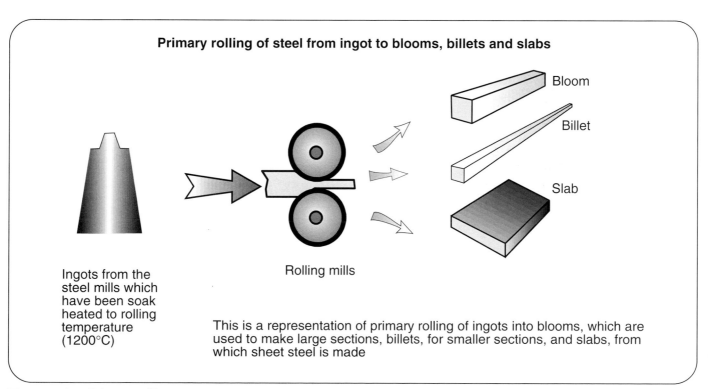

Primary rolling of steel from ingot to blooms, billets and slabs

Bloom

Billet

Slab

Ingots from the steel mills which have been soak heated to rolling temperature (1200°C)

Rolling mills

This is a representation of primary rolling of ingots into blooms, which are used to make large sections, billets, for smaller sections, and slabs, from which sheet steel is made

FIGURE 1   *Primary rolling stages.*

Sections in demand

You will be familiar with some of the sections in which steel is available. It may be bought in a wide variety of cross-sectional shapes, and in various lengths. Bars may be round, square, flat, hexagonal, octagonal, and special shapes such as equal-angle, unequal-angle, U-shaped or channel, H-shaped girders, etc. As well as these, steel is available as sheets of different thickness, hollow sections of various shapes, and as wires. So, the variety of steel shapes produced is very wide.

Stages in rolling steel

1 Heating of ingots to rolling temperature

2 Primary rolling to blooms, billets or slabs

3 Cooling followed by inspection

4 Re-heating in a re-heating furnace

5 Rolling to the required shapes

The semi-finished products (blooms, billets, and slabs) are generally allowed to cool before being inspected, prior to further processing. Cracks and voids can be detected by the use of ultrasonic and magnetic tests, which are described under Non-Destructive Testing (page 171). Once passed, the units are sent for reheating, which takes place in a reheating furnace. In this particular furnace, the blooms are pushed along by each other, so that each time one is pushed into the entry side, one falls out the exit side, onto a conveyor.

Blooms are rolled into structural sections, such as girders, channels, beams, and angles. These are used in building bridges, ships, high buildings, vehicle bodies, trailers, TV towers, factory and barn roofs, electricity pylons, etc. Some blooms go on to be rolled down to billets, which are 50 mm to 120 mm square, in a billet mill.

Usually about eight passes are required from bloom to billet. Billets leave the mill at a speed of around 180 metres per minute. Billets are cut to lengths of 9 metres, while they are moving. A special cutting machine, called a *flying shear* is used. The word *flying* comes from the fact that the cutting blades move along with the billet at the same speed while the cut is being made. Once a cut is made, the flying shear returns to make the next cut.

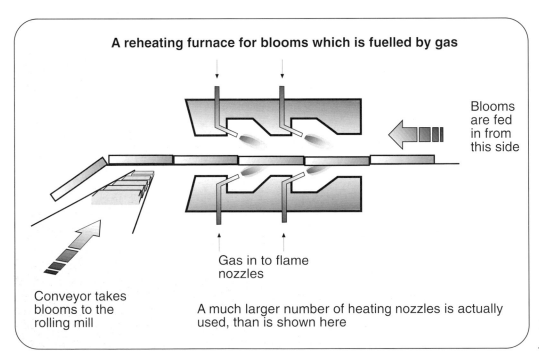

A reheating furnace for blooms which is fuelled by gas

Blooms are fed in from this side

Gas in to flame nozzles

Conveyor takes blooms to the rolling mill

A much larger number of heating nozzles is actually used, than is shown here

FIGURE 2 *Reheating furnace.*

FIGURE 3 *This a travelling crop saw, which has a circular blade with cutting teeth. The blade can be seen to the right, under the safety guard. (Courtesy: Irish Steel)*

Bars, rods and wire are all made from billets in a great variety of sizes, and for a large number of applications, including reinforcing for concrete, shafts, wire for steel cables and light fabrication.

Slabs are rolled to produce:

a Steel plate used to build ships
b Sheet steel from which car bodies, cookers, fridges, barns, computer cabinets, are made

c Tinplate for the food canning, and drinks industries
d Strip steel in various widths for general use
e Welded tubing for fabrication, such as furniture, etc.

Before going on to final rolling, slabs usually have their rough ends cut off by an extremely powerful hydraulic cutting machine known as the *crop shear*.

FIGURE 4 *Here you can see a continuous rolling mill operation. Notice the mills are in line. (Courtesy: Irish Steel)*

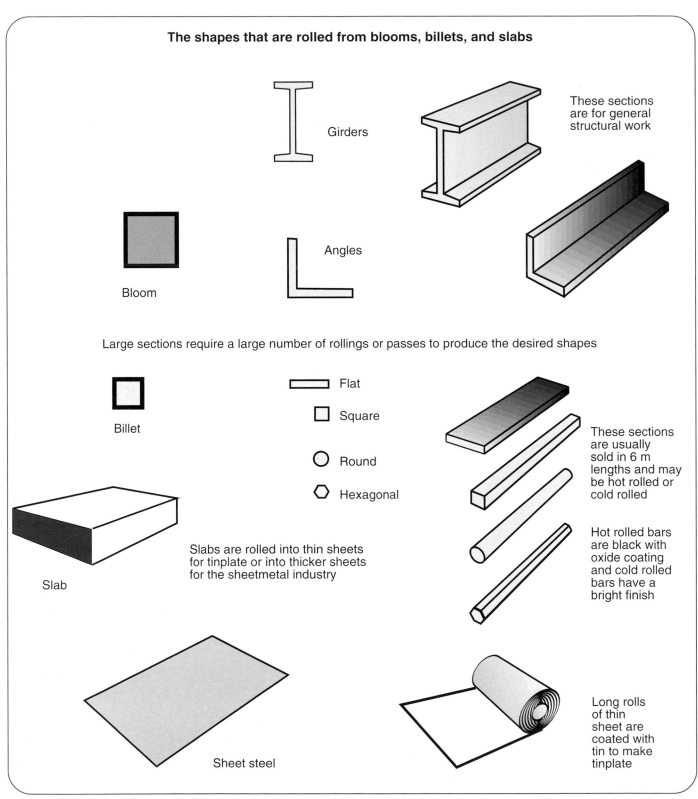

The shapes that are rolled from blooms, billets, and slabs

Girders

These sections are for general structural work

Bloom

Angles

Large sections require a large number of rollings or passes to produce the desired shapes

Billet

Flat

Square

Round

Hexagonal

These sections are usually sold in 6 m lengths and may be hot rolled or cold rolled

Slabs are rolled into thin sheets for tinplate or into thicker sheets for the sheetmetal industry

Slab

Hot rolled bars are black with oxide coating and cold rolled bars have a bright finish

Sheet steel

Long rolls of thin sheet are coated with tin to make tinplate

FIGURE 5 *Rolled shapes.*

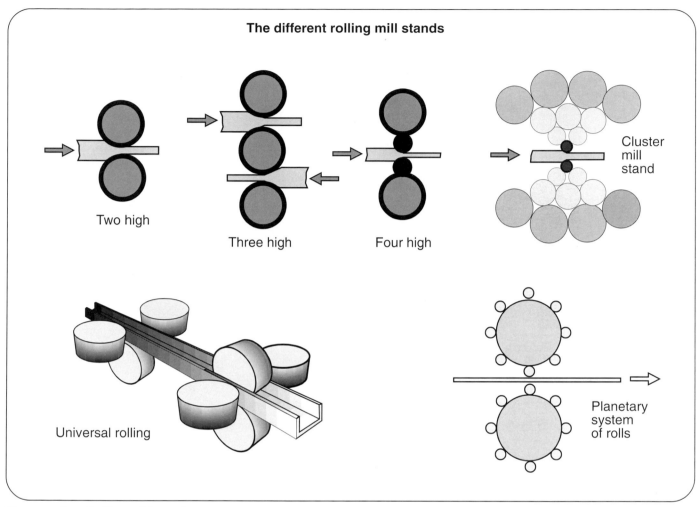

FIGURE 6 *Rolling mill stands.*

As already mentioned, rolling mills need to be very powerful, and consequently, are very expensive to run. Indeed, there are mills which use enough power to run five ferry ships, similar to those which travel between Ireland and Britain! The rolls, together with the electric motors which drive them, are housed in a very strong frame and the whole assembly is known as a *rolling mill stand*.

Rolling mill stand types

The mill stands get their name from the way in which the rolls are arranged. It is the actual number of rolls, or the way in which the rolls are arranged, that gives a rolling mill its name. **FIGURE 6** illustrates six common types of rolling mill.

1 *Two high mill stand* which has two rolls, one placed above the other, hence the name *two high*. This is the type of mill stand which is used for semi-finishing, and it is usually reversing. Reversing simply means that the metal being rolled goes through the rolls first in one direction, and then in the reverse direction. To reverse the mill, roll rotation direction is changed.

2 In a *three high mill stand*, the rolls do not reverse, but the metal being rolled is lifted, or lowered, as required, to the next rolling gap, for the next pass.

3 *Four high mill stand*. Although there are four rolls, only two come in contact with the metal. The other two large rolls are to prevent the working rolls from bending, because of the large forces

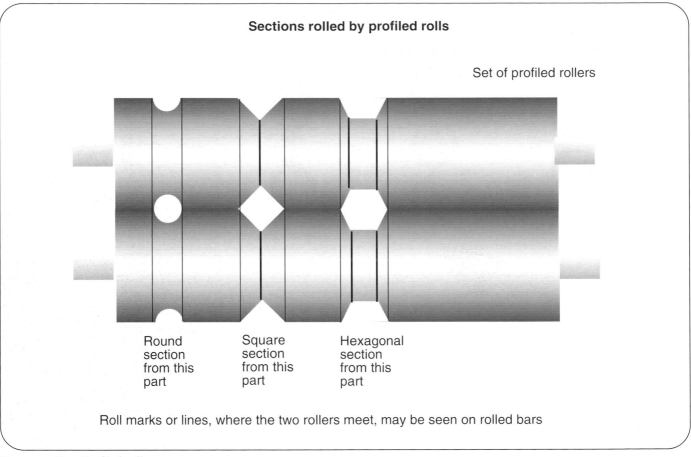

Sections rolled by profiled rolls

Set of profiled rollers

Round section from this part

Square section from this part

Hexagonal section from this part

Roll marks or lines, where the two rollers meet, may be seen on rolled bars

FIGURE 7 *Profiled rolls.*

involved. Four high mills are usually reversing and are mainly used to produce plates and strips.

4 The *planetary mill stands* are so called because the arrangement resembles the movement of planets. This term is also used in the description of certain gear systems. Plate and sheet are produced by this mill, and due to the big number of working rolls, greater rolling force can be exerted on the hot steel. Therefore, a large change in metal thickness is possible in a single pass.

5 *Cluster mill stands.* This arrangement provides great rigidity for rolling cold sheet accurately. This is one of the most expensive systems to set up.

6 In a *universal mill stand*, a combination of vertical and horizontal rolls is used to produce sections by rolling all faces in one pass. Universal stands are the type used to produce channels and I or H beam sections. Commonly referred to as RSJ Rolled Steel Joist).

Different types of roll

The main types of rolls used in rolling mills are:

• **Plain Rolls**
• **Profiled Rolls.**

Plain rolls are plain cylinders, and are used to roll flat products such as plate, sheet, strip, as well as being used in primary rolling.

Profiled rolls are specially shaped rolls. Each pair of rolls is profiled, or shaped so that a particular section is rolled. To roll round rods, each of the profiled rolls has a semi-circular groove cut in it. As can be seen from **FIGURE 7**, round, square, hexagonal may be rolled by the same set of rollers.

FIGURE 8   *In this photograph, you can see very long lengths of hot rolled steel angle section, usually called **angle iron**, cooling on a cooling bed. (Courtesy: Irish Steel)*

Cold rolling of steel

The two main reasons for using cold rolling are that first, much better accuracy is possible than can be achieved with hot rolling and, secondly, the finish obtained is smooth.

Since steel is not very malleable when it is cold, major problems arise in cold rolling as much more power is required, than for hot rolling. This increases production costs. Friction between the rolls and the metal being rolled, is very great indeed. An application of a suitable lubricant, such as palm oil, helps to reduce the friction. Even so, cold rolling is a very complex, and a very difficult operation to control. Cold rolled steel has a clean finish, but during the rolling process, it becomes hard and stiff. In this condition, it is not as easy to work with, as is hot rolled steel, and for some uses it is annealed.

SUMMARY

Steel from the mills must be processed into useful shapes or sections. This may be carried out by rolling. Primary rolling shapes heated ingots into blooms, billets or slabs, which are later rolled into other shapes.
A mill stand is an assembly of rolls, frames and electric motors, used in steel rolling.
Plain rolls are cylinder-shaped rolls, which produce flat surfaces.
Profiled rolls are shaped in pairs, so that a particular section, such as a square section, may be produced.
Cold rolling of steel is very complex and requires a lot of power to drive the mill.

Non-Ferrous Metals and Alloys

INTRODUCTION

The non-ferrous metals and alloys are those which do not contain iron. Steel is a ferrous metal because it contains iron. Non-ferrous metals, in general, have excellent resistance to corrosion. *Copper*, which is reputed to be the first metal put to use by mankind, has some interesting properties. It is fairly easy to form because it is malleable and ductile. Evidence suggests that this ease of forming, was put to good use by our ancestors. Examples of pre-historic copper bowls, used as utensils, which were hammered into shape by hollowing, have been found in many parts of the world. On the other hand, *aluminium*, a very common metal today, only began to feature at the end of the nineteenth century. Without these two metals, the development of the modern world would have been severely hindered. In this chapter, we consider the main non-ferrous metals as well as some of their alloys.

COPPER

Copper came to prominence through the industrial revolution in Britain in the nineteenth century. Up until that time, it was used for its decorative appeal and also for utensils and roofs. It was because of its special properties that copper found its new role. Copper is malleable and ductile. It is a good conductor of both heat and electricity, and it can be rolled into sheets or drawn into wire. This metal found many industrial applications. Among the most important of these was, and still is, its use in electrical generators. Copper wires were used to distribute the electricity, and to convey telegraphic signals. It is still used for these purposes, although it is being replaced to some extent by aluminium.

Copper ore

Underground and open pit mining are used to extract copper ore, which is usually *chalcopyrite*. Chalcopyrite and pyrite are often mistaken for gold because of their colour and weight. This is why these are known as *fool's gold*. Copper ore is found mainly in the following countries: United States, Canada, Peru, Zambia, Zaire and the Philippines.

Copper production in modern times

An Irishman called *Marcus Daly*, who was born and reared near Ballyjamesduff, County Cavan, was almost entirely responsible for the development of copper mining techniques and smelting processes. No single person had such an influence on the introduction of copper to the modern world. When Daly went to America, as a young man, he travelled a bit, but eventually ended up in the state of Nevada, where silver mining was in full swing. The remarkable Irishman became famous, in a few short years, as a specialist in mining, and his services were in great demand. He went to Montana, became joint owner of the famous *Anaconda* silver mine, which originally belonged to a man called Healey. Daly developed the mine but was troubled by large veins of copper, in which there was little interest at the time. Taking a chance that the copper might become important, Daly sent a ship full of copper ore to Wales to have it smelted. Just at the same time, the need for copper wire, for electricity, emerged, and Daly capitalised on this need. The smelting of copper, on a large scale, first began in Montana, by Marcus Daly, in the 1880's. Soon, other countries followed suit, and all used the methods developed by Daly. Prices of copper fluctuated enormously from 1882 until 1890. Daly, the remarkable Cavan man, put the United States in a commanding position in the supply of copper to the world.

The production of copper

Copper production is divided into three main stages:

1 Matte-smelting
A reverberatory furnace is used to produce a *matte*, which contains from 30% to 50% copper. The ore is

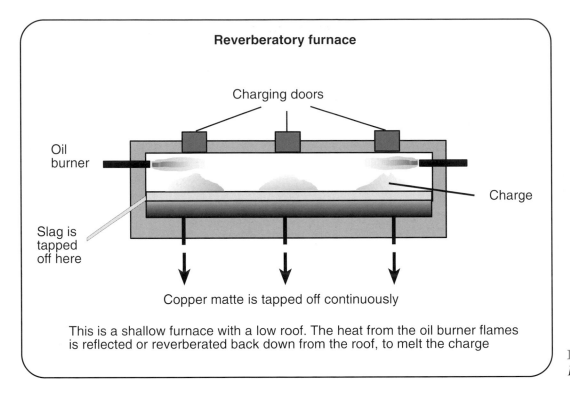

Reverberatory furnace

Charging doors

Oil burner

Charge

Slag is tapped off here

Copper matte is tapped off continuously

This is a shallow furnace with a low roof. The heat from the oil burner flames is reflected or reverberated back down from the roof, to melt the charge

FIGURE 1
Reverberatory furnace.

first concentrated at a mill near the place of mining. To concentrate the ore, it is first crushed, and then concentrated by *leaching* or *flotation*. Leaching is a method of extracting the metallic parts of an ore by using a solvent such as dilute acid. The solution is then treated to recover the metal.

Next, the ore is roasted or smelted in an oil-fired furnace, as shown in **FIGURE 1**, at a temperature below the melting point of copper.

This process produces copper matte, which is a metal-like material that contains the sulphur and iron from the chalcopyrite ($Cu Fe S_2$).

2 Converting
Iron and sulphur are removed by blowing air through the heated matte in a converter vessel, **FIGURE 2**.

Molten matte is placed in the converter, and the converting process produces sufficient heat to keep the charge molten during the blowing time, which is about eight hours. Blowing continues until the converter contains only copper sulphide, or white metal, which is finally blown to produce *blister copper*. Blister copper is up to 99% pure. Blister copper is further refined in a fire refining furnace, to remove the remaining oxygen. It is then cast into ingots known as *anodes*.

3 Refining by electrolysis
Electrical applications of copper require a purity of 99.99%, and this can only be achieved by *electrolytic* refining. Electrolytic tanks are arranged as laid out in **FIGURE 3**.

Fire refined blister copper anodes are connected to the positives DC supply, while thin cathode plates, which are electrolytically deposited, are connected to the negative supply. Tanks may contain about 30 anodes, and the electrolyte, normally a mixture of copper sulphate and sulphuric acid at 50°C, is circulated by pumps. Copper from the anodes is electrolytically deposited at the cathodes. The current density is usually about 200 amps per square metre.

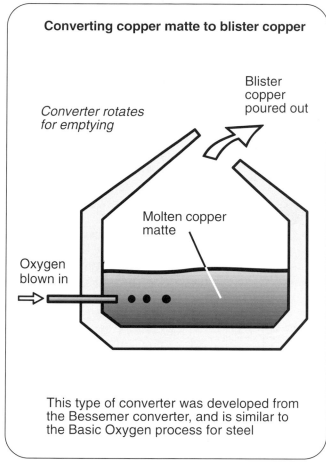

Converting copper matte to blister copper

Blister copper poured out

Converter rotates for emptying

Molten copper matte

Oxygen blown in

This type of converter was developed from the Bessemer converter, and is similar to the Basic Oxygen process for steel

FIGURE 2   *Converting copper matte.*

Applications of copper

Over half of all copper produced is used in the electrical industry. Copper wire, for transmission, accounts for a large amount of this use, **FIGURE 4**.

Central heating and plumbing are two other major applications of copper. The hot water cylinder in your hot press at home is more than likely made of copper, as is much of the piping used to distribute water in buildings. Some very fine copper roofs can be seen, usually on large buildings such as schools and churches. Traditionally, car cooling and heater radiators have been made from copper, but there is a modern trend towards the use of an aluminium and plastic configuration. The recycling of copper is extensive, and accounts for around 40% of total production.

ALUMINIUM

Many say that this is the steel age, but such is the prominence of aluminium that there are those who say that this is the aluminium age. Aluminium was, at one time, regarded as a precious metal, because only a small amount of it had been extracted. This very versatile metal has only been in commercial production for about seventy five years. Next to steel, it is the most used metal in the world. Even so, the production of aluminium is only 6% that of steel. Aluminium has a very wide range of uses, from cooking foil to aircraft. Its properties make it suitable for many applications. It is light, does not corrode, is a good conductor of electricity and heat and is cheaper than copper. Many heavy electricity transmission cables are now being manufactured from aluminium because the price of copper is so high. Aluminium can be cast, rolled, extruded, forged, drawn, etc., to give us the numerous shapes of the aluminium objects that we see every day.

Mining

It has been estimated that eight per cent of the earth's crust is made up of aluminium, which makes it the most plentiful metal. However, there is a problem, in that it is also the most difficult to extract from its ore. It does not occur in natural form but combined with other elements. The principal ore is *hydrated aluminium oxide*. This oxide was first found to be an ore of aluminium in *Les Baux* in France, and, because of this, it is known as *Bauxite*. The main areas where bauxite is found are:

France	Australia	Jamaica
Russia	Guinea	Brazil
Greece	Yugoslavia	Hungary
India	China.	

Mining method

Open cast mining is carried out using large earth-moving equipment. First, the soil or sand is removed and stored. After mining, it is customary to re-profile the land. Bauxite is first crushed and, if necessary, washed to remove silicon oxide.

Production of aluminium from bauxite

The production of aluminium is very energy intensive, and requires very large amounts of electrical

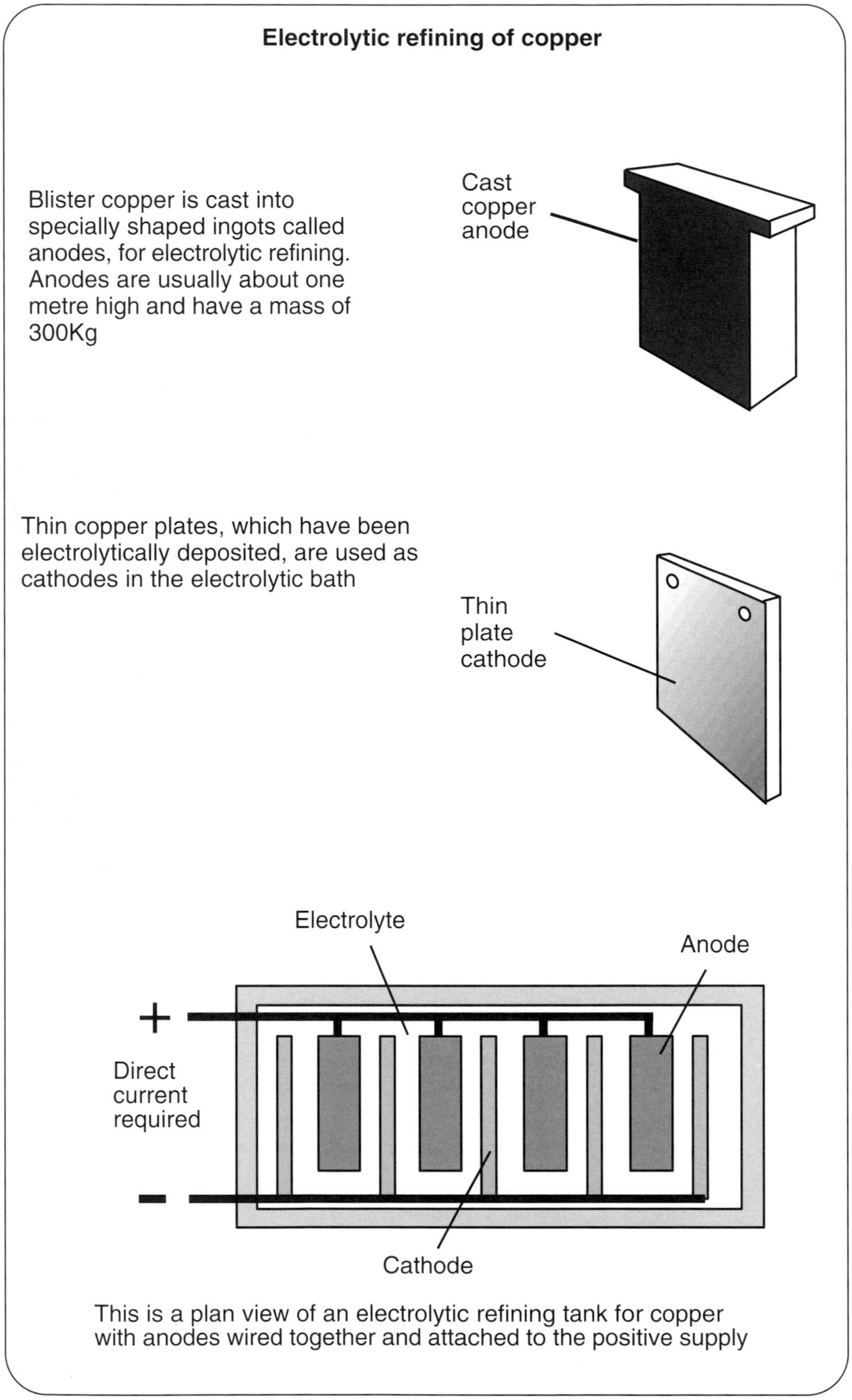

Electrolytic refining of copper

Blister copper is cast into specially shaped ingots called anodes, for electrolytic refining. Anodes are usually about one metre high and have a mass of 300Kg

Cast copper anode

Thin copper plates, which have been electrolytically deposited, are used as cathodes in the electrolytic bath

Thin plate cathode

Electrolyte

Anode

Direct current required

+

−

Cathode

This is a plan view of an electrolytic refining tank for copper with anodes wired together and attached to the positive supply

FIGURE 3 *Electrolytic refining of copper.*

energy. As a result, most aluminium production plants are situated near hydro-electric power stations, which produce a cheap supply of electricity. Examples are to be found in USA, Brazil, Norway and Canada (with its St. James River's array of hydro dams). Cheap electricity is available also from coal in Australia and Germany, so these are aluminium-producing countries too.

Two-stage process
The first stage in the two-stage production of aluminium from bauxite is the purification. This is shown in a simplified graphic form in **FIGURE 5**.

After being mixed with a caustic soda solution, the bauxite is sent to heated pressure vessels where the alumina hydrated aluminium oxide dissolves in the caustic soda. The impurities, or waste materials (iron oxide, titanium, and silicon), are removed as *red mud* (they do not dissolve). Alumina hydrate crystallises out of the solution when cooling takes place. It is then *roasted* or *calcined* (Bayer process). Although alumina plants are generally built near the mines, there are some exceptions, e.g. the alumina plant near Limerick, in Ireland.

Reduction of alumina to aluminium
Electrolysis is used to convert the alumina to aluminium **FIGURE 6**. Alumina has a melting point of 2000°C and cannot, therefore, be easily liquefied. It is first dissolved in *cryolite* before being converted to metal. The effect of the cryolite is to lower the conversion

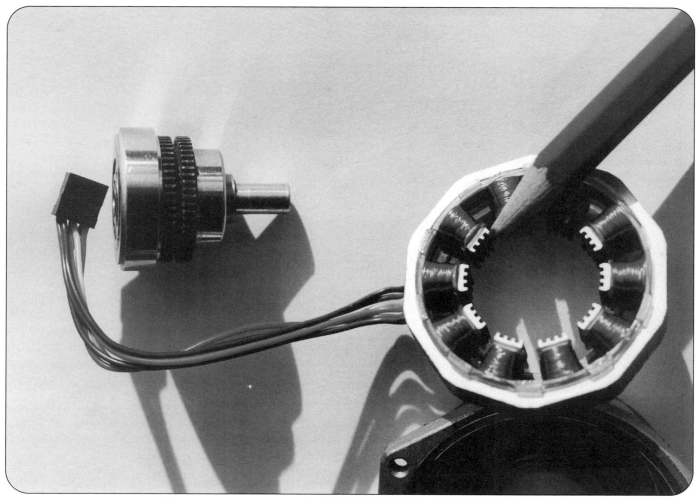

FIGURE 4   *An example of copper cable used in a miniature application. (Courtesy: the Authors).*

temperature and in doing so, drastically reducing the amount of energy required. First discovered in the 1880s by Hall and Heroult, the *cryolite factor* made the production of aluminium feasible. Even so it still takes 2 tonnes of alumina and 15,000 units of electricity to make 1 tonne of aluminium.

Recycling of aluminium
In terms of cost alone, it costs only 5.3% of initial cost to recycle aluminium. Recycled aluminium costs 800 units of electricity per tonne, compared to 15,000 units per tonne for aluminium produced from alumina. So it makes good economic sense to recycle this metal. It is important to remember that the supply of bauxite is limited. To cut the cost of

production, a large amount of aluminium is recycled. Thus, recycling accounts for 25% of the total world production of this metal. This is a huge saving indeed!

Applications of aluminium
As already mentioned, there are many uses of aluminium in everyday life. One of the largest applications is for electric cables. In this respect, aluminium is often used in place of copper, in order to reduce weight in certain electrical applications. Aluminium is also alloyed with metals such as copper, magnesium, nickel and zinc, to produce alloys with many special properties. Aluminium alloys are dealt with later on.

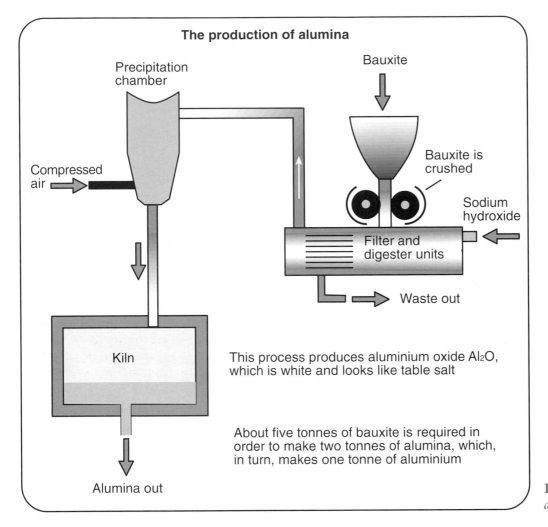

The production of alumina

Precipitation chamber

Bauxite

Bauxite is crushed

Compressed air

Sodium hydroxide

Filter and digester units

Waste out

Kiln

This process produces aluminium oxide Al₂O, which is white and looks like table salt

About five tonnes of bauxite is required in order to make two tonnes of alumina, which, in turn, makes one tonne of aluminium

Alumina out

FIGURE 5 *Production of aluminium.*

LEAD

Lead has a *low melting point*, is malleable and does not corrode. These properties made it suitable for use by the Romans for their very sophisticated water distribution systems. Nowadays, about half of all the lead produced is used to make *lead-acid batteries* for starting cars, and other vehicles. Lead has another use in cars, which is thought to be an undesirable one by many. It is added to petrol to improve the antiknock rating of this fuel. Lead is a toxic material and it is not good to have lead-containing fumes issuing from the tailpipes of millions of cars. There has been a growth in the opposition to the use of lead in petrol, which results in pollution of our atmosphere. As a result of this opposition, more

unleaded petrol is being used by motorists, and petrol vehicles are being fitted with catalytic converters. These converters chemically transform hydrocarbons and carbon monoxide, into carbon dioxide and water vapour, and also convert oxide of nitrogen into nitrogen and oxygen. The catalysts used are the metals platinum and palladium, which resemble one another in appearance. Another alternative to the use of lead compounds in petrol, and perhaps a kinder one to the atmosphere, is to add ethanol to petrol, up to about 15%, by volume. This is being done to a large extent in Brazil, where many cars run on alcohol only!

Lead-tin solders are essential in the electronics industry. Components mounted on PCB boards are

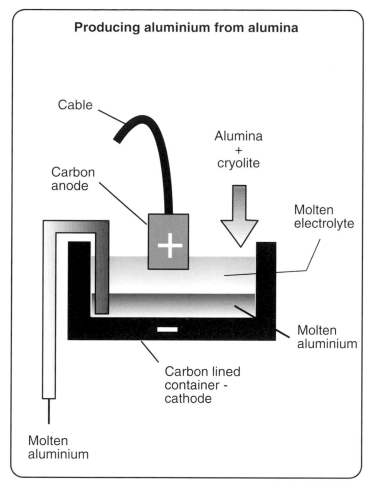

Producing aluminium from alumina

Cable

Alumina + cryolite

Carbon anode

Molten electrolyte

Molten aluminium

Carbon lined container - cathode

Molten aluminium

FIGURE 6 *Production of aluminium from alumina.*

bath soldered with a 62% tin + 38% lead. Also, soft soldering is the normal method of making permanent joints between wires and electronic components. Some other uses for lead include: sheaths for underground cables, bearing materials, radiation protection shields (X-ray and nuclear).

TIN

The story is told of a Russian Czar who stored away tonnes of tin in an extremely cold store somewhere in Russia. Later, when he went to see his tin, he found that it had disintegrated into a powdery substance. He was not amused. When tin is stored below 13.2°C, it slowly transforms into grey tin, and then disintegrates into a white powder! This is called 'tin disease'. The main source of tin in Roman times was Britain, where this metal was mined in Cornwall.

Tinplate
About 40% of tin produced is used in making tinplate. Tinplate is produced by dipping steel sheet into baths of molten tin. The *canned* or *tinned food* industry is based on the tinplate can. Food is first prepared, and then canned under special conditions, in *tinplate cans* or *tins*, as they are most often called. Canned food stays good in the cans for a long period of time. This fact has led to a huge tinned food industry, in which all kinds of canned foodstuffs are sold off the shelves of shops. The *tin can*, as we call it, is mostly steel, the tin coating making up only 1% of the can!

ZINC

Zinc is a *silvery white* metal which is a poor conductor of both heat and electricity. Canada is the main producer of zinc. *Sphalerite* is the main ore of zinc, and it is nearly always found along with *galena*, which is the main ore of lead.

One large use of zinc is in the protection of steel against corrosion, by galvanising. It is usually applied by *hot dipping*, but can also be applied by *electrogalvanising*. Because of its electrochemical properties, zinc protects steel by *cathodic* or *sacrificial protection*, as well as providing a mechanical protection.

Zinc is used in *dry batteries* such as those used in lamps, radios, personal tape players, etc. It is alloyed with other metals to make die castings. *Brass* is an alloy of copper and zinc, and it is in this form that zinc was first found. It was only later that zinc was separated. Zinc also has applications in the chemical and cattle food industries.

NICKEL

Almost as strong and hard as iron, nickel is *magnetic*, and has great *resistance to corrosion*. Because of its resistance to corrosion, nickel is contained in stainless steel, which helps to give this special steel its corrosion resistance. *Pentlandite* is the principal ore of nickel, and comes mainly from Canada. Canada's largest source of the ore was accidentally found during the construction of that great railway, the *Canadian Pacific Railway*.

FIGURE 7 *In this photograph you can see a jet engine in the final stages of assembly. Turbines in such engines are normally manufactured from titanium.* (Courtesy: Rolls Royce Ltd)

Nickel is extensively used in the *electroplating industry*. When nickel is added to steel, it gives increased *hardness* and *strength*, as well as resistance to rust.

MAGNESIUM

Early photographers made use of *magnesium powder* to give bursts of light to help get good exposures. When magnesium powder is ignited, it burns with an instantaneous white light. Electronic flashes have long ago replaced this use of magnesium.

Magnesium looks a little like aluminium, with its silvery white appearance. It has many uses in the aircraft industry, where advantage is taken of its good strength to weight ratio. Magnesium–aluminium alloy car wheels are very popular.

TUNGSTEN

Tungsten is sometimes called *Wolfram*. This very hard and very heavy metal, (over twice as heavy as steel), has the very high melting point of 3380°C. It

Aluminium alloys - compositions and applications		
Alloy type	Percentage composition Balance of aluminium	Common applications
Wrought aluminium alloys - Not heat treated	1.2% manganese + 2.5% magnesium	Suitable for general use: for the manufacture of saucepans, lorry bodies, ship fittings, chemical plant containers
Heat treated	4% copper + small amounts of magnesium, manganese, and silicon	This is the best of the alloy known as duralumin and it age hardens. This alloy is used extensively in the aircraft industry
	1% magnesium + 1% silicon + 0.7% manganese	This is the alloy used for electric wires and also for: ladders, scaffolding
Cast aluminium alloys - Not heat treated	11.5% silicon	Mainly used for die casting and sand casting of pump housings, gearbox housings, etc
Heat treated	4% copper + small amounts of silicon, magnesium, nickel and titanium	Most alloy engine blocks, cylinder heads and pistons are cast from this type of alloy - it is known as Y-alloy

FIGURE 8   *Aluminium alloys – compositions and applications.*

is widely used for filaments for *incandescent* electric lamps, or bulbs, because it gives off white light at high temperatures. *Edison* carried out an extremely large number of experiments in his attempt to find a *filament*, as he called it, that would not burn out in a short time. Tungsten proved to be the most suitable material. One of the hardest substances in use in an engineering room, is *tungsten carbide*, which is used for high speed lathe cutting tools, etc.

MOLYBDENUM

Molybdenum is a strong whitish malleable metal that melts at 2526°C. In France, near the end of the nineteenth century, it was used to make armour plate, by being alloyed with iron. Today, it is used in the making of special HSS tools, rocket components, and as a lubricant in the form of *molybdenum disulphide.*

FIGURE 9 *Examples of coins made from coinage bronze (copper coins and coins made from cupro-nickel (silver coloured) are to be seen in the photograph. (Courtesy: the authors)*

TITANIUM

This metal is *light* and has *high strength*, as well as exceptional resistance to corrosion. Titanium is malleable and ductile, and resembles iron. It was discovered in Cornwall, England, in 1791, by a man called *Gregor*. Titanium is named after the Titans, who, in Greek mythology, were the sons and daughters of Uranus and Ge. The most common ore is *rutile*. Titanium is used to make strong, light structures. It is used to make turbine blades, and other parts for aircraft, because of the properties already mentioned, and also because it has good heat resistant qualities, see **FIGURE 7**.

NON-FERROUS ALLOYS

This is a very large group of alloys indeed. Any alloy which does not contain iron, is a *non-ferrous alloy*. Steel holds the number one position in the league of usage of alloys. But aluminium alloys, and copper alloys are not far behind. These are about the two most important families of non-ferrous alloys.

ALUMINIUM ALLOYS

Aluminium alloys are divided into the groups:

- **Wrought alloys**
- **Cast alloys.**

Wrought alloys

These are alloys which can be *worked*. They may be rolled, forged, extruded, or drawn. Some of these wrought alloys are *not heat treated* and some are *heat treated*.

Non heat-treated wrought alloys are hardened by cold working processes. Manganese is added to these alloys, to impart strength, and magnesium is added to increase corrosion resistance. Wrought alloys which can be heat treated include *age-hardening alloys*. Age-hardening alloys contain copper, magnesium and silicon. The age-hardening is due to the precipitation of $CuAl_2$, which happens a few days after treatment. *Duralumin* is a well known alloy of this type, and it contains 4% copper.

Cast alloys

As the name implies, these alloys are used for casting, whether it be for *sandcasting* or for *die casting*. As with the wrought alloys, some are heat treatable, and others are not. One of the most important non heat-treatable aluminium casting alloys, is the

Minerals and the metals that may be extracted from them

Metal	Name of mineral contained in the ore	Metallic compound contained in mineral	
		Chemical name	*Chemical symbols*
Copper	Chalcopyrite	Copper-iron sulphide	$CuFeS_2$
Aluminium	Bauxite	Hydrated aluminium oxide	$Al_2O_3.3H_2O$
Lead	Galena	Lead sulphide	PbS
Magnesium	Magnesite	Magnesium carbonate	$MgCO_3$
	Dolomite	Magnesium-calcium carbonate	$MgCa(CO_3)_2$
Molybdenum	Molybdenite	Molybdenum sulphide	MoS_2
	Wulfenite	Lead molybdate	$PbMoO_4$
Zinc	Sphalerite *Zinc Blende*	Zinc sulphide	ZnS
	Smithsonite *Calamine*	Zinc carbonate	$ZnCO_3$
Nickel	Pentlandite	Nickel-iron sulphide	$(Fe,Ni)gS_8$
Tungsten	Wolframite	Iron manganese wolframate	$(Fe, Mn) WO_4$
	Scheelite	Calcium wolframite	$CaWO_4$
Tin	Casserite	Tin oxide	SnO_2

The minerals listed are not necessarily the only ones from which particular metals may be extracted. However, these are the most common minerals used.

FIGURE 10   *Minerals and ores.*

aluminium-silicon series of alloys. This series is used for all kinds of casting, because it has excellent casting characteristics. In this series, a *eutectic* is formed with between 10% and 13% silicon. A widely-used alloy is LM6, which contains 11.5% silicon. If copper is added to the aluminium silicon series, then the alloy will respond to heat treatment, and is often used for die casting. FIGURE 8 indicates some applications of aluminium alloys.

SPECIAL ALLOYS

Y-alloy

This alloy was composed at the *National Physical Laboratory* during World War I. It is used for pistons because of its ability to perform well at high temperatures. This alloy contains copper, nickel and magnesium.

Hiduminium

This alloy was also developed for working under conditions of high temperature. Hiduminium is similar to Y-alloy, but it has better properties, and is used for the manufacture of parts for aircraft engines.

COPPER ALLOYS

Brasses are copper-zinc alloys, which can contain up to 50% zinc, and sometimes small amounts of other alloying elements. Because of the presence of the zinc, brasses are yellowish in colour and very attractive, and so, brasses are used a lot for ornamental work. Cold working brasses are alloys suitable for all sorts of cold working processes such as rolling, pressing, wire drawing. An example of a cold working brass, is *cartridge brass*, so-called because of its ductility, which allows it to be made into cartridge cases. Hot working brasses are suitable for hot working processes. This group of brasses is used to make castings, extrusions and stampings. *Muntz metal* is a 60% copper, 40% zinc alloy, which is sometimes called *yellow metal*. It is used for brazing. High tensile brasses are basically 60/40 brass, with other elements added. Elements added include iron, aluminium, manganese, lead, nickel and, sometimes, silicon. These brasses are used where strength, toughness, and corrosion resistance are required. Ships' propellers can be made from high tensile brass which is often wrongly called *manganese bronze*.

Nickel silver contains no silver but is a copper-zinc combination. Once nickel is added to brass, the yellow colour becomes less prominent and, at about 20% nickel, the alloy looks like silver. This is why it is known as nickel silver. Nickel silver is often silver plated, or chromium plated when used for cutlery, etc. EPNS (electroplated nickel silver), is usually stamped on such products.

Monel metal

A typical composition for *monel metal* is 68% nickel, 29.5% copper, 1.25% iron and 1.25% manganese. This alloy has very good mechanical properties, combined with excellent *corrosion resistance*. The *Concorde* aircraft is held together by 300,000 monel metal rivets. This accounts for nearly three-quarters of a tonne of the aircraft's weight. This might be reduced if a suitable aluminium, or titanium alloy was available.

Bronzes

These are the copper-tin alloys and were one of the earliest alloys used by humans. Bronzes are much harder than copper, and there are many combinations in this alloy group. Some of the more important bronzes are considered here.

Coinage bronze is used to make bronze coins and contains 3.5% tin, and 1.5% zinc. Most *copper coins* are made of this alloy. Another alloy used to make coins is *cupro-nickel*. It is not a bronze, but it is worth mentioning because this is the alloy contained in modern day *silver* coins! Some modern coins are shown in FIGURE 9.

Gunmetals are excellent for casting and they have good mechanical properties. *Admiralty gunmetal* is the best known gunmetal, and it is used for marine fittings, steam fittings, and also for ornamental casting. It has the following composition: 88% copper, 10% tin, and 2% zinc.

Phosphor bronze is widely used to make bearings and castings of all shapes. The most used phosphor bronze contains 10% tin, and about 0.5% phosphorus. Many machine parts, which need to have bearing-type surfaces, and still be able to support heavy loads, are cast from phosphor bronze.

Bearing bronze is when lead is added to bronze containing 10% tin, the bearing properties of the alloy are improved considerably. Lead may be added anywhere in the range from 8% up to 25%. If a bearing bronze with good plasticity is required, then the lead content is kept high. This would be the case when the alloy is to be used as bearings for mild steel shafts.

Aluminium bronzes are a range of alloys with copper and aluminium as the basis. Other elements which are often contained in aluminium bronzes are: iron, nickel, and manganese. These alloys are extremely good for service at medium temperatures, at which an alloy's strength, and resistance to corrosion, are satisfactory.

There are two divisions into which aluminium bronzes are divided:

1 Alloys which are *ductile* and *corrosion-resistant*. They are suitable for cold working and contain around 6% aluminium. These alloys are widely used for heat exchangers in thermal plant and in chemical plant. Alloys of this type, have a beautiful golden colour, and an excellent protective *surface oxide* which helps to prevent tarnishing.
2 Duplex aluminium bronzes. These have an aluminium content of 9% to 10%, with about 2% iron being added, along with a little nickel. This kind of alloy gives strength, toughness, resistance to corrosion and oxidation and, therefore, has many applications in marine engineering, such as propellers, pump bodies, valves, etc.

ZINC ALLOYS FOR DIE CASTING

Zinc has a low melting point and from this point of view is attractive for casting purposes. Zinc-based alloys are widely used for pressure die casting (see under Manufacturing, page 181). Two such alloys are common. These are the mazaks: mazak 3 and mazak 5. A large number of components, both domestic and industrial, are manufactured from the *mazaks*. Some examples are: carburettors, door handles for cars, washing machine parts, miniature toy cars. Mazak 3 contains 4% aluminium and 0.5% magnesium, which gives an *ultimate tensile strength* (UTS), of 275 N/mm². Mazak 5 is similar, but with 1% copper, and has a UTS of 350 N/mm². In both

cases, the four nines – 99.99% zinc, is used in making the alloy, which is necessary for good quality castings.

SUMMARY

Non-ferrous metals and alloys are those which do not contain iron.
Copper is one of the major non-ferrous metals. It is malleable, ductile and is an excellent conductor of electricity.
Chalcopyrite is the name given to the copper-iron sulphide ore, from which copper may be extracted. It is also known as *fool's gold*.
Matte-smelting is the first stage in the production of copper. Matte contains 30% to 50% copper.
Blister copper, which is up to 99% pure, is produced from matte copper in a converter.
Pure copper results from an electrolysis process in which copper from copper anodes is electrolytically deposited at a prepared cathode.
Bauxite, or hydrated aluminium oxide, is the ore from which aluminium is extracted in two stages.
Alumina is produced from bauxite in the first stage of aluminium production. There is an alumina plant at Aughinish Island, on the Shannon.
In the electrolysis process used to convert alumina to aluminium, large amounts of electrical energy are consumed.
Cryolite is used to lower the melting point of alumina, which is normally about 2000°C.
Lead has a low melting point, and does not corrode. A major use of lead is in lead-acid batteries, which provide starting power for vehicles.
Zinc is a poor conductor of heat and electricity but is used extensively in galvanising.
Aluminium alloys are divided into wrought alloys and cast alloys. Wrought alloys can be worked, whereas cast alloys are for casting.
The two most widely used copper-based alloys are the brasses and bronzes.
Brass is an alloy of copper and zinc. The greater the percentage of zinc, the more yellow the brass.
Bronze is an alloy of copper and tin. It is much harder than copper and was the first alloy used by mankind, to make good quality tools.
Mazaks are low melting point alloys based on zinc + aluminium + magnesium compositions.

Plastics

INTRODUCTION

Any solid substance which can be moulded into a new shape under pressure is said to be *plastic*. Today a large group of synthetic materials is known by the general term plastics. This term came into use because most of these materials are in a plastic condition at some time, usually when they are being moulded into some shape or object.

When we refer to plastics we usually mean *polymers,* since plastic is a condition or state of a material. Metals when heated to certain temperatures can also be plastic. And, on the contrary, certain polymers are no longer plastic after moulding.

Plastics can be produced in any colour. They can be moulded into very complex shapes. Numerous items such as household equipment, toys, building materials, decorative objects, containers, packaging, aircraft parts, motor car parts, safety screens, are made from plastics. This variety of uses demands that plastics have different properties. For example, a plastic grille on the front of a motor car must be *decorative* and *tough* whereas a plastic drinking cup may have to withstand temperatures up to 100°C.

Plastics can be transparent or opaque, hard or soft, rigid or flexible. As a general rule plastics are poor conductors of heat and electricity. This makes some of them suitable for use as insulating materials.

FIGURE 1   *Interior of the "Opel Omega MV6". Many of the materials used are plastic. (Courtesy: Opel Ireland Ltd.)*

TYPES OF PLASTICS

Plastics can be divided into three categories:

1 Natural plastics.
2 Modified natural plastics.
3 Synthetic plastics.

1 Natural plastics

Decorative objects, trinket boxes and even house-hold items were made as far back as the 1860's from natural plastics. Some of the more popular natural plastics are:

- **Amber**
- **Animal horn**
- **Natural rubber**
- **Shellac.**

Amber is a resinous substance which oozes from pine trees and solidifies. It is a fairly soft material and can be easily carved into shape. The carved object can then be polished. Pine trees which produce amber generally grow in the Baltic region. Fossilised amber derived from extinct coniferous trees occurs in many places world-wide.

Animal horn is composed completely or partly of *keratin*. This is a fibrous protein which is found in the outer layers of the skin. Finger nails and hair are other examples of keratin.

Natural rubber is a cream coloured elastic material extracted from the rubber tree. It is more often referred to as a natural polymer than a natural plastic. See page 123.

Shellac is a resinous substance. It is produced by parasitic insects which live on trees, generally in India. Shellac was once important as an adhesive and wood polish.

2 Modified natural plastics

These are natural materials which have been modified in some way. Examples are:

- **Cellulose**
- **Casein.**

About 1850, Professor Alexander Parks added *camphor* to cellulose nitrate – a substance produced by treating cotton with nitric acid. The material he produced was called *parkesine*. In 1869 an American, John Wesley Hyatt, was attempting to find a substitute material for *ivory* which was at that time used in billiard balls. (A prize of $10,000 was offered to the inventor of such a material.) He improved on the work done by Parks and began to manufacture the new material under the name *celluloid*.

In the early 1900's a Belgian chemist, Leo Baekeland, produced a plastic which he called *Bakelite*. This was the first truly synthetic "plastic" (although it is in fact rigid once formed and by no means "plastic" in the sense that its shape could be changed).

Cellulose is a material manufactured from cotton fibre and from wood pulp.

Casein is obtained from cow's milk.

3 Synthetic plastics

A synthetic plastic is one which is produced entirely by human-controlled chemical processes.

Synthetic plastics are manufactured from two sources:

- **By-products of the production of gas from coal**
- **By-products of the distillation of crude oil (known as *cracking* of crude oil).**

Coal is almost completely carbon and oil is a compound of carbon. They are called *organic* substances. This is because they once lived on the earth as vegetation and animals. Over millions of years they have been pressed deep into the earth's surface. Carbon has the ability to form an endless number of compounds by combining with elements such as Hydrogen, Oxygen, Nitrogen, Chlorine and Fluorine.

POLYMERISATION

The vast majority of polymer substances that we use are compounds of carbon. The word polymer comes

The mechanism of polymerisation

In this example the monomer Ethylene is polymerised. The new molecule is Polyethylene (more usually known as Polythene)

Ethylene monomer

Carbon atoms

Hydrogen atoms

Double bond

Polymerisation of Ethylene

Step 1

A catalyst (free radical) is added to the ethylene
A free radical is a reactive atom (or group of atoms) containing an unpaired electron. This is represented by the large dot (●)

Step 2

One of the bonds has been broken and the carbon atom is now ready to link up with similar carbon atoms

Step 3

Long-chain molecules form in a fraction of a second

Polymer

Covalent bond

Mer

Termination (This is just one of a number of methods)

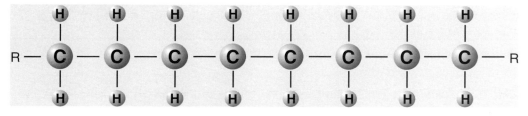

The catalyst provides two radicals which serve to **initiate** and **terminate** the polymerisation process

FIGURE 2   *The mechanism of polymerisation.*

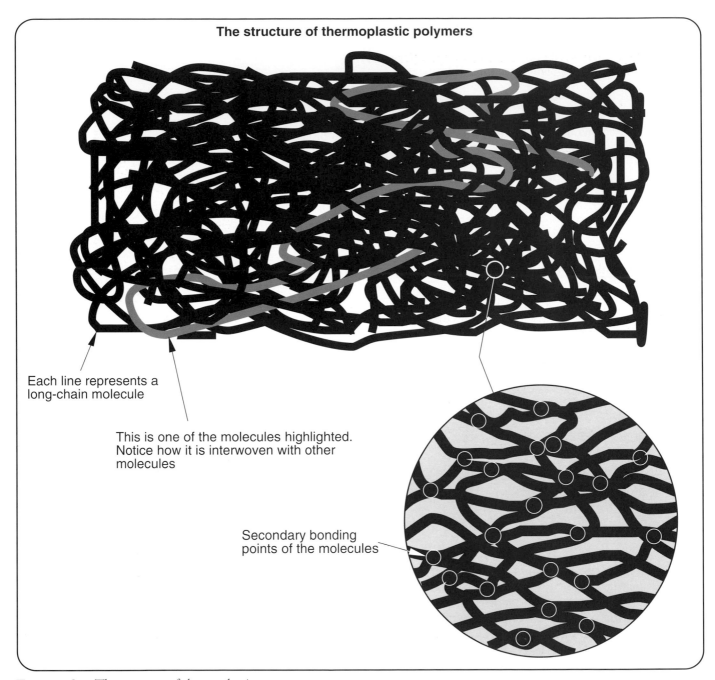

The structure of thermoplastic polymers

Each line represents a long-chain molecule

This is one of the molecules highlighted. Notice how it is interwoven with other molecules

Secondary bonding points of the molecules

FIGURE 3 *The structure of thermoplastics.*

from the Greek for "many parts". Polymer molecules are the result of the joining together of a number of basic units known as *monomers*. Within the polymer molecule there is a repeated unit known as a *mer*. Mers are the building blocks of long-chain molecules or network molecules.

The process in which monomers are joined together is known as *polymerisation*. This process can occur in two ways:

1 Addition polymerisation (also known as chain-growth).

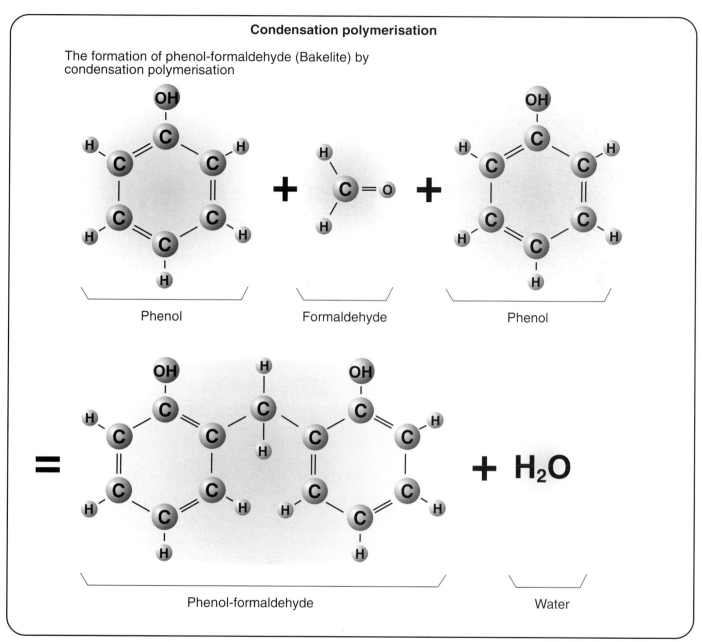

FIGURE 4   *Condensation polymerisation.*

2 Condensation polymerisation (also known as step-growth).

1 Addition polymerisation
Addition polymerisation is essentially adding together large numbers of mers so that they form into long-chain molecules. Many of the common polymers are produced in this way. By studying the production of polyethylene in **FIGURE 2** you can see how addition polymerisation works. The basic substance or monomer (shown at the top of the diagram) from which polyethylene is produced is ethylene (ethene). An ethylene molecule is composed of two carbon atoms and four hydrogen atoms.

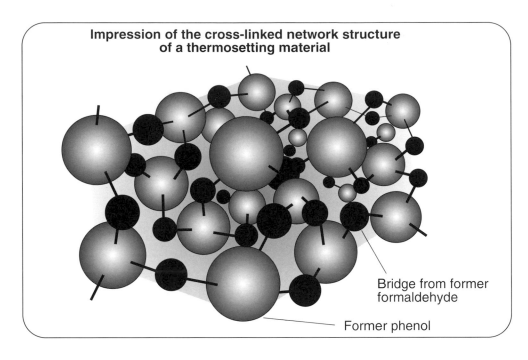

Impression of the cross-linked network structure of a thermosetting material

Bridge from former formaldehyde

Former phenol

FIGURE 5   *Cross-linked network.*

A double bond exists between the two carbon atoms. This is indicated by the double lines. The lines represent the covalent sharing of two pairs of valence electrons. Adding a *catalyst* starts the polymerisation process. A catalyst is a substance that increases the rate of a chemical reaction. In polymerisation the catalyst generates *free radicals*.

A free radical is an atom containing an unpaired electron. The reaction converts the double bond of the monomer into a single bond and this forms a mer. The mer now has an unpaired electron and behaves as a radical itself. Its unpaired electron reacts with the next nearest monomer. This extends the chain by another unit. The reaction continues while there are unreacted monomers near by or until the reaction is *terminated*. A second radical (from the catalyst) can act as a terminator or chain stopper.

The long-chain molecules form a complex coiling structure similar to spaghetti. **FIGURE 3** gives an impression of this structure. Several thousand mers can be joined by addition polymerisation in a single second.

2 Condensation polymerisation
The polymerisation of phenol formaldehyde by the step-growth process is shown schematically in **FIGURE 4**.

The two phenol molecules are linked by the formaldehyde molecule during the reaction. When this happens, the phenols each give up a hydrogen atom and the formaldehyde gives up an oxygen atom. These combine to produce water (H_2O) as a by-product. The water is condensed out leaving the structure *cross-linked*. This method of polymerisation is known as condensation polymerisation. It is a slow process compared to addition polymerisation.

The phenol molecule shown at **FIGURE 4** has several possible points of contact where it can link up with other molecules. This linking generates a *three-dimensional network* which is shown in **FIGURE 5**. (Compare this with the polyethylene molecule in **FIGURE 2** which has only two points of contact. Having only two points of contact forces the polymerised molecule into a *linear structure*.)

Johannes Diderick van der Waals was a Dutch physicist (1837–1923) who carried out research on secondary bonding. He was a headmaster of a secondary school and later became a professor at the University of Amsterdam.

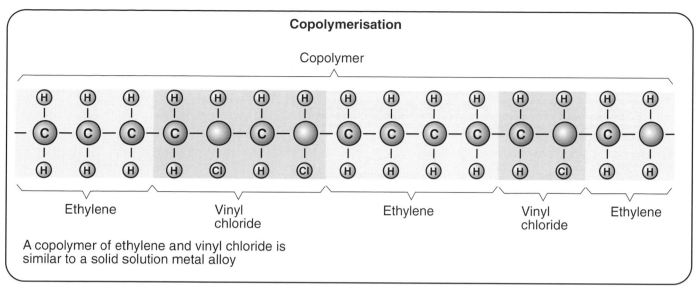

Copolymerisation

Copolymer

Ethylene   Vinyl chloride   Ethylene   Vinyl chloride   Ethylene

A copolymer of ethylene and vinyl chloride is similar to a solid solution metal alloy

FIGURE 6   *Copolymerisation.*

COPOLYMERISATION

The process in which mers of *different* kinds are linked together in the same addition chain is called *copolymerisation*. The process of copolymerisation makes it possible to produce many different polymers with a great variety of properties. **FIGURE 6** shows an example of a copolymer molecule.

CLASSIFICATION OF POLYMERS

Polymers can be classified under two main headings:

1 Thermoplastic materials.
2 Thermosetting materials.

These two terms *thermoplastic* and *thermosetting* refer to the way the respective material responds to a rise in temperature.

1 Thermoplastic materials
Addition polymers are made up of long-chains of bonded carbon atoms. These have pendants or side-structures of hydrogen (as you can see in **FIGURE 2**) or chlorine or other elements. All of the bonds within the polymer molecule are *primary* bonds. Primary bonds are very strong chemical bonds.

They have a high resistance to rupture. Raising the temperature of the material has no effect on the strength of these primary bonds.

The bonds between adjacent molecules are, however, *secondary* bonds. Secondary bonds (or *van der Waals forces*) are relatively weak forces of attraction.

Secondary bonds can be weakened even further by raising the temperature of the material. This is why thermoplastic materials soften at elevated temperatures but strengthen again when the temperature is lowered. They can, therefore, be resoftened and moulded repeatedly. When the temperature of some of the common thermoplastics is raised above 100°C the molecules can slip past each other – the material softens. In this state the material can easily be moulded into shape by one of the processes discussed in Manufacturing with Plastics, page 207.

The "slippage" of the molecules at normal temperatures is restricted if the molecules are very long. Very long molecules (high molecular mass) would form a stronger material. Other methods of increasing the strength of thermoplastics are:

Connecting the long-chains at various points with primary bonds (see vulcanisation of rubber on page 123).

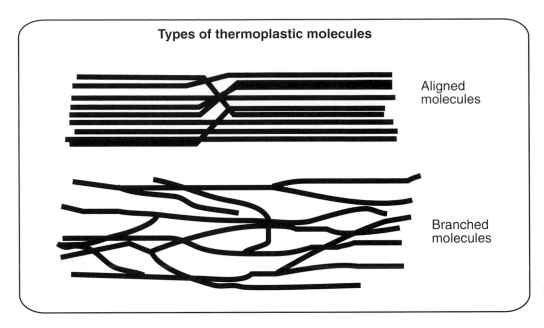

Types of thermoplastic molecules

Aligned molecules

Branched molecules

FIGURE 7 *Types of thermoplastic molecules.*

Crystallising the structure to produce an aligned, parallel arrangement of the adjacent molecules (**FIGURE 7**).

Producing molecules with very large "pendants" or side-structures (for example, polystyrene) that become entangled in each other and so increase the stiffness of the material.

Branching is another method of increasing strength. This is done by adding an agent to start a chain-growth off the side of a molecule (**FIGURE 7**).

2 Thermosetting materials

Thermosetting materials are usually polymerised by the condensation process. In these polymers, primary bonding occurs. This results in the formation of a rigid, cross-linked structure as shown in **FIGURE 5**. In this structure the atoms are connected by strong covalent bonds. The cross-linking process is known as *curing*. It can be assisted by applying heat and pressure. Thermosetting materials have a non-reversible (primary bonded) structure and cannot be resoftened by heating. They will retain their mechanical properties almost until they begin to burn.

ADDITIVES USED IN PLASTICS

Polymers are not always used in engineering in their pure state. They are often combined with other materials to give them certain desired properties.

These other materials can be summarised as:

- **Fillers**
- **Plasticisers**
- **Colour pigments**
- **Stabilisers**
- **Antioxidants**
- **Flame retardants**
- **Lubricants.**

The final products or compounds are commonly known as *plastics*.

Fillers are added to polymers to improve their mechanical properties. They also tend to reduce the amount of the polymer present – often making them cheaper. Common fillers are:

Wood flour – gives fair strength and good mouldability
Cloth fibre – gives good impact strength
Glass fibre – gives high strength and allows translucence
'Whiskers' of metal – gives very high strength
Asbestos fibre – improves heat resistance
Mica – very good electrical insulating properties

When fillers are used with a polymer resin, the resin

behaves as a *binder*. The binder surrounds the filler material and holds the mass together.

Plasticisers added to polymers improve their flexibility. This happens because the plasticiser separates the molecules and reduces the forces of attraction between them.

Colour pigments give the plastic the desired colour.

Stabilisers and antioxidants help to prevent the degrading effects of heat, ultraviolet light and oxidation on the polymer.

Flame retardants are important where, for example, the plastic is to be used as a building material or for clothing or furniture.

Lubricants added to a polymer make it easier to mould. Waxes and soaps are examples of lubricants. Usually very little is used because they affect the engineering properties of the moulded material.

DEGRADATION OF PLASTICS

All plastics can be destroyed by fire. Ultraviolet light, which is a component of sunlight, can also have a very serious effect on most plastics. Ultraviolet light is made up of photons capable of altering chemical bonds. The combined heat and ultraviolet light of the sun can damage polymer molecules by establishing free radicals. Many recombine without damage, but if oxygen reacts with these free radicals, molecular chains may be broken. This reduces the molecular mass and weakens the plastic. Another possible effect is that it may start cross-linking. This will increase molecular mass and reduce the flexibility of the plastic, making it brittle and prone to cracking.

Plastics intended for use outdoors can be protected against degradation by including an ultraviolet absorbing pigment, such as carbon black. Also the use of antioxidants which trap oxygen free radicals can help prevent reactions.

PROPERTIES AND USES OF COMMON THERMOPLASTICS

Polyethylene (polythene)
In the production of polyethylene, careful control of the polymerisation process can produce either of two polymer types. One type, *high density polyethylene* (HDPE), has mainly linear molecules that pack closely together. The other type, *low density polyethylene* (LDPE), although it has branched molecules, is much weaker but more ductile. Polyethylene has a wide range of applications because of its properties. It is a good electrical insulator and is very durable, capable of resisting attack by chemicals. The major disadvantages are a very low softening point and low strength.

Polyethylene is widely used in the form of sheet and film for protecting objects and food. It is also one of the most important materials from which water pipes and electric cable insulation are made.

Acrylonitrile butadiene styrene (ABS)
This is an important copolymer. It can be compounded in varying degrees of hardness, flexibility and toughness. It is often used in applications where conditions would damage polymers. It can withstand temperatures up to 105°C. This makes it suitable for sink waste pipes. It is also used in telephone and electrical hand tool casings.

Acetals (polyoxymethylenes POM)
These are highly *crystalline* thermoplastics (the molecules are in a tight parallel alignment). They are very strong and are resistant to attack by hot water. Plastic jug kettles are manufactured from acetals.

Polypropylene
This is a higher strength material than polyethylene and it has better durability and temperature resistance. Because of its high flexibility this material is often used in food containers with 'hinged' lids. It is used extensively in the manufacture of moulded articles such as toys, hospital and laboratory ware, pipes and sheets.

Polyvinylchloride (PVC)
This material is more rigid than polyethylene. It has good strength and resists attack by most chemicals. A plasticiser added to PVC makes it more flexible. For example, PVC water pipes are rigid. With increased amounts of plasticiser PVC becomes suitable for substitute leather upholstery for car seats.

Polystyrene

This is a polymer with a disorganised structure (*amorphous* polymer) because of the very bulky molecules which have large side structures. It results in the production of a clear transparent polymer. Polystyrene is a good electrical insulator and has good resistance to chemical attack. Its important uses are electrical fittings and as clear sheets and films for packaging. It is relatively easy to mould by heat forming. Foamed polystyrene is made by blowing steam into the specially-prepared polymer. In this form it is used as thermal insulating material ('aeroboard') in building. It is also used as ceiling tiles.

Polysulphones

These include *polyphenylene sulphide* (PPS) and *polyetherethereketone* (PEEK). Developed to withstand temperatures over 200°C for long periods, these are very expensive and often difficult to process.

Polymethylmethacrylate

The polymerisation of *methylmethacrylate* results in an amorphous (non-crystalline) structure. This polymer is therefore transparent. It is better known by its trade name 'perspex'. It is often used in the form of transparent sheet as a glass substitute. This material is tough and resistant to weathering, so it is used in roof lights, signs and other outdoor applications. It does not have a high resistance to chemical attack.

Polytetrafluorethylene (PTFE)

This polymer is noted for its excellent resistance to chemical attack and its low co-efficient of friction. It can also withstand high temperature. It is used to coat surfaces to give them non-stick properties. "Teflon" is a well known trade name for PTFE coated saucepans and frying pans.

Polyamides

Nylon is a term which is often used to describe a number of polyamides. The original material was nylon 6.6. It was developed as a fibre and was used in the manufacture of textiles. There are many different types of nylon, each identified by a number, for example, nylon 6.10, nylon 11, and so on. The number comes from the arrangement of atoms in the structure of the material. Nylons have very high strength. They are often used as gear wheels and bearings in engineering.

Cellulose derivatives

Cellulose is a natural polymer obtained from plants. A number of important polymers are derived from cellulose.

These are:

Cellulose nitrate – used in paint finishes.
Cellulose acetate – used in packaging, containers and electrical parts.
Cellulose acetate butyrate – this is a copolymer used in the manufacture of car parts and containers.

PROPERTIES AND USES OF COMMON THERMOSETTING MATERIALS

Bakelite

This was the first fully synthetic plastic. Bakelite is a plastic which is manufactured by polymerising phenol and formaldehyde (See **Figure 4**). Remember that this material differs from thermoplastics in that there is cross-linking (primary bonding) between the molecules. Bakelite is hard and heat-resistant. It is also a good electrical insulator. Its uses include electrical components and handles on the handwheels of machines and on some cooking utensils.

Amino plastics (aminoplasts)

The two important types are *urea-formaldehyde* and *melamine-formaldehyde*. Both these materials have good resistance to chemical attack. Urea-formaldehyde can be used as a bonding material to laminate plywood for exterior uses. It is also used for electrical fittings. Melamine-formaldehyde is used as a decorative and highly durable laminate for tables and work tops. 'Formica' is an example of this material.

Epoxy resins

Epoxy resins, when cured are very tough and resistant to chemicals. One of the main uses of epoxies is as adhesives ('Araldite' is an example). The strength of epoxies can be increased by reinforcing with fibres.

SAFETY NOTE:
Some of the chemicals used in association with epoxies are toxic and can cause irritation.

Polyesters

By using 'modifiers' the extent of the cross-linking can be carefully controlled when producing polyesters. This makes it possible to produce a range of polyesters with different properties. The important properties are good strength, rigidity and resistance to chemical attack. They can, however, be affected by some alkalis.

Polyesters, when reinforced with glass fibres, are used in the manufacture of boats and car bodies. Reinforced polyesters have extremely high strength.

Polyurethanes

These are a large group that can range from thermoplastic materials to thermosetting materials. The forms in which polyurethanes can be produced include flexible and rigid foams and liquids. The flexible foams are used as padding in seat upholstery ('foam rubber' is actually polyurethane foam). The rigid foams are used for thermal insulation in buildings and refrigerators. The liquids are used as clear varnishes for furniture.

Silicones

These are similar to hydrogen-carbon molecules but the carbon is replaced by silicon. These materials can be liquid, elastomer or thermosetting plastic. They have high resistance to heat, water and chemical attack.

Elastomers

These are polymers produced by addition polymerisation. They can allow a very large amount of *elastic deformation*. Some can be stretched to several times their own length as in the case of a common rubber band. When the stretching force is removed the elastomer tends to return to its original length.

Elastomer molecules are in the form of long-chains which are coiled. When the elastomer is stretched, the molecules uncoil in a manner similar to a spring. When the load is removed the molecules recoil and this returns the elastomer to its original shape. In practice, however, when you stretch an elastomer, there may also be a small amount of sliding of the molecules over each other. If this happens the material will not fully recover its original shape when the load is removed. This *deformation* can be prevented by a small amount of carefully controlled cross-linking of the coiled molecules.

Small amounts of cross-linking leaves the elastomer flexible but prevents sliding of the molecular chains. This gives the elastomer strength.

Rubber

Natural rubber is processed from the sap of certain tropical trees. When combined with other substances and fillers, many different materials can be produced. Charles Goodyear discovered in 1839 that natural rubber could be *vulcanised* (cross-linked) by adding sulphur and heating to a suitable temperature.

Synthetic rubbers can be manufactured with many desired properties "Neoprene" and "Nitrile" are examples of high performance manufactured rubbers.

These materials have limited cross-linking and have a *glass transition temperature* below room temperature. (Glass transition temperature means, in general terms, that below a certain temperature a material is a rigid solid. Above this temperature the material becomes leathery, rubbery or liquid. A rubber tube placed for a period of a few minutes (or less) in liquid oxygen will break like glass if dropped on the floor!)

Silicone rubbers

These have excellent resistance to high and low temperatures. They also resist attack by oils and chemicals. Because they are chemically inert, they are sometimes used in medical implants. They will not cause reactions in surrounding body tissue.

COMPOSITE MATERIALS

A composite material is a combination of two or more components. These combine to produce properties which are not found in any of the individual components. A common example of a composite is concrete reinforced with steel bars used in the construction of buildings and bridges. In the automotive and aerospace industries, fibrous composites are used. Commonly used composites are fibre reinforced plastics (FRP). Examples include *glass*

Plastic	Type	Main properties	Main uses
Acrylonitrile butadiene styrene (ABS)	Thermoplastic (Copolymer)	Very tough. Resists chemical attack	Telephones. Domestic waste pipes
Acetals	Thermoplastic (Crystalline)	Very strong. Resistant to hot water	Plastic jug kettles
Low density polyethylene (LDPE) (polythene)	Thermoplastic	Good electrical insulator. Translucent. Fairly flexible	Food protection film. Electric cable covering. Plastic bags
High density polyethylene (HDPE) (polythene)	Thermoplastic	Translucent. Fairly stiff and hard	Plastic bottles
Polypropylene (PP)	Thermoplastic	Very flexible in thin sections. Stiff and hard in thicker sections	Food boxes. Food boxes with hinged lids
Polyvinyl chloride (PVC)	Thermoplastic	Transparent if no fillers or colour added	Guttering and down pipes. Car seat upholstery when plasticised
Polystyrene (PS)	Thermoplastic	Stiff and hard	Yogurt cartons. Disposable cups. 'Airfix' kits
Expanded polystyrene (EPS)	Thermoplastic	Can be crumbled in the hand. Highly buoyant in water	Ceiling tiles. Packing material for delicate instruments
Polymethalmethacrylate (Perspex)	Thermoplastic (Amorphous)	Highly transparent. Good surface gloss.	Illuminated signs. Rear lights for motor vehicles
Polytetrafluorethylene (PTFE)	Thermoplastic	Opaque (usually white). Smooth texture	Non-stick coatings on cookwear
Nylon (Polyamide)	Thermoplastic	Opaque, stiff and hard	Curtain rails. Bearings and gears. Ropes
Cellulose acetate (CA)	Thermoplastic	Transparent if no fillers added. May be flexible if plasticiser added	Photographic film. Tool handles
Cellulose nitrate (CN)	Thermoplastic	Transparent if no fillers added. May be flexible if plasticiser added	Table tennis balls
Polyester *film*	Thermoplastic	Transparent. Stiffer than other plastic films	Audio tape. Cooking bags
Polyurethane foam (PU)	Thermoplastic	Soft and flexible. Rigidity can be varied	Cushion and upholstery filling.
Urea formaldehyde (UF)	Thermosetting plastic	Very hard and stiff. Hard wearing	Plug tops. Switch covers
Melamine formaldehyde (MF)	Thermosetting plastic	Very hard and stiff	Table wear. Work tops
Phenol formaldehyde (PF)	Thermosetting plastic	Good electrical insulator Hard and stiff. Flame resistant	Handles for domestic cooking utensils
Polyester *resin*	Thermosetting plastic	Very stiff and hard. Excellent binder for fibre reinforcement	Boat building. Car and aircraft parts

TABLE 1   *Properties of common plastics.*

fibre reinforced polyester, *"Kevlar"* and *carbon fibre* reinforced epoxy resin. "Kevlar" is the trade name for the strongest of all the human–developed organic fibres (its *specific* tensile strength is many times that of steel). It was discovered by Du Pont scientist Stephanie Kwolek in 1965. Kevlar and carbon fibre reinforced resin is used in the construction of many structural parts in modern aircrafts. Wood and leather are examples of natural composites.

SUMMARY

Plastics or polymers are organic substances which can be moulded into useful objects. The molecular composition of polymers determines their characteristics, engineering properties and their end uses.

Polymer molecules are formed by a process called *polymerisation*. The two types of polymerisation are *addition* polymerisation and *condensation* polymerisation. In addition polymerisation, individual mers are formed from monomers by the action of a catalyst. The mers link together to form long-chain polymer molecules. *Thermoplastic* materials are made up of these molecules. The molecules are held together in the plastic by *secondary bonding* or weak forces of attraction. Thermoplastics can be resoftened and remoulded many times.

Copolymerisation is a process in which mers of different monomers are joined together in the same addition chain.

Condensation polymerisation produces a network of *primary bonded,* cross-linked molecules. This results in the formation of plastics which are hard and rigid. They are known as *thermosetting* materials. They cannot be resoftened by heating.

Common plastics and their uses (see **TABLE 1**). Additives in plastics (see **TABLE 2**).

Additive	Purpose
Fillers	Improve mechanical properties
Plasticisers	Improve flexibility
Colour pigments	Give desired colour
Stabilisers	Prevent degradation
Flame retardants	Reduce flammability
Lubricants	Make the plastic easier to mould

TABLE 2 *Additives in plastics.*

ENGINEERING TECHNOLOGY

Metrology

INTRODUCTION

Metrology is the science of measurement. The term metrology comes from the Greek word *metron* meaning 'measure'. Metrology covers a wide range of activities in measurement but here we will concentrate on the measurement of lengths, angles and surface roughness.

Precise measurement of length and angles is a very important part of engineering manufacture. Measurement is a basic form of inspection. Inspection ensures that the component being manufactured is in accordance with the specification. There are two methods of inspecting a component.

1 By using measuring instruments to determine its actual dimensions. This is *measurement*.
2 By using gauges to simply determine whether it is useful or unusable (good or bad). This is *gauging*.

MEASUREMENT

Measurement gives full information about the magnitude of each dimension of the component. To measure an engineering component successfully you must use a system of measurement which can be understood and one which is used by other people. Many countries now use *le Système International d'Unités* (SI units). The standard SI unit of length is the metre.

Standards of measurement

Measurement in engineering depends mainly on end standards. The end standards in general use are slip gauges.

Slip gauges are small blocks of alloy steel or tungsten carbide. They are usually rectangular in shape although square and round types are also available. They have two very flat and parallel surfaces at opposite ends. These surfaces are the measuring faces of the slip gauge. Steel slip gauges are carefully heat treated to ensure that they can retain their accuracy.

Regardless of the material they are made from, slip gauges are made in a variety of sizes ranging from 100mm down to 1.0005mm. The measuring faces of slip gauges have such a good surface finish that when you place two gauges together with their

> It was Simon Stevin (born in 1548 and died in 1620) who devised the decimal unit of measurement. Talleyrand worked on the idea of a system of international decimal units based on the metre. In the 1790s there was an attempt to establish the metre as 1/40000000 of the earth's meridian passing through the Paris observatory.
>
> In 1889 the standard metre was defined as the distance between two lines which were engraved on a specially made platinum-iridium bar. This was the international prototype metre. It is kept at the *Bureau International de Poids et Measures* at Sevres in France. A major disadvantage of the standard metre was the need to make copies which introduced the possibility of making errors.
>
> In 1960 the metre was defined as the length equal to 1 650 763.73 wavelengths, in vacuum, of orange light radiation of krypton 86. This definition made it possible to reproduce the metre anywhere if the equipment to produce the correct light and the means to count the wavelengths were available. The possible error with this system is about four parts per billion (a little over a metre in the distance from the earth to the moon). As the wavelength of this light never changes, the length of the standard metre (by that definition) does not change. At a General Conference on Weights and Measures in 1983 the metre was redefined. It is now the distance light travels through space in 1/299 792 458 of a second. (Light travels at exactly 299 792 458 metres per second.) Because the metre is now based on time, the accuracy of the metre will improve as the methods of measuring time improve.

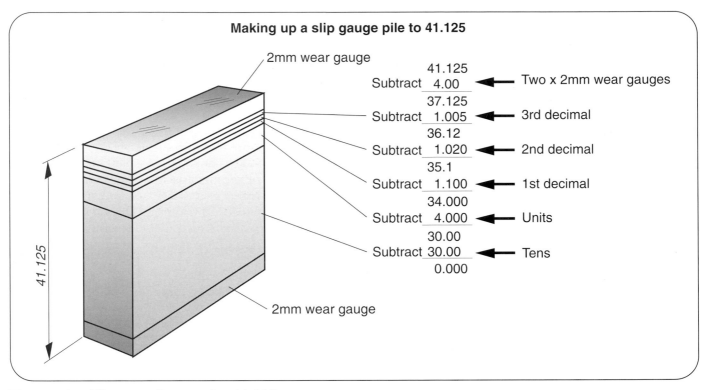

Making up a slip gauge pile to 41.125

2mm wear gauge

	41.125	
Subtract	4.00	← Two x 2mm wear gauges
	37.125	
Subtract	1.005	← 3rd decimal
	36.12	
Subtract	1.020	← 2nd decimal
	35.1	
Subtract	1.100	← 1st decimal
	34.000	
Subtract	4.000	← Units
	30.00	
Subtract	30.00	← Tens
	0.000	

41.125

2mm wear gauge

FIGURE 1   *Slip gauge pile measuring 41.125.*

FIGURE 2   *A slip gauge set. (Courtesy: Mitutogo (U.K.) Ltd.)*

measuring faces in contact, and slide one gauge over the other, they will wring together. Wringing slip gauges together is a method used to build up dimensions from selected gauges. **FIGURE 1** shows a slip gauge pile measuring 41.125mm.

Slip gauges are made up in sets. A typical set is shown in **FIGURE 2**. Each set is carefully packed in a sturdy case in which there is a separate compartment for each gauge. Slip gauge sets are designated by a number. An M32/1 set would be made up as follows: M = metric gauges; 32 = thirty two slip gauges in the set; 1 = 1mm base. Another example would be M42/2.

Slip gauges are made in different grades of accuracy.

- **Calibration grade and grade 00**
- **Grade 0**
- **Grade 1**
- **Grade 2.**

The calibration grade and grade 00 are extremely accurate and are used to check the accuracy of other slip gauges and also for calibrating very precise instruments. Generally, when checking for accuracy in manufacture, grade 2 gauges are used. Grade 0 gauges are used where more accurate checking is needed.

Standard measuring temperature

All measuring instruments will be affected by changes in temperature. Because of this, a standard measuring temperature of 20°C has been adopted. Slip gauges and other end standards are the correct size at this temperature. When engineers need to measure accurately, they often work in a laboratory which has a controlled temperature of 20°C.

Limits, tolerances and allowances

In manufacturing, it is not possible to make an engineering component to an exact size. It is of course possible to make something to an exact size by chance but to set out to make a part on a lathe, for example, to an exact diameter of 20.0000mm would be impractical.

First of all you would need a very high quality lathe. The slightest inaccuracies or vibrations in the lathe would reduce the possibility of machining to the required accuracy. Even the most minute wear on the tool would cause a variation in the size of the

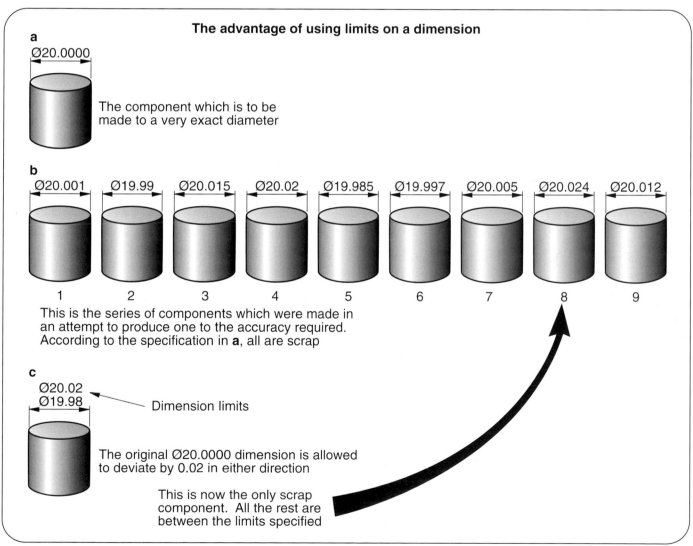

The advantage of using limits on a dimension

a Ø20.0000 — The component which is to be made to a very exact diameter

b Ø20.001 Ø19.99 Ø20.015 Ø20.02 Ø19.985 Ø19.997 Ø20.005 Ø20.024 Ø20.012
1 2 3 4 5 6 7 8 9

This is the series of components which were made in an attempt to produce one to the accuracy required. According to the specification in **a**, all are scrap

c Ø20.02 Ø19.98 — Dimension limits

The original Ø20.0000 dimension is allowed to deviate by 0.02 in either direction

This is now the only scrap component. All the rest are between the limits specified

FIGURE 3   *Using limits on a dimension.*

component between the start of the cut and the end. Both the lathe and the workpiece would be affected by temperature changes and would ideally need to be in a laboratory where the temperature was maintained at exactly 20°C. You would need very accurate measuring instruments to check that the component was being accurately made and these would also have to be used at a strictly controlled temperature of 20°C. So you can see that to make a component to a very precise size would be expensive indeed.

If you study **FIGURE 3(a)** you will see the component that was referred to above. All of the components in **FIGURE 3(b)** are various attempts by a highly skilled operator to produce the component. You can see that none is the right size. This would be a very costly manufacturing exercise – every single piece is scrap!

Now look at **FIGURE 3(c)**. Here we have allowed the size to *deviate* a little from that which was originally required. We have also set *limits* (limit dimensions) on the amount by which the size of the part can deviate from the dimension specified. What this means is that the original component, instead of being exactly 20.0000mm, will be acceptable if it measures up to 20.02mm or down to 19.98mm. Any size in between these two will be accepted. Now if we check the pieces that were made we find that only one (number 8) is scrap.

Manufacturing engineers set limits on the dimensions of components. Setting limits makes it easier and faster to make components. Generally, the greater the limits, the cheaper it is to make. But the limits decided on by the engineer must take the end use of the component into account. For example, a part for an aircraft engine will usually require much smaller limits than a part for a washing machine.

Tolerance

The required size of a component, before the limits are set, is the *basic* size. It is also known as the *nominal* size. When the engineer sets limits, he/she is introducing a *tolerance* into the size. A tolerance is the amount by which a dimension is allowed to deviate from the nominal size.

If the nominal size of the part is 25.00mm then the limits could be given as

25.01 – this is known as the upper limit
24.98 – this is known as the lower limit

If you subtract the lower limit from the upper limit the result will be the tolerance.

   25.01 upper limit
   24.98 lower limit
    0.03 tolerance

If you subtract the nominal size from the upper limit the result will be the upper deviation

   25.01 upper limit
   25.00 nominal size
    0.01 upper deviation

If you subtract the nominal size from the lower limit the result will be the lower deviation

   24.98 lower limit
   25.00 nominal size
   – 0.02 lower deviation

A tolerance is *bilateral* if it is spread over both sides of the nominal size. A *unilateral* tolerance is one which is either above or below the nominal size.

Allowance

If moving parts in machines are to function properly, then rotating shafts for example, have to be able to run freely in their bearings. A shaft which has to run freely in a bearing must have enough space to do so. It must also have enough space for a film of oil between the two in order to prevent wear. If the shaft has too much space it will vibrate, wear quickly and may even cause something to break resulting in serious damage to the machine. In engineering, the relationship between the size of a part and the size of the part which fits into it is of extreme importance.

The space between the shaft and the bearing is known as the *allowance*. An allowance is the desired difference between the sizes of two parts which fit together. Note how this is different from tolerance. Tolerance is the permitted variation in size (the difference between the limits). The allowance determines the type of *fit* between two parts. **FIGURE 4** shows the meaning of allowance. A large

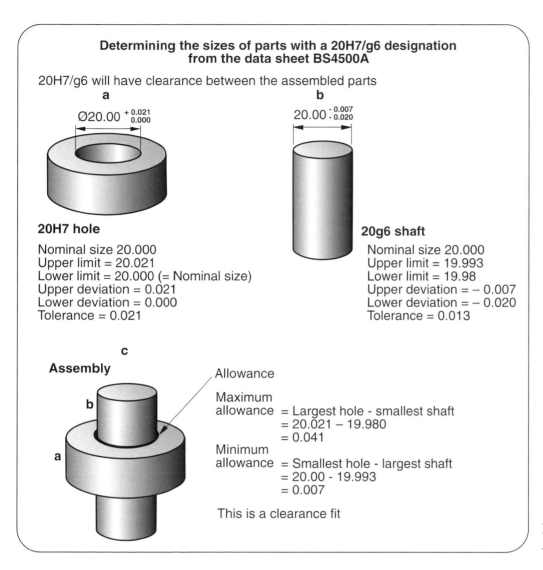

Determining the sizes of parts with a 20H7/g6 designation from the data sheet BS4500A

20H7/g6 will have clearance between the assembled parts

a

$\varnothing20.00 \, ^{+0.021}_{0.000}$

20H7 hole

Nominal size 20.000
Upper limit = 20.021
Lower limit = 20.000 (= Nominal size)
Upper deviation = 0.021
Lower deviation = 0.000
Tolerance = 0.021

b

$20.00 \, ^{-0.007}_{-0.020}$

20g6 shaft

Nominal size 20.000
Upper limit = 19.993
Lower limit = 19.98
Upper deviation = − 0.007
Lower deviation = − 0.020
Tolerance = 0.013

c

Assembly

Allowance

Maximum
allowance = Largest hole - smallest shaft
= 20.021 − 19.980
= 0.041

Minimum
allowance = Smallest hole - largest shaft
= 20.00 - 19.993
= 0.007

This is a clearance fit

FIGURE 4 *Determining sizes from the data sheet.*

allowance will give a loose fit. A small allowance will give a close fit.

Limits and fits

When the engineer has decided on the type of fit for the parts in an assembly, he/she will use a table of *limits and fits* (**TABLE 1**, page 150) to determine the correct tolerances for sizes of the parts. Once the tolerances are known, the limits on the nominal sizes can be written down.

The ISO system of limits and fits

The ISO system of limits and fits gives a range of sizes to which parts should be made if the type of fit is known. There are two systems of fits in use:

1 Hole basis system
2 Shaft basis system

The hole basis system of fits

This is the preferred system. All holes are manufactured to a fixed size and the shaft size is varied. This system is preferred because reamers, for example, are made in a range of standard sizes. (It would be impossible to make a range of reamers to cover all types of fit.)

The shaft basis system of fits

In this system the shaft is the fixed size and the hole sizes are varied. This system is sometimes used when a variety of components, such as bearings, couplings and gears have to fit the same shaft.

The following is a list of fits in use in the ISO system:

- **Clearance fit**
- **Transition fit**
- **Interference fit.**

Clearance fit
In this assembly there is a space between the two parts. The shaft is always smaller than the part it fits into.

Transition fit
This is a range of fits which can be either clearance or interference. The shaft can be larger or smaller than the part it fits into.

Interference fit
In this assembly there is no space between the parts. In fact the shaft is always made larger than the part into which it is intended to fit. This means that force is required to assemble the parts.

Selected fits in the hole basis system
The ISO limits and fits system gives a number of selected tolerances. Selected tolerances are given a code. In the hole basis system all holes are coded 'H' and the shaft tolerances are denoted by a lower case letter. The letter H in the code indicates the deviation and the number in the code indicates the tolerance grade.

Selected hole tolerances H11; H9; H8; H7
If a hole is to be made with 20mm diameter the tolerance should accompany the dimension to give the limits on the size of the hole, for example, 20H7.

Selected shaft tolerances c11; d10; e9; f7; g6; h6; k6; n6; p6; s6
A shaft size could be given as 20g6.

If the basic size changes then the limits may also change. You can see a full range of tolerances in the data sheet on page 150.

INSPECTION BY MEASUREMENT

Measurement is very important in manufacturing. Many different instruments have been developed which allow measurements to be taken quickly and accurately. Some instruments are hand-held and the size of the measured component is read from the instrument. Hand-held measuring instruments are easy to use and give a quick and accurate interpretation of the size of the part being measured.

Other instruments are fixed to machines for 'in-process inspection'. In-process inspection is used to automatically control the size of the workpiece. In this system, information about the size of the workpiece is fed back from the inspection instrument to the machine control unit. The control unit adjusts the cutting tool until the size of the component is correct.

The accuracy of a system of measurement can be affected by:

Misreading the instrument. Where line-matching is the basis of how the instrument functions, misreading is a possibility.
Parallax errors (where the line of sight onto the instrument reading is not correct).
Distortion of the instrument due to over-tightening or exerting too much pressure on the measuring faces.
The temperature of the instrument and the component being measured. The size of all engineering components are affected to some extent by changes in temperature. Accurate measurements should be taken at the standard measuring temperature.

Linear measuring instruments
There are two types of linear measuring instruments

1 Direct-reading instruments
2 Indirect-reading instruments

Direct-reading instruments have a scale and the size of the component is matched directly with this scale. An engineer's rule is a typical example. This is basically a line-matching instrument.

Indirect-reading instruments transfer the size of the component to a special scale. Micrometers and

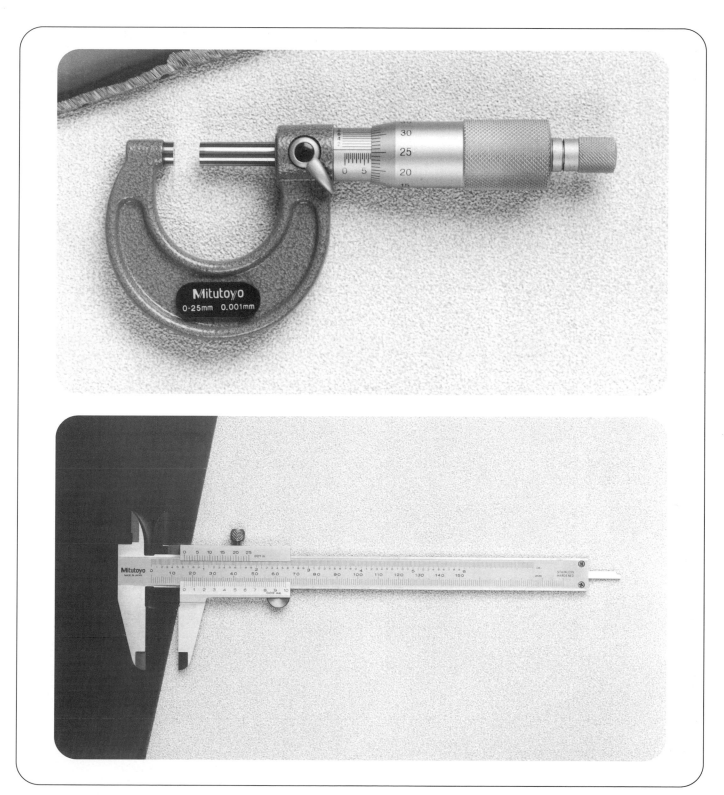

FIGURE 5 *Measuring instruments. Top photograph shows a micrometer, bottom shows a Vernier callipers. (Courtesy: Mitutoyo (UK) Ltd)*

The problem of inaccurate reading of instruments is solved by the use of digital readout systems attached to the instruments. The digital readout can be built into the instrument or it can be a separate unit. FIGURE 6 shows an electronic height guage (notice the digital readout). Some very sensitive measuring instruments have pressure indicators attached to the measuring faces. When the correct pressure on the measuring faces is indicated, the reading is taken.

Modern inspection equipment can be connected to a computer. The measurements taken are entered directly to a file on the component being measured. This system allows accurate record-keeping for every component inspected. Also, persistent errors in the manufacturing process can be quickly seen by comparing the results of a number of components.

Dial gauges

Dial gauges are used for linear measurement. When the plunger is pushed in, the distance it moves will be shown directly on the dial by the deflection of the pointer or on the digital readout.

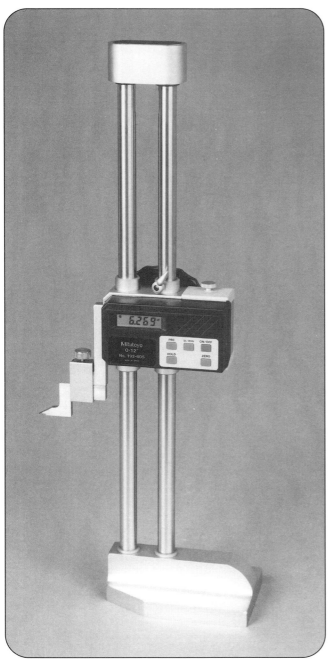

FIGURE 6   *A height guage with a digital readout. (Courtesy: Mitutoyo (UK) Ltd.)*

Vernier callipers are examples of direct reading instruments. These are also examples of end-measuring instruments. They are usually easier to use and are more accurate than line-matching devices. FIGURE 5 shows both measuring instruments.

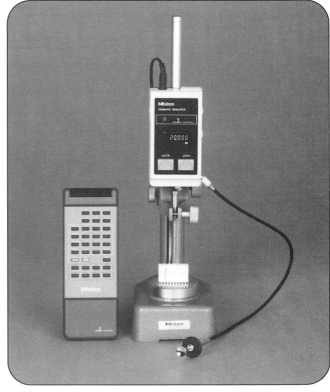

FIGURE 7   *A comparator. (Courtesy: Mitutoyo (UK) Ltd.)*

Dial test indicator (sometimes referred to as a DTI)
These instruments are suitable for taking measurements in very confined spaces. The pointer will rotate when the lever is moved up or down. To set these indicators to zero you have to rotate the bezel.

Comparator
A simple comparator, shown in **FIGURE 7**, consists of a dial gauge fixed to a sturdy stand. The reference surface of the comparator is flat. The comparator is set by setting the gauge to zero using slip gauges as a reference. The instrument then compares the size of the component with the length of the slip gauges.

Slip gauge accessories

These accessories are made to the same accuracy as slip gauges.
The accessory set will enable you to make up very accurate

- **Height gauges**
- **Internal gauges**
- **External gauges.**

Angle-measuring instruments

Precision measurement of angles is possible using two methods.

1 By measuring the angle directly in degrees.
2 By taking linear measurements and using trigonometry to determine the angle.

An angle can be measured in degrees using a vernier protractor (shown in **FIGURE 8**). The stock and the blade are put into contact with faces of the component. The angle between the faces is then read off the vernier scale. The vernier protractor is capable of measuring to within 5 minutes of an arc.

Angles can also be measured using the combination angle gauges shown in **FIGURE 9**. Combination angle gauges are very precisely made. The gauge faces are finished to an accuracy similar to slip gauges and they can be wrung together to make a large variety of angles. Angle gauges are packed in sets. Their accuracy is within ± 2 seconds of a degree.

FIGURE 8 *Vernier protractor. (Courtesy: Moore and Wright Ltd)*

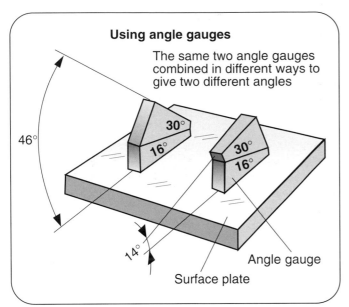

Using angle gauges

The same two angle gauges combined in different ways to give two different angles

46°

30°
16°

30°
16°

14°

Angle gauge

Surface plate

FIGURE 9 *Combination angle gauges.*

A number of methods can be used to determine or set up angles using calculations. These include:

• **The sine bar**
• **Precision cylinders (or precision rollers)**
• **Precision balls.**

The sine bar

The sine bar is made from high quality steel. The two rollers are the same diameter and are true cylinders. The common axis of the rollers is parallel with the working surface of the sine bar. The distance between the rollers is known and it is this distance which designates the size of the sine bar. Popular sizes are 100mm; 200mm; 300mm.

With a sine bar you can set up and measure angles very accurately. It is used on a flat reference surface as you can see in **FIGURE 10**. The working surface of the sine bar forms an angle with the reference surface when slip gauges are placed under one of the rollers.

Precision cylinders

A precision cylinder is very accurately made from high quality steel. One of the principal features of the precision cylinder is that its diameter is extremely accurate over its entire length. If you are required to measure accurately the angles of dovetails

such as machine slide ways, or external tapers such as a morse taper, you could use precision cylinders. You can see a method of measuring a dovetail slide in **FIGURE 11** and a method of measuring a taper component is shown in **FIGURE 12**.

Precision balls

It is very difficult to measure the angle of small internal tapers directly. Precision balls make it possible to take linear measurements from which you can calculate the angles. In **FIGURE 13** you can see a method of using precision balls to measure an internal taper. The diameter of each ball is known and their height from the end of the taper can be found by measuring with a depth micrometer. A triangle is constructed from which the required angle is calculated.

Measurement of screw threads

The features of a screw thread which are usually measured are:

• **The major diameter**
• **The minor diameter**
• **The thread form. (This includes the crest and root radii and the flank angles)**
• **The pitch**
• **The pitch diameter.**

The major diameter can be measured using a hand-held outside micrometer. It is preferable, however, to use the specially made bench micrometer or a floating carriage diameter measuring machine.

The minor diameter is also measured using an outside micrometer and thread measuring prisms. The prisms are shaped so that they can contact the root of the thread. A more accurate method of measuring the minor diameter is to use a floating carriage diameter measuring machine.

The most important measurement of a thread form is measurement of the flank angles. The more common method of measuring the thread form is by using an optical contour projector such as shown in **FIGURE 14**. The image of the screw thread is projected onto the screen and the flank angles can be measured using a type of protractor.

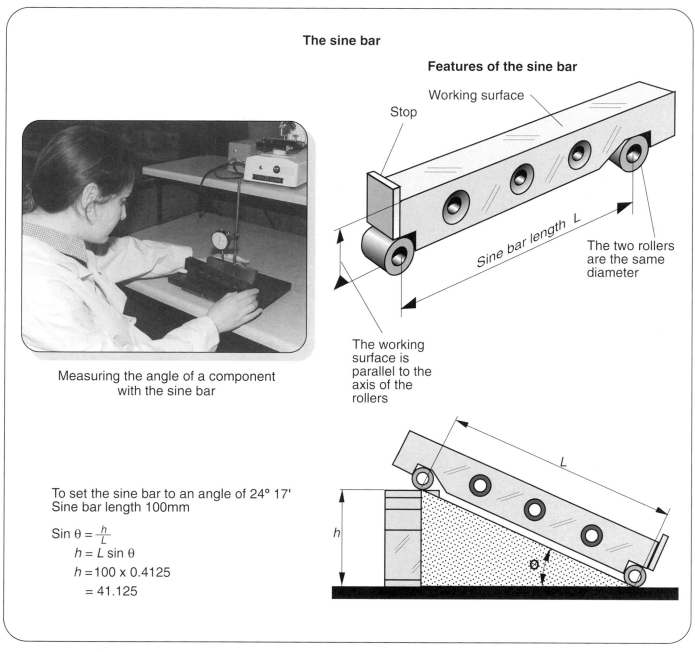

The sine bar

Features of the sine bar

Working surface

Stop

Sine bar length L

The two rollers
are the same
diameter

The working
surface is
parallel to the
axis of the
rollers

Measuring the angle of a component
with the sine bar

To set the sine bar to an angle of 24° 17'
Sine bar length 100mm

$\sin \theta = \frac{h}{L}$

$h = L \sin \theta$

$h = 100 \times 0.4125$

$= 41.125$

L

h

FIGURE 10   *The sine bar. (Inset photograph: using the sine bar to check the angles of a component. Courtesy: the authors)*

The pitch diameter is measured using small precision cylinders under the faces of the micrometer. The precision cylinders are selected so that they contact the flanks of the thread about half way down. A floating carriage diameter measuring machine is normally used to ensure that the measurement is taken at right angles to the thread axis.

An outside micrometer and three cylinders can be used. This is known as the three-wire measuring

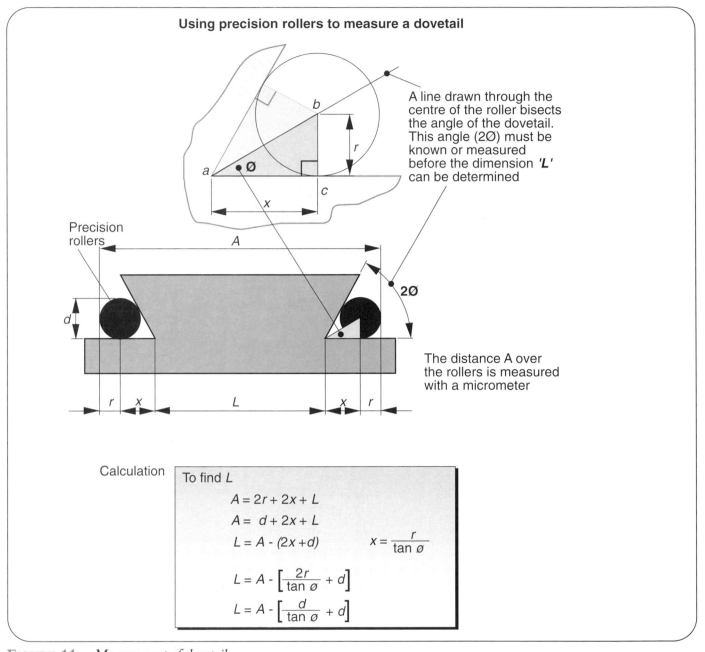

Using precision rollers to measure a dovetail

A line drawn through the centre of the roller bisects the angle of the dovetail. This angle (2Ø) must be known or measured before the dimension *'L'* can be determined

Precision rollers

The distance A over the rollers is measured with a micrometer

Calculation

To find L

$$A = 2r + 2x + L$$
$$A = d + 2x + L$$
$$L = A - (2x + d) \qquad x = \frac{r}{\tan ø}$$
$$L = A - \left[\frac{2r}{\tan ø} + d \right]$$
$$L = A - \left[\frac{d}{\tan ø} + d \right]$$

FIGURE 11   *Measurement of dovetails.*

method. The third cylinder ensures that the measurement axis is at right angles to the thread axis.

In the two methods above, the diameter of the cylinders must be known and taken into consideration when calculating the pitch diameter. The exact point at which the cylinder contacts the flank can be calculated, knowing the cylinder diameter and the flank angle of the thread.

INSPECTION BY GAUGING

The use of any system of limits and fits makes it possible to *gauge* the size of a component. When you

Measuring the included angle of an external taper

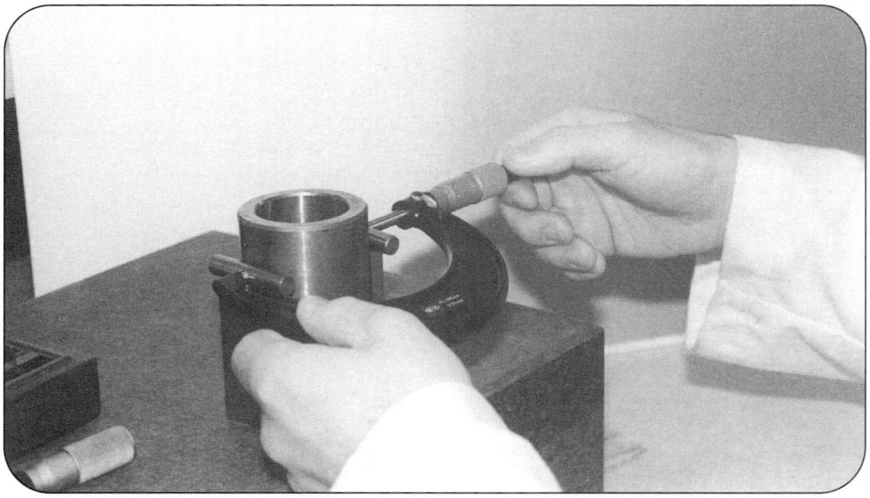

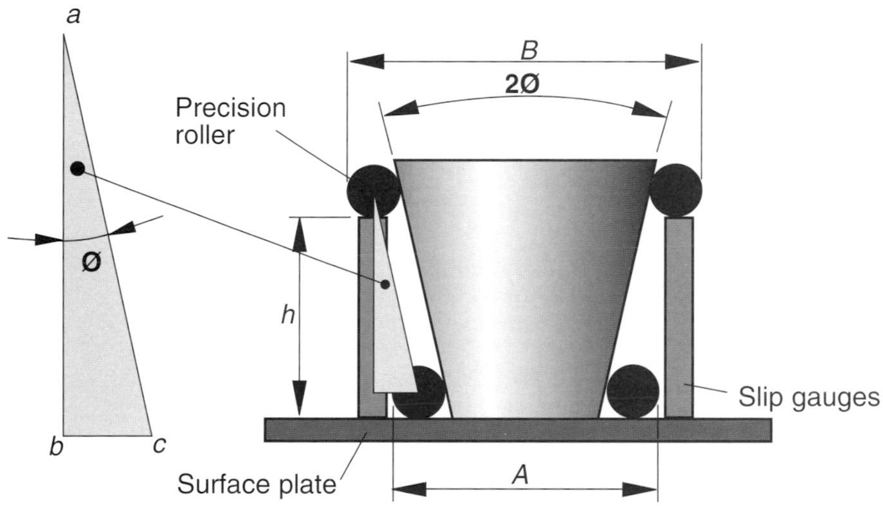

a

Precision
roller

B

$2\emptyset$

$\emptyset$

h

Slip gauges

b c

Surface plate

A

Calculation

To determine the included angle
of the tapered component

$\text{Tan } \emptyset = \dfrac{bc}{ab}$

but $bc = \dfrac{B - A}{2}$

$\text{Tan } \emptyset = \dfrac{B - A}{2ab}$

$\boxed{2\emptyset = \text{Tan}^{-1} \dfrac{B - A}{ab}}$

FIGURE 12 *Measuring with precision roller. (Photograph courtesy: the authors)*

141

Measuring the angle of an internal taper

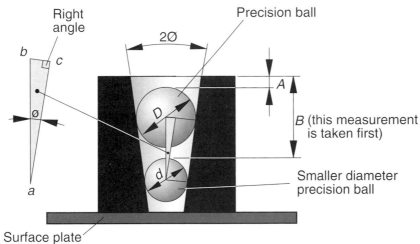

Right angle

Precision ball

2Ø

b ∘ *c*

A

Ø

D

B (this measurement is taken first)

a

d

Smaller diameter precision ball

Surface plate

To determine the internal angle of the component

$$\text{Sin } \varnothing = \frac{bc}{ab}$$

$$\text{but } bc = \frac{D - d}{2}$$

$$\text{and } ab = \left[B + \frac{d}{2} \right] - \left[A + \frac{D}{2} \right]$$

$$\text{if } \frac{D}{2} = R \text{ and } \frac{d}{2} = r \text{ then } \quad 2\varnothing = 2 \text{ Sin}^{-1} \frac{R - r}{(B + r) - (A + R)}$$

FIGURE 13 *Measuring the angle of an internal taper using precision balls. (Photograph courtesy: the authors)*

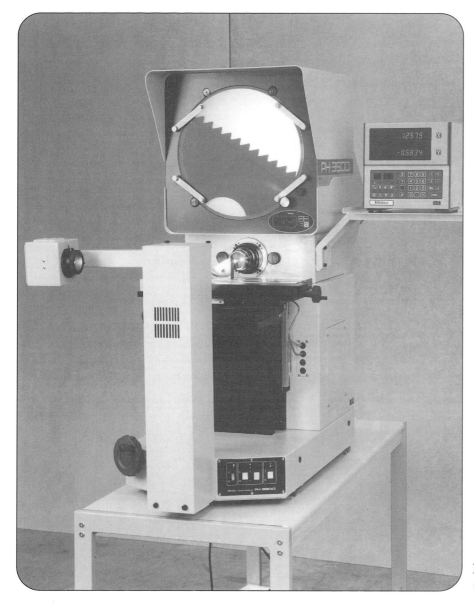

FIGURE 14   *Optical projector.*
(Courtesy: Mitutoyo (UK) Ltd.)

use *limit gauges* to inspect a component, you make no attempt to determine its actual size.

Gauging a component is carried out to ensure that the actual size is within the specified limits. To do this you need two gauges for each basic size:

1 One gauge for the upper limit.
2 One gauge for the lower limit.

Gauging a shaft
You can check that the size of a shaft is within limits using *gap* (or snap) gauges. One gap gauge is made to the upper limit. This is the 'GO' gauge. The other gauge is made to the lower limit. This is the 'NOT GO' gauge. In practice the GO and NOT GO gauges are often combined in the same instrument.

The GO gauge should fit over the shaft. The NOT GO gauge should not be able to pass over the shaft.

If the GO gauge did not fit over the shaft then the shaft diameter would be too large.

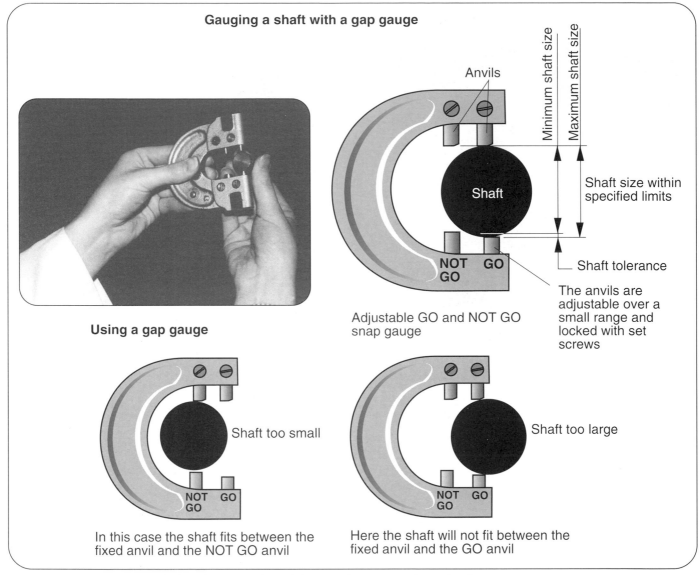

Gauging a shaft with a gap gauge

Using a gap gauge

Adjustable GO and NOT GO snap gauge

Anvils

Minimum shaft size

Maximum shaft size

Shaft

Shaft size within specified limits

Shaft tolerance

The anvils are adjustable over a small range and locked with set screws

Shaft too small

In this case the shaft fits between the fixed anvil and the NOT GO anvil

Shaft too large

Here the shaft will not fit between the fixed anvil and the GO anvil

NOT GO   GO

FIGURE 15   *Gauging a shaft with a gap gauge. (Photograph courtesy: the authors)*

If the NOT GO gauge passes over the shaft then the shaft diameter would be too small. **FIGURE 15** shows a gap gauge and how it is used to gauge the size of a shaft.

Gauging a hole
You can check that the size of a hole is within limits using plain plug gauges.

The 'GO' plug gauge is made to the lower limit. The 'NOT GO' plug gauge is made to the upper

limit. If the NOT GO plug gauge passes through the hole then the hole diameter is too large. If the GO plug gauge does not enter the hole then the hole diameter is too small.

In **FIGURE 16** you can see a plain plug gauge and how it is used to gauge the size of a hole.

Special gauging equipment
Air gauging
For rapid gauging of mass produced parts, specially–

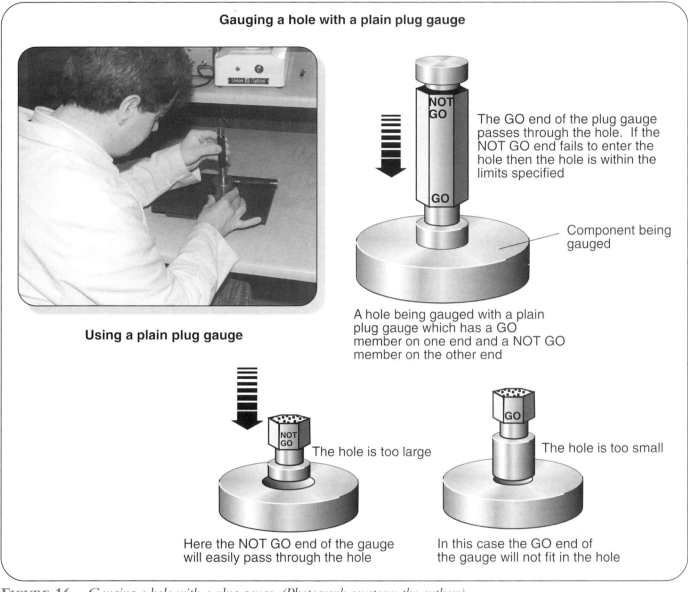

Gauging a hole with a plain plug gauge

Using a plain plug gauge

NOT GO

GO

The GO end of the plug gauge passes through the hole. If the NOT GO end fails to enter the hole then the hole is within the limits specified

Component being gauged

A hole being gauged with a plain plug gauge which has a GO member on one end and a NOT GO member on the other end

NOT GO

The hole is too large

Here the NOT GO end of the gauge will easily pass through the hole

GO

The hole is too small

In this case the GO end of the gauge will not fit in the hole

FIGURE 16   *Gauging a hole with a plug gauge. (Photograph courtesy: the authors)*

designed air gauging apparatus speeds up the operation. Air gauging is very accurate and a number of features can be checked at the same time.

Interchangeability

In manufacturing, components are usually made in large batches. This is because it is more efficient to set up a machine to produce just one type of component at a time. If parts which have to be assembled together are manufactured within limits, and are then selected at random from the batches, they will always fit.

Interchangeability is very important because parts for assemblies are sometimes made in different areas of a factory and even in different countries.

Selective assembly

In selective assembly all the parts which have been manufactured within limits are measured before

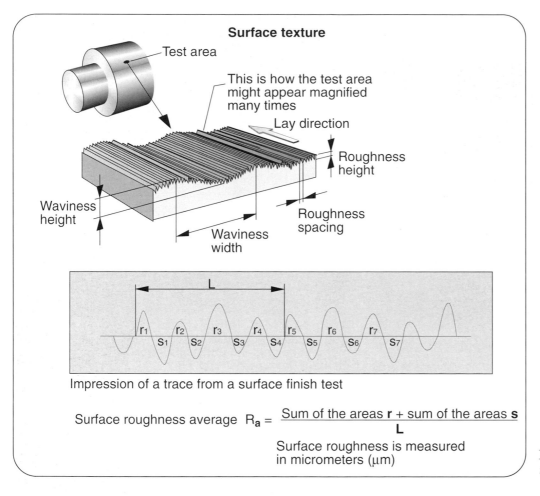

Surface texture

Test area

This is how the test area might appear magnified many times

Lay direction

Roughness height

Waviness height

Waviness width

Roughness spacing

Impression of a trace from a surface finish test

$$R_a = \frac{\text{Sum of the areas } r + \text{sum of the areas } s}{L}$$

Surface roughness average

Surface roughness is measured in micrometers (μm)

FIGURE 17 *Surface roughness.*

assembly. The parts which give the most satisfactory fit are then assembled together.

SURFACE ROUGHNESS

In precision manufacture there is a constant effort to produce components which have "perfect" surface finish. Good quality surface finish has many benefits. One of the most important is resistance to fatigue because roughness facilitates cracking.

Measurement of surface roughness

The measurement of a surface is concerned with the following aspects:

* **The lay of the surface**
* **The roughness of the surface**
* **The waviness of the surface.**

Eli Whitney, an American teacher and engineer, was given an order for 10,000 muskets for the government. Because the time he had been given to deliver the muskets was so short (15 months), he devised a system of manufacturing whereby each workman made just one component part continuously. Each part was so accurately made that they were all interchangeable. The system of production involved such ideas as: limiting the travel of the slideways on the lathes using stops; using special attachments to guide the workman's files; using jigs to drill holes in exactly the right places and so on.

Whitney demonstrated the success of his system by selecting at random 10 samples of each component part of a musket. He took the parts to the Treasury Office in Philadelphia where he allowed officials to assemble a musket using a component selected from each group.

FIGURE 18   *Surface roughness instrument. (Courtesy: Rank Taylor Hobson Ltd.)*

The lay of any surface is generally determined by the process which produces the surface. For example, the lay on the end of a bar which has been faced on the lathe is circular. A surface produced on a shaping machine has a linear lay.

Roughness refers to finely spaced surface irregularities. A machined surface is in reality not smooth but consists of a series of minute peaks and valleys. They are caused by the machining operation.

Waviness is caused by deflection of tools and work during the machining operation. It can also be the result of warping of the work. You can see these details in **FIGURE 17**

Method of measuring surface roughness

The roughness of a surface is measured by instruments which use a stylus to traverse the surface.

The movement of the stylus is converted into electrical impulses, which are amplified and fed into a recording machine or into a computer.

In practice the vertical movement of the stylus is magnified on the printout to a much greater extent than the horizontal movement of the stylus.

The section of the surface over which the stylus is moved is known as the sampling length. The sampling length can vary from 0.25mm to 0.8mm depending on the method used to produce the

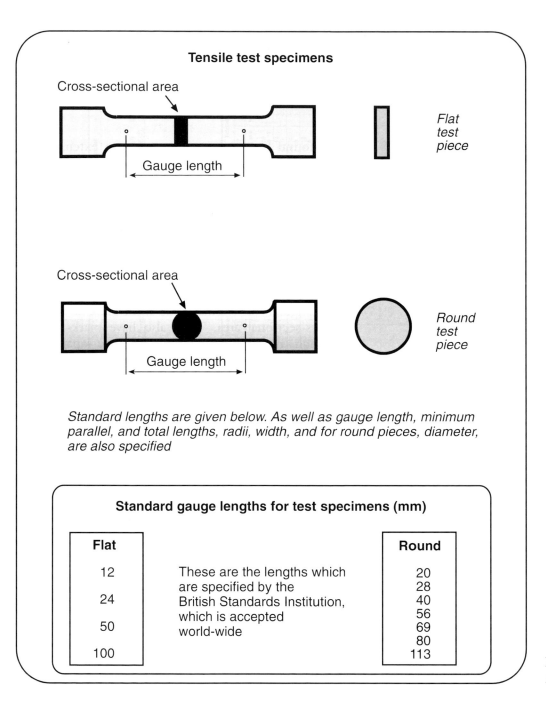

Figure 1 *Tensile test specimens.*

In the tensile testing of metals, a stage is reached when the metal will not return to its original length – it stays stretched. This shows the end of its elasticity, and the material has reached its elastic limit. Up to the elastic limit, there is *proportionality*, as explained above, and the elastic limit is also known as the *limit of proportionality*.

Once the elastic limit has been reached, an increase in the load on the specimen produces a much larger extension than in the earlier part of the test. This is called the plastic region. At the end of this state, the extension is even greater, and a *yield point* is reached, as seen in **FIGURE 2**. A further increase in the load causes the specimen firstly to thin uniformly, then to

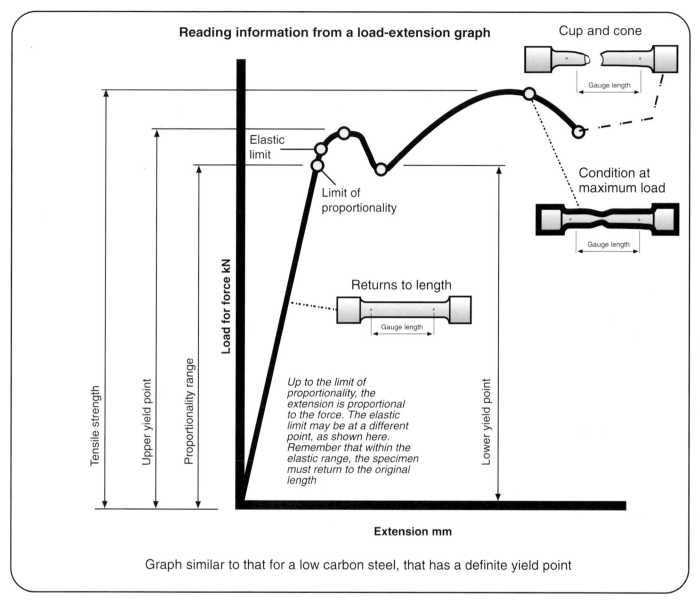

Reading information from a load-extension graph

Cup and cone

Gauge length

Elastic limit

Limit of proportionality

Condition at maximum load

Gauge length

Load for force kN

Returns to length

Gauge length

Up to the limit of proportionality, the extension is proportional to the force. The elastic limit may be at a different point, as shown here. Remember that within the elastic range, the specimen must return to the original length

Tensile strength

Upper yield point

Proportionality range

Lower yield point

Extension mm

Graph similar to that for a low carbon steel, that has a definite yield point

FIGURE 2   *General tensile graph.*

neck, and then start to break, or fracture. When the fracture occurs, one side of the broken specimen has a rough *cone* shape, and the other has a rough *cup* shape. This is known as the *cup and cone* fracture, which is to be seen in **FIGURE 2**.

FIGURE 3 shows the graph of the elastic part of a tensile test on a 0.2% carbon steel specimen. When the load is plotted against the extension, the result is

a straight line. It was Robert Hooke who first noted that, in elastic materials, the extension is proportional to the load and naturally this is called *Hooke's Law.*

Stress
When a load or force is applied to a piece of metal, the load is carried by the whole area of the cross section. In other words, each unit of area, usually

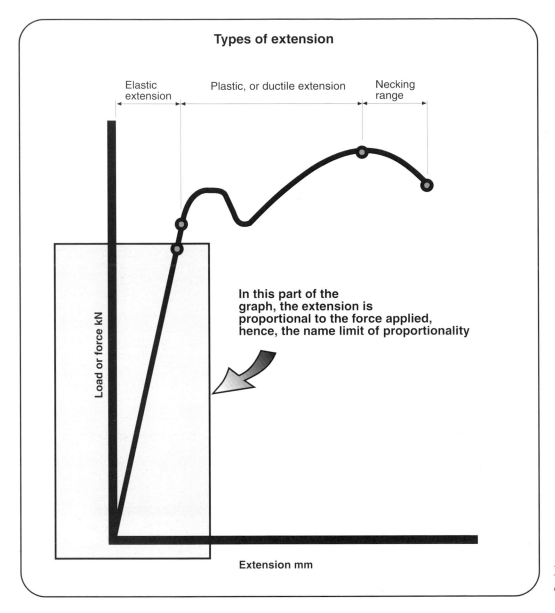

Types of extension

Elastic extension

Plastic, or ductile extension

Necking range

Load or force kN

In this part of the graph, the extension is proportional to the force applied, hence, the name limit of proportionality

Extension mm

FIGURE 3 *Types of extension.*

1 mm², carries an equal amount of load. So, 1 mm² might have a force of 250 newtons (N), acting on it, which is stated as 250 N per mm². This is normally written as – 250 N/mm². It is the amount of load or force carried by a unit area, and it is known as stress. **FIGURE 4**

Stress is a very important ratio, and, as we will see later, there are various types of stress. It is the amount of load or force carried by a unit area that is called stress.

Strain
The amount that a metal specimen stretches in the elastic range is very small. It is only a small fraction of the length of the specimen gauge length, or original length. When a tensile test is carried out, the information is presented in graphical form. It may be presented as in **FIGURE 2** and **FIGURE 3**, where load is plotted against extension, or it may be presented as shown in **FIGURE 5**, where stress is plotted against strain.

Stress, strain, and Young's Modulus of elasticity

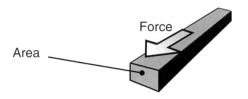

Force

Area

$$\text{Stress} = \frac{\text{Load or Force}}{\text{Sectional area}}$$

If this bar, 15 mm wide x 8 deep, is pulled with a force of 360 kN, the stress is found as follows:

$$\text{Stress} = \frac{\text{Load or Force}}{\text{Sectional area}}$$

Force = 360 kN

Cross-sectional area = 120 mm²

Then stress = $\dfrac{360 \text{ kN}}{120 \text{ mm}^2}$

= **3 kN / mm²**

$$\text{Strain} = \frac{\text{Extension}}{\text{Original length}}$$

The extension is the amount by which the length changes and in a tensile test the original length is the gauge length

If the bar above measures 2 metres before the force is applied, and 2.05 metres when the force is applied,

then :

$$\text{Strain} = \frac{2.05 - 2.0}{2.0}$$

= **0.025**   **Note that there are no units – the value is a ratio**

$$\textbf{Young's Modulus of elasticity} = \frac{\textbf{Stress}}{\textbf{Strain}} \text{ GN / m}^2$$

From the above figures the modulus of elasticity (E) = 120 kN / mm²

FIGURE 4   *Explaining stress, strain and Young's Modulus.*

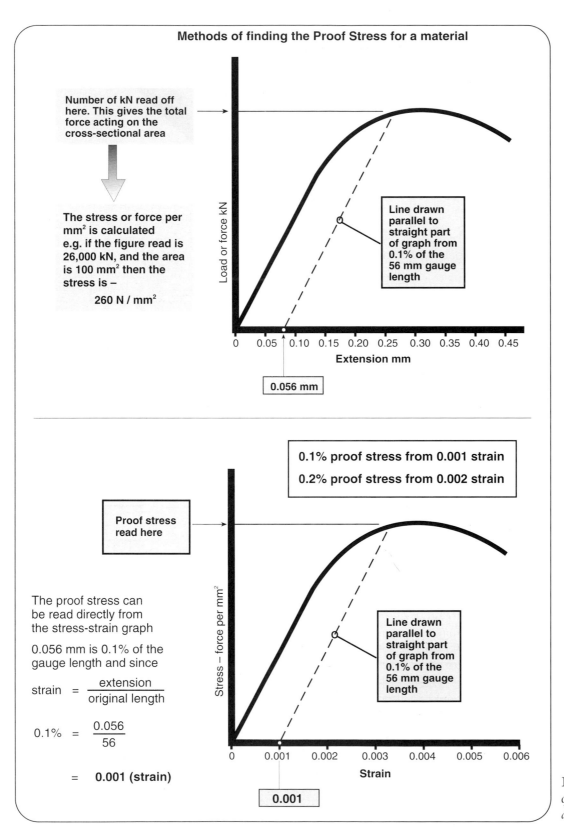

Methods of finding the Proof Stress for a material

Number of kN read off here. This gives the total force acting on the cross-sectional area

The stress or force per mm² is calculated e.g. if the figure read is 26,000 kN, and the area is 100 mm² then the stress is –

260 N / mm²

Load or force kN

Line drawn parallel to straight part of graph from 0.1% of the 56 mm gauge length

Extension mm

0.056 mm

0.1% proof stress from 0.001 strain

0.2% proof stress from 0.002 strain

Proof stress read here

Stress – force per mm²

Line drawn parallel to straight part of graph from 0.1% of the 56 mm gauge length

The proof stress can be read directly from the stress-strain graph

0.056 mm is 0.1% of the gauge length and since

$$\text{strain} = \frac{\text{extension}}{\text{original length}}$$

$$0.1\% = \frac{0.056}{56}$$

$$= \mathbf{0.001 \ (strain)}$$

Strain

0.001

FIGURE 5 *Two kinds of graph – load/extension and stress/strain.*

Ductility and shear strength

Ductility One of the properties that may be measured by a tensile test is the ductility – it may be measured as:

Percentage elongation

Percentage reduction in area

This information is calculated from the results recorded during a test as follows:

$$\text{Percentage elongation} = \frac{\text{extension}}{\text{original length}} \times 100$$

The more the specimen stretches then the greater the percentage elongation

$$\text{Percentage reduction in area} = \frac{\text{Reduction in area}}{\text{original area}} \times 100$$

The original area being referred to is the area of cross-section of the specimen and the reduction in area is found by finding the final area of cross-section (at fracture) and subtracting this from the original area

Shear strength

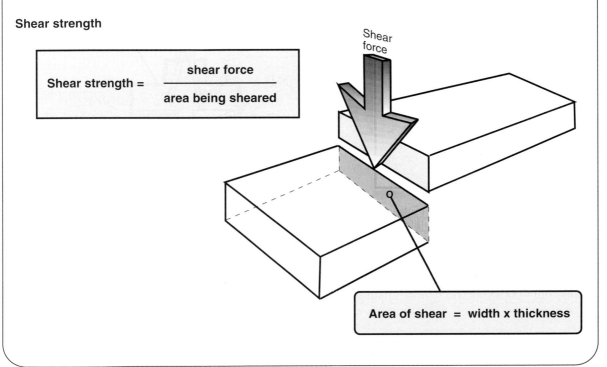

$$\text{Shear strength} = \frac{\text{shear force}}{\text{area being sheared}}$$

Shear force

Area of shear = width x thickness

FIGURE 6
Ductility and shear strength.

In the stress-strain graph, the load at each stage of the test is divided by the cross-sectional area of the specimen, to give the stress, and the extension is divided by the original length, to give the strain.

In the load-extension graph, the load applied to the specimen is plotted, and the measured extension for the particular load, is also plotted. However, in the stress-strain graph, instead of the load on the specimen, the load per mm^2 (stress), is used. Also, instead of the actual extension, the extension per mm (strain) is plotted. So, for a stress-strain graph, the load is for each unit of cross-sectional area, and the extension is per mm of gauge length, making the values independent of the size and shape of the specimen.

Modulus of elasticity

In the elastic range of a material, stress is directly proportional to strain, which is another way of stating Hooke's Law. The ratio of: Stress/Strain, for any material, is constant in the elastic range, and it gives an indication of how much stiffness a material displays in use. The ratio, is called Young's Modulus, and is represented by E. The value of E for a material, is usually expressed in kN/mm^2.

A good way of thinking about stiffness, is to get some bars of different material, say, steel, PVC, brass, aluminium and wood, about a metre long, and 12 mm in diameter. If you do this, you will find that the bars differ in stiffness, or rigidity. Some bars are less likely to bend or yield. The stiffer, or more unbending a bar is, the greater the value of E.

Young's Modulus can also be read from a stress-strain graph. It is the slope of the straight line part of the graph (i.e. slope = stress/strain).

Generally, if the temperature of a material is raised, then ductility increases, while strength and modulus of elasticity decrease. If the temperature is lowered, ductility decreases, and fractures become brittle. Many materials, especially steels, have a clearly defined temperature at which fractures become brittle. The temperature at which the change, or transition takes place is termed the *transition temperature*.

Tensile strength

Tensile strength is the maximum force or load, in newtons or kilonewtons, applied to the specimen

FIGURE 7 *Rockwell indenter. This is a close-up of an indenter which is pressed into the surface of a material in order to measure hardness. This type of indenter is known as a Rockwell Cone indenter. (Courtesy: NPL, London)*

before it breaks or fractures, divided by the original cross-sectional area. It may be read from a graph of test results.

Proof stress

Materials such as hardened steel, polymers and non-ferrous metals normally do not have a well defined yield point, or an indication at what stress yield occurs. That is, if a graph of results is studied, there is no obvious point where the material starts to yield, such as is shown in **FIGURE 2**. To overcome this, a value of stress, known as *proof stress*, is used.

Proof stress from a force-extension graph

Proof stress is evaluated from a graph of tensile test results. In a force-extension graph, a distance equal to 0.1% of the gauge length, from the origin, is

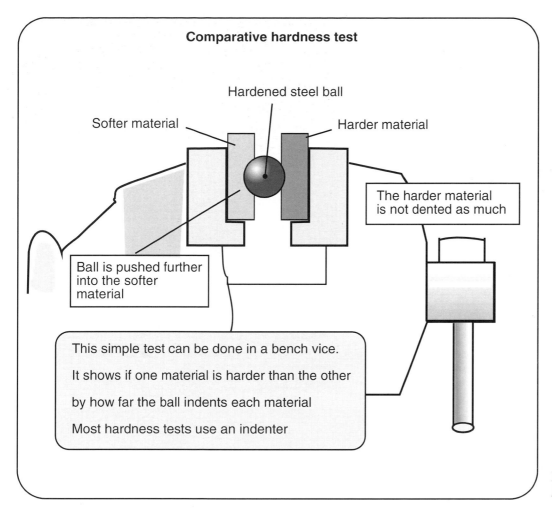

Comparative hardness test

Softer material

Hardened steel ball

Harder material

The harder material is not dented as much

Ball is pushed further into the softer material

This simple test can be done in a bench vice.

It shows if one material is harder than the other

by how far the ball indents each material

Most hardness tests use an indenter

FIGURE 8 *Comparative hardness test.*

located. If the gauge length is 56 mm, then the distance from the origin for 0.1% proof stress is 0.056 mm. A line, parallel to the straight part of the graph, is drawn from the 0.056 mm mark, until it cuts the graph line. This is shown in **FIGURE 5**. The stress at that point is the 0.1% proof stress, and it gives the engineer, or designer, an indication of how the material will perform in practice.

Proof stress from a stress–strain graph

Proof stress is much easier to find from a stress–strain graph than from a force or load-extension graph. The lower part of **FIGURE 5** shows how it is done. Proof stress is read almost directly from this type of graph. If the 0.1% proof stress is required, then a line is drawn from 0.001 strain parallel to the straight part of the plot, in a similar manner as before.

Sometimes it is the 0.2% proof stress that is required. In this case, the line is drawn from the 0.002 strain mark on the strain axis.

Shear

A shear force tends to shear the material into two parts. Shear force is used in cutting with scissors, tinsnips, guillotine and in 'punching' or piercing with a press. **FIGURE 6** shows a bar of metal being sheared.

FACTOR OF SAFETY

It is not enough to calculate the size or cross-sectional area of a component that will stand up to the load required. If this were the case, and any increase in load occurred perhaps due to a shock load, or an extra load due to wind, as in the case of a bridge, there would be many more failures of components in service, than actually occur.

When an engineer designs a component, he/she calculates the forces which have to be taken into account. If a particular part has to withstand a force of 600 kN, the engineer might allow for a force of 1800 kN, which is three times the calculated load. In this case, the calculated load is multiplied by three. The number used is called the *Factor of safety.* Different factors are used for different applications. A normal factor might be 2.5, while a much larger factor is allowed where, say, a bridge is subjected to high winds.

HARDNESS OF MATERIALS

Hardness is tested by measuring the material's resistance to indentation, or scratching of its surface. Hardness in metals may vary, or indeed, may be changed by heat treatment (see under Heat Treatment, page 217) to some desirable degree. It is, therefore, necessary to be able to test the hardness of metal surfaces to ensure that the correct hardness has been achieved. There are also tests for various polymeric materials (plastics).

How a hardness test is carried out

A hard piece of metal, called the indenter, is pressed against the surface of the material being tested, with a measured force. The softer the material is, the deeper the indentation will be, and vice versa.

A very simple comparative test, for comparing the hardness of two pieces of metal, using a steel ball and a vice, is shown in **FIGURE 8**.

Two materials, which may be metallic or non-metallic, are placed in an engineer's vice, with a hardened steel ball between them, as is shown. When the vice is tightened, the force applied causes the ball to be pushed into the materials. The amount of indentation is greater in the softer material. You can try this test out quite easily using a piece of soft material, say aluminium, and a piece of harder material such as carbon steel. A ball-bearing makes a suitable indenter.

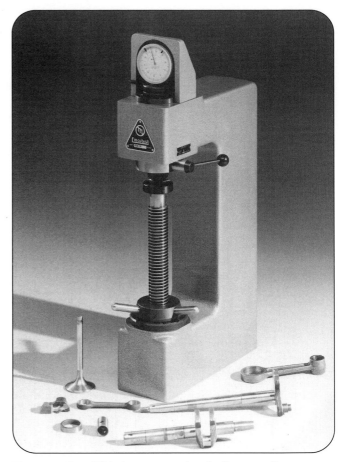

FIGURE 9   *This is a conventional, direct reading hardness testing machine. (Courtesy: Emcotest Ltd)*

The different hardness tests

The photograph in **FIGURE 9** shows a conventional hardness testing machine. The value of the hardness is read from the dial at the top. You can see various components in front of the machine, which may be hardness tested on such a machine. A small crankshaft, a connecting rod, and a poppet valve are easily identified. Components like these usually receive heat treatment, and are normally hardness-tested before going into service.

In **FIGURE 10**, you can see where the item or component to be tested is placed. The table on which the item is placed can be adjusted for height using the screw and adjusting nut.

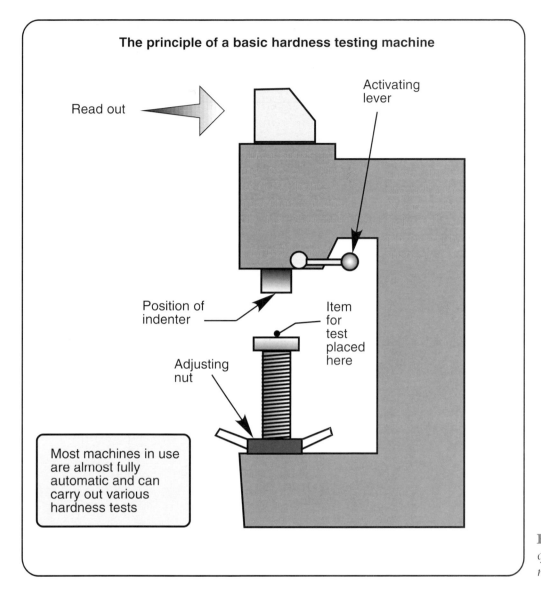

The principle of a basic hardness testing machine

Read out

Activating lever

Position of indenter

Item for test placed here

Adjusting nut

Most machines in use are almost fully automatic and can carry out various hardness tests

FIGURE 10 *The principle of a basic hardness testing machine.*

There are different tests which use similar machines:

The *Brinell* test, which is named after Dr. Johan Brinell, uses a ball indenter

The *Vickers* test, which uses a diamond-square based pyramid indenter

The *Rockwell* hardness test, which originated in the United States and is very fast.

These three hardness tests are compared briefly in **FIGURE 11**. Brinell and Vickers numbers have

approximately the same values for materials with hardness numbers up to about 300 HB or 300 HV.

Tensile strength and hardness
A very general approximate relationship exists between the tensile strength of a material and the material's HB or HV. The relationship is shown in **FIGURE 11**. Although this cannot be taken as accurate, it is a very good guide in forecasting material properties.

The *Knoop test* was developed at the US National

	Hardness tests	
Hardness test	**Indenter details**	**Notes on use**
Brinell	Hardened steel or tungsten carbide ball 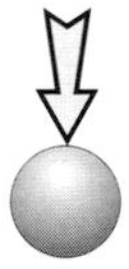 Diameter = 10 mm or 5 mm or 1 mm	Cannot be used on very thin sections Ball deforms with very hard materials Ball indents too far in soft materials
Vickers	Square Pyramid type indenter  Angle = 136°	Similar to Brinell but may be used on hard materials and easier to use Brinell hardness numbers (HB) are about equal to Vickers Hardness numbers (HV) up values of 300
Rockwell	Two most common indenters are Ball – B and Cone – C	Uses small steel ball for soft materials and a diamond cone for hard materials – see FIGURE 7

Both the Brinell and Vickers hardness tests measure the surface areas that the indenters make to determine the hardness numbers but the various Rockwell tests measure how far the indenter moves into the material tested

Tensile strength is approximately = 3.5 x HB or HV N/mm^2

FIGURE 11
Hardness tests.

Bureau of Standards for *microhardness testing*. It uses a sensitive diamond indenter which leaves a long diamond shaped mark. A small portable hardness testing instrument, known as a *scleroscope* from the Greek word *skleros* for hard, uses a *diamond-pointed hammer*. The *hammer*, which is contained in a clear

Hardness values	
Material	Approximate Brinell and Vickers hardness values
Tool steel	700 - 800
Mild steel	180 - 200
Grey cast iron	150 - 250
Brass	80 - 120
Aluminium	60 - 100
Polythene	10 - 15

FIGURE 12   *Hardness values.*

graduated glass tube, is allowed to fall from a height of 250 mm onto the surface to be tested. The rebound height of the hammer gives the hardness number.

Which test is best?

Each test has definite advantages which makes it suitable for certain applications. The Brinell test, which measures hardness as the force applied to the indenter, divided by the circular area of indent made by the ball, is mostly used for iron castings and drop forgings. However, the Brinell test is unsuitable for either very hard, or very soft materials. This is because the ball indenter may, in very soft materials sink in too far, i.e. up to, or past the diameter, or in the case of very hard materials, make no measurable indentation.

The Vickers test, which uses a square pyramid diamond indenter, converts to a hardness number from the length of the diagonal of the diamond-shaped indentation. The Vickers test tends to be more accurate than the Brinell test. Some approximate HB/HV hardness values are given in FIGURE 12.

The Rockwell system has a large range of hardness scales. Each scale has a set size and type of indenter, as well as a specified indenting force. Two basic types of indenters are used – a ball and a cone. Scales are denoted by letters, e.g. the C scale denotes that a diamond cone of a particular size is used, and that the range is suitable for steels and cast irons. In general, the Rockwell system is more flexible than those already mentioned, and has a wide range of applications, but is entirely empirical.

Notched bar or impact testing

There are two well-known methods of testing for toughness. These are the:

- **Izod test**
- **Charpy test.**

A more accurate name for this type of testing would be *notched bar testing*, because it is the notch and not the impact that is the most important feature. An impact testing machine in the *at rest* position is to be seen in FIGURE 13, while FIGURE 14 shows a test about to be carried out. Here, the operator is placing the specimen to be tested.

Notched test pieces are held in a vice and are struck by a pendulum. By measuring the energy absorbed in breaking the test piece, a numerical value for toughness is given. When the striker at the end of the pendulum strikes the prepared specimen, energy is absorbed by the specimen.

The Izod test

FIGURE 13. This shows the features of a testing machine in which a weighted pendulum strikes from a set height. The striking energy is 167 joules. When the pendulum strikes and breaks the test piece, it swings past and up the other side. The height it swings to indicates the amount of energy used in breaking the test piece.

Charpy testing

Most notched-bar testing machines can be used for both the Izod and the Charpy tests. Both tests are similar but the Charpy test releases the pendulum from a higher position and has a striking energy of 300 J. FIGURE 15 shows some Charpy test specimens.

FIGURE 13   *This is a conventional impact testing machine which a capacity of 300 joules (300 J). The machine is securely anchored to the floor. (Courtesy: National Physical Laboratory, London)*

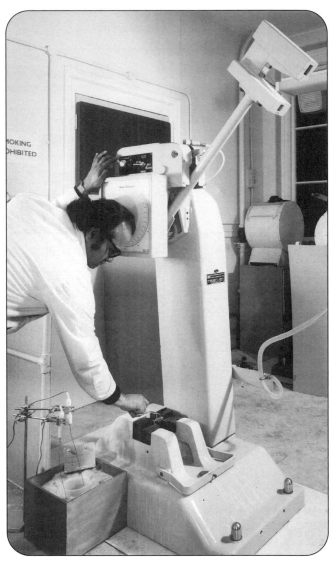

FIGURE 14   *In this picture, the engineer is placing a specimen for a Charpy test. The pendulum is in the raised position, and the required energy level has been set. (Courtesy: National Physical Laboratory, London)*

An explanation of the various parts of an impact testing machine is given in **FIGURE 16**.

In the Izod test, the specimen is held vertically, as may be seen in **FIGURE 17** and **FIGURE 18**, but in the Charpy test, the specimen is held horizontally. See **FIGURE 18**.

Creep

If a weight is hung by a thin strip of lead, for a number of days, the lead strip stretches. This slow deformation of the metal is known as creep. Lead will creep at ambient temperatures. In general, the higher the melting point of the metal, the higher the resistance to creep.

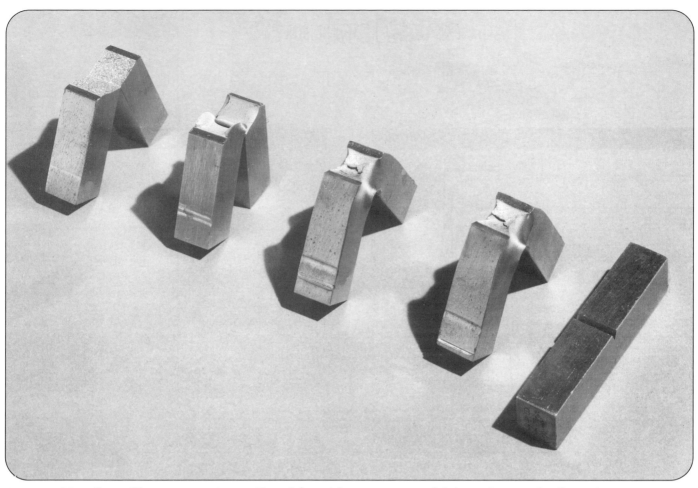

FIGURE 15 *Some Charpy test specimens. From left to right, you can see a brittle specimen, a ductile specimen, two very tough samples, and an unused specimen. (Courtesy: National Physical Laboratory, London)*

High temperatures and time are the causes of creep in components under constant load. The result of creep is that components may fail at a stress well below the tensile strength of the metal.

Creep is very important where metal components operate at high temperatures, such as in the case of turbine blades in gas turbine, and steam turbine plant. These turbines rotate at very high speed, and the blades are under constant load both from the force exerted by the expanding steam, and from centrifugal forces. You can see a turbine with the upper part of the housing removed in **FIGURE 19**.

Creep testing
Creep testing is complex because the specimens must be kept at a certain temperature (perhaps up to 1000°C), for long periods of time.

Specimens like those used in tensile testing are used, and strain gauges monitor the extension. Creep resistant alloys have been developed for certain applications at high temperatures. These are nickel-based alloys. See **FIGURE 20**.

Fatigue
In the early 1860s, a man called Fairbairn did some experiments with iron girders. When a girder was supported at both ends, he found that a load of about 12 tonnes would cause the girder to fail. However, when he loaded, and then unloaded, a load of only 3 tonnes, 3 million times in succession,

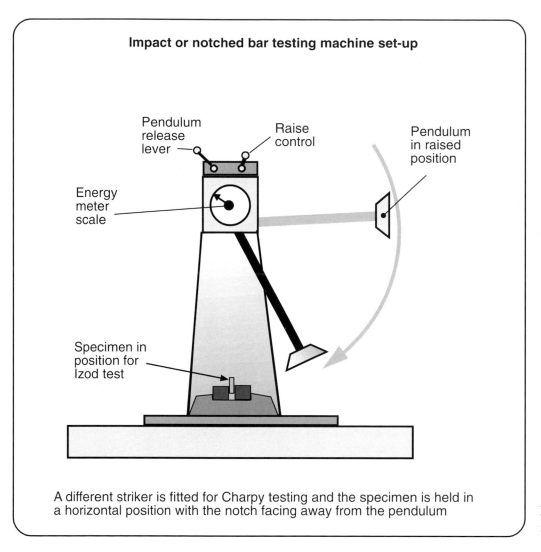

Impact or notched bar testing machine set-up

Pendulum release lever

Raise control

Pendulum in raised position

Energy meter scale

Specimen in position for Izod test

A different striker is fitted for Charpy testing and the specimen is held in a horizontal position with the notch facing away from the pendulum

FIGURE 16 *Impact or notched bar testing machine.*

on a girder, the girder failed. This type of failure, due to repeated on/off loading or cyclic stressing, is known as *fatigue*.

In a car engine each piston can go up and down, or to and fro, thousands of times in a minute. Thus the connecting rods are being pushed for one stroke and being pulled for the next. This is an example of cyclic stressing.

Fatigue caused many problems in early aircraft propellers and, indeed, in wind machines. The aircraft industry is one industry which has to take the whole question of fatigue and fatigue failure, very seriously. Airframes and wings are subjected to

tremendous buffeting during flights, and must be carefully monitored to prevent failure in operation. All aircraft are very susceptible to fatigue. It is probably true to say that fatigue is the most common cause of failure in metal components, and has been the cause of many aircraft accidents. One of the methods of testing for the fatigue characteristics of a material is shown in **FIGURE 21**.

How fatigue causes failure
Fatigue may start as a little crack on the surface of the component. Slowly the crack increases, and moves across the section of the component, until the uncracked bit is not strong enough to support the load, and so the component breaks. The failing or

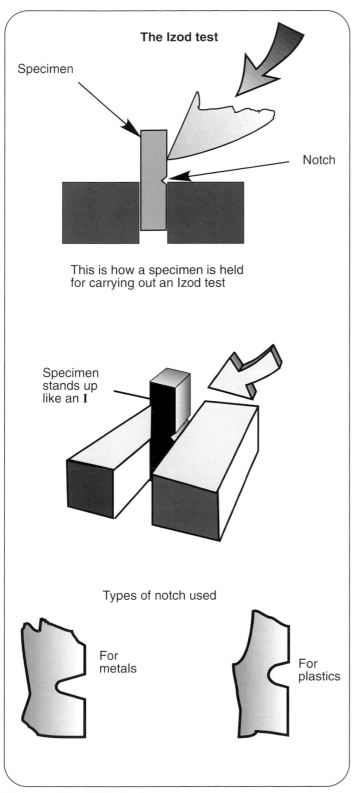

The Izod test

Specimen

Notch

This is how a specimen is held for carrying out an Izod test

Specimen stands up like an **I**

Types of notch used

For metals

For plastics

FIGURE 17 *The Izod test.*

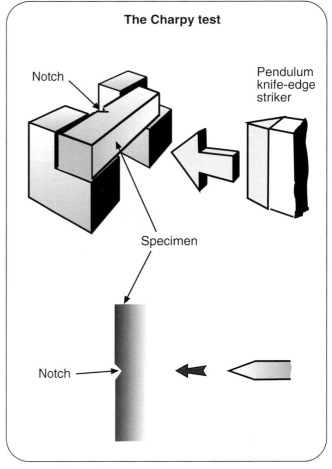

The Charpy test

Notch

Pendulum knife-edge striker

Specimen

Notch

FIGURE 18 *Charpy test.*

breaking process usually occurs over a considerable period of time. Fatigue fractures are not brittle fractures.

Fatigue failure

Even though allowances for fatigue are made in the design of components, fatigue still occurs. A component may be designed to withstand many times the expected load, and yet may fracture as a result of fatigue. Vibrations can be the cause in many instances.

Certain elements of design are taken into consideration in an effort to prevent fatigue. These include:

Surface finish – a poor or rough surface can lead to the start of a fatigue crack. Surfaces should have a smooth finish.

Sharp corners should be avoided.

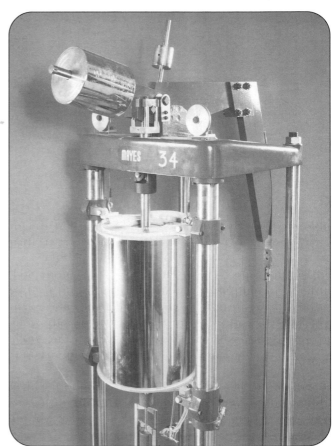

FIGURE 19   *This is a power plant turbine with the upper half of the housing not yet in place. You can see the turbine blades quite plainly at the rear of the unit. They look like spokes. (Courtesy: Asea Brown Boveri)*

FIGURE 20   *This photograph shows the top part of a constant stress cam lever creep testing machine. The specimen under test is just visible at the bottom of the picture – it is the small round piece with the small cylinders above and below. (Courtesy: National Physical Laboratory, London)*

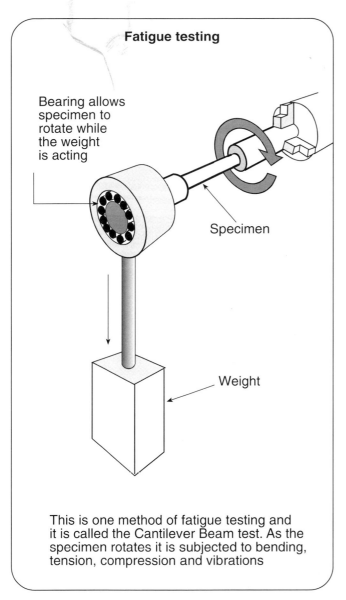

Fatigue testing

Bearing allows specimen to rotate while the weight is acting

Specimen

Weight

This is one method of fatigue testing and it is called the Cantilever Beam test. As the specimen rotates it is subjected to bending, tension, compression and vibrations

FIGURE 21   *Fatigue testing.*

Steps should be taken to prevent corrosion. Corrosion can be a cause of fatigue cracks, which may start where pitting has taken place.

SUMMARY

Tensile testing gives information relating to tensile strength, elastic limit and ductility.

Stress is equal to the force applied divided by the cross-sectional area of the component in question. Stress is expressed in N/mm^2.

Strain is the amount of stretch divided by the original length. Strain is always a small number.

Young's Modulus of elasticity is equal to stress divided by strain. It gives an indication of how stiff or flexible a beam or other component would be in service.

Proof stress is used for materials without a well-defined yield point, e.g. polymers and non-ferrous metals.

Hardness is the resistance a material has to indentation.

Impact testing tests specimens for toughness. In the Izod test, the specimen stands straight up, while in the Charpy test, the specimen is horizontal.

Non-Destructive Testing

INTRODUCTION

Non-destructive testing, or NDT, as it is generally known, takes its name from the fact that this type of testing does not damage the material or specimens being tested. The object of this type of testing is to detect flaws or faults which may not be visible during a visual inspection. Stringent NDT testing is normal procedure in the repair of, and rebuilding of aircraft engines and airframes. NDT has many applications which we will discuss later in the chapter. Non-destructive testing may be conveniently divided into:

- **Testing for surface flaws such as cracks**
- **Testing for flaws which are internal or below the surface.**

DETECTION OF SURFACE FLAWS

The cheapest and simplest technique in detecting surface flaws is by visual inspection. This is the most common form of NDT. Good light is essential for this type of work, and usually some form of magnification is used. Even with magnification up to about 5 times (5x), surface faults may not be noticed.

Penetrant testing for flaws

In the simplest form of penetrant testing, coloured dye is carried by a penetrant which is allowed to soak into the material under test. Excess penetrant is removed and the penetrant which penetrated the surface flaws is encouraged to emerge. The *oil and chalk* method is the oldest form of this type of NDT.

Nowadays, however, the penetrants used are fluorescent when viewed under *ultraviolet* (UV) light. Any penetrant which enters cracks fluoresces under the UV light. The principle of fluorescent penetrant testing is described in **FIGURE 1**.

BELOW-THE-SURFACE FLAW DETECTION

Thermal tests

Tests have been developed which are based on the high thermal conductivity of metals. Any flaw present will affect the heat transfer in the metal being tested and is shown up by the use of heat-sensitive coatings.

Magnetic methods of testing

In *ferro-magnetic* materials, cracks and cavities cause distortions in magnetic fields set up in components under test.

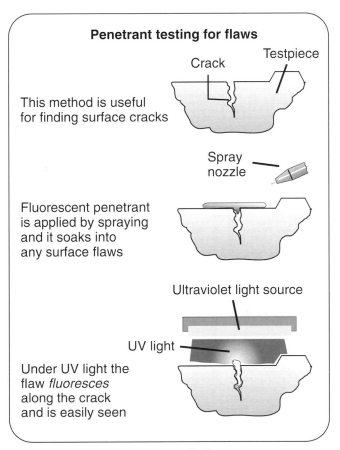

Penetrant testing for flaws

Crack — Testpiece

This method is useful for finding surface cracks

Spray nozzle

Fluorescent penetrant is applied by spraying and it soaks into any surface flaws

Ultraviolet light source

UV light

Under UV light the flaw *fluoresces* along the crack and is easily seen

FIGURE 1   *Penetrant testing for flaws.*

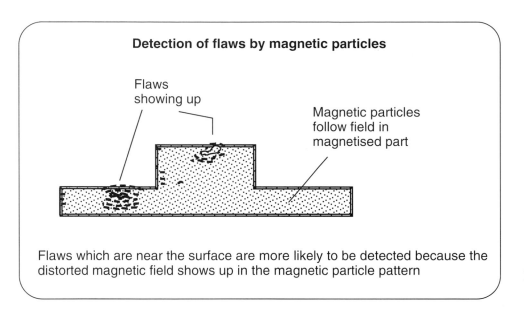

Detection of flaws by magnetic particles

Flaws
showing up

Magnetic particles
follow field in
magnetised part

Flaws which are near the surface are more likely to be detected because the
distorted magnetic field shows up in the magnetic particle pattern

FIGURE 2   *Detection flaws by magnetic particles.*

Magnetic particle method

This method can detect surface flaws or flaws very near the surface. Flaws show up best when the crack or flaw is at right angles to the magnetic field.

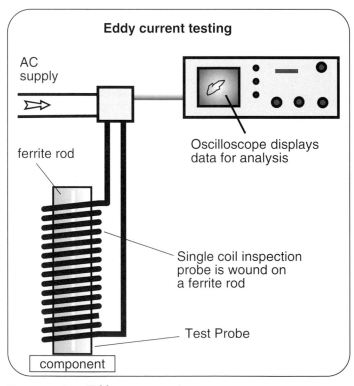

Eddy current testing

AC
supply

ferrite rod

Oscilloscope displays
data for analysis

Single coil inspection
probe is wound on
a ferrite rod

Test Probe

component

FIGURE 3   *Eddy current testing.*

Magnetic particles may be used dry, or in a liquid suspension. When applied to the magnetised component, the particles show the magnetic field with distortion, if flaws are present. Close examination of the pattern of the magnetic particles on the surface of the component under test, may show a bending of lines or distortion of the magnetic field – a flaw is thus detected.

Components for testing must be magnetised. A permanent magnet may be used, but various types of magnetisation machines are available. FIGURE 2 shows how the magnetic field of particles may be distorted by flaws. After testing, components should be demagnetised.

Eddy current testing

This type of testing is widely used for non-ferrous metals, mainly for bars of uniform section. An induction coil, fed with an alternating current (AC) is used to set up eddy currents in the metal under test. There is, of course, a magnetic field around the coil.

As can be seen in FIGURE 3, an inspection or search coil is used. The AC coil sets up the eddy or secondary currents in the component. These currents produce a magnetic field in the component. The magnetic field in the test-piece and the magnetic field around the coil oppose one another

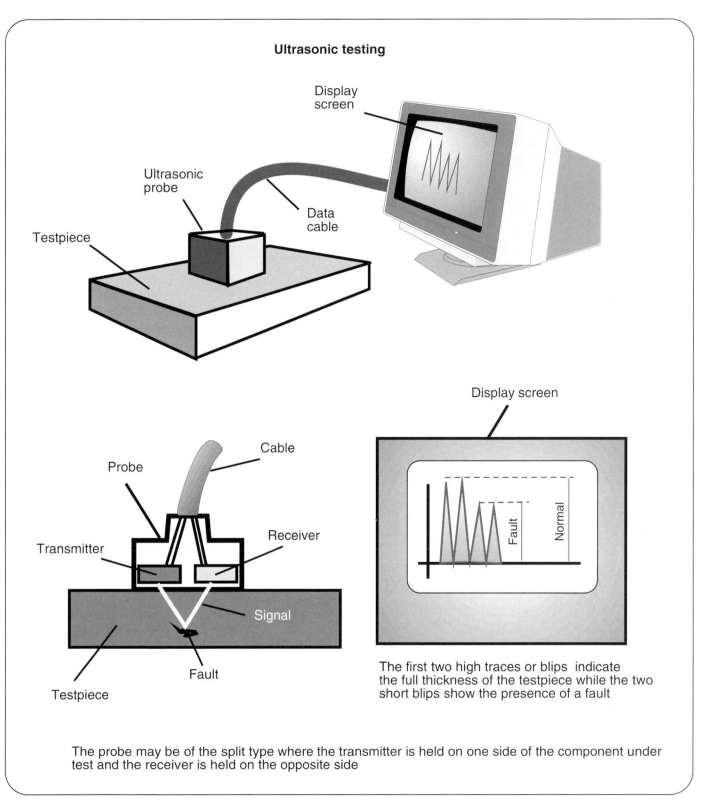

Ultrasonic testing

Display screen

Ultrasonic probe

Data cable

Testpiece

Display screen

Cable

Probe

Receiver

Transmitter

Signal

Fault

Testpiece

Fault

Normal

The first two high traces or blips indicate the full thickness of the testpiece while the two short blips show the presence of a fault

The probe may be of the split type where the transmitter is held on one side of the component under test and the receiver is held on the opposite side

FIGURE 4   *Ultrasonic testing.*

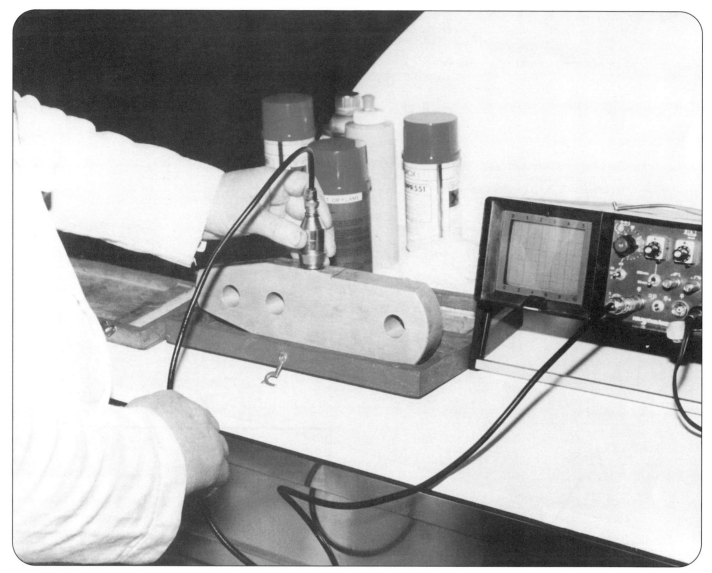

FIGURE 5   *Here you can see an ultrasonic probe being used on a component, with holes in it, in order to demonstrate the principle of ultrasonic testing. The blips, which cannot be seen in the photograph, appear on the screen on the right.*

and cause changes in the current flow in the coil. Any change in the flow of current in the coil, which is displayed on the screen of an oscilloscope, indicates a flaw at the surface, or near the surface.

Ultrasonic testing
If you stand among high buildings or in an empty hall and shout, you may hear an *echo*. What is the echo? The sound you make travels through the air, bounces off a wall or other hard surface, and returns

to your ear. It takes a little time for the sound to make the over and back journey, and so you hear a *second* sound or echo which is a reflection of the first sound. **FIGURE 4**

This principle is used by ships for checking the depth of the water in which they are sailing. It can also be used to detect shoals of fish or submarines. Seismic surveys at sea (oil prospecting) also use the sonic principle, whereby a shot is sounded (by

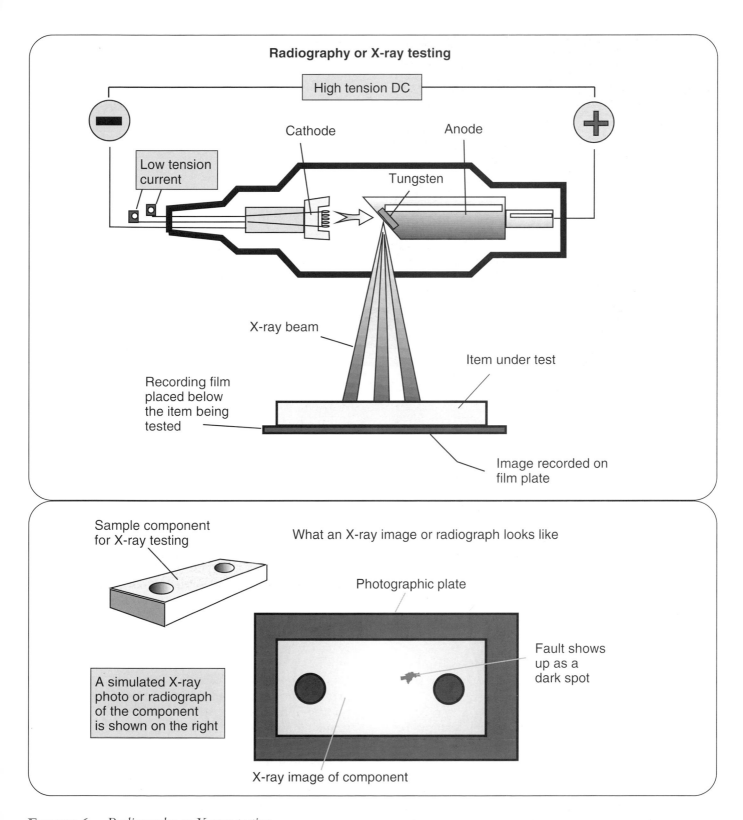

Radiography or X-ray testing

High tension DC

Cathode

Anode

Low tension current

Tungsten

X-ray beam

Item under test

Recording film placed below the item being tested

Image recorded on film plate

Sample component for X-ray testing

What an X-ray image or radiograph looks like

Photographic plate

A simulated X-ray photo or radiograph of the component is shown on the right

Fault shows up as a dark spot

X-ray image of component

FIGURE 6   *Radiography or X-rays testing.*

FIGURE 7   *This is a photograph of the turbine of a turbocharger for a Diesel engine. The turbine has been repaired by a specialised welding technique, and is under inspection. An X-ray inspection is fairly normal practice in a case like this. (Courtesy: Asea Brown Boveri)*

compressed air), and the reflection is picked up by a *geophone*. Geophysicists can determine rock structures from the information so received.

Ultrasonics refers to sound waves which cannot be heard because they are above the audible limit (above 20,000 cycles/sec or 20,000 hertz). These ultrasonic waves can be generated using a quartz crystal. In flaw detection, the most common method used is the *pulse reflection* method. The probe is moved along the test piece and pulses and echoes are

shown on a cathode ray tube CRT (like a TV screen). If a flaw is present, then the pulse is reflected off it, and the echo returns in a faster time than it would do if there were no flaw, thus producing a shorter trace or 'blip' on the screen.

This method of NDT has wide applications including large forgings, castings and in weld inspection.

X-ray testing

Invented by the German engineer, Willhelm Konrad Roentgen, in 1895, X-rays are produced in a high voltage discharge tube. The inventor was awarded the 1901 Nobel Prize, which did not, as it does now, include a substantial sum of money. In a truly unselfish manner, Roentgen refused to patent his invention, which has been of tremendous importance in the fields of engineering and medicine since that time.

X-ray radiation is of the same type of radiation as light, but the wavelength is very short in comparison. The wavelength of light falls within the range: 4×10^{-7} to 8×10^{-7} while X-rays are in the range: 5×10^{-9} to 6×10^{-12}. The units are metres.

Electrons are released by heating the cathode to a high temperature. The released electrons are then accelerated by a high DC voltage and aimed at a target *anode*. Some electrons penetrate the atoms of the metal anode and when this happens, energy is released as X-rays. The target or *anticathode* is angled so that the X-rays are directed towards the workpiece. This may be seen in **FIGURE 6**.

X-rays can penetrate materials which ordinary light will not penetrate. The X-ray image may be viewed on a fluorescent screen (Fluoroscope), or may be printed on photographic film, to produce an X-ray photograph or *radiograph,* which is more usual. A simulated radiograph is shown in **FIGURE 6**.

X-rays used for NDT have shorter wavelengths than those used in medicine. This makes them more dangerous to human body tissues, so stray radiation must be shielded against. X-ray NDT is used extensively for the examination of welds.

SUMMARY

Visual inspection is carried out with the help of a magnifying lens, which may incorporate a powerful light.

NDT does not damage the material being tested, and is used to detect flaws which may not be detected by visual inspection.

Penetrant testing uses a penetrant which soaks into surface cracks in the material being tested. The cracks then show up under ultra violet (UV) light.

Thermal testing works on the principle that if there are internal flaws in a material, its thermal conductivity is affected.

Magnetic particles suspended in a liquid may be applied to a component under test. When the component is viewed in a magnetic field, flaws may be seen as distortions in the field.

Eddy currents induced into a magnetic material can be used to detect flaws. The currents set up a magnetic field in the material, which is opposed by an outside field, to detect changes in current flow in the test-piece.

Ultrasonic testing makes use of sound waves above 20,000Hz, which are reflected back off surfaces and flaws. If an echo returns in a faster time than it should, a fault is probably indicated.

X-ray radiation penetrates materials which ordinary light will not penetrate, and may be used to produce photographic images called radiographs, to allow inspection for internal faults.

ENGINEERING TECHNOLOGY

Manufacturing

INTRODUCTION

In today's world, *to manufacture* is generally taken to mean: to produce in large numbers, using the necessary machinery. Originally, the word referred to the making of things by hand processes, but as the *making technology* progressed, mass production systems were developed and refined, under the influence of people such as Henry Ford, who introduced a moving assembly line. The number of manufacturing methods is quite large, and a study of them would require a volume of text on its own. In this book we consider just some of the common methods. Automation in manufacture has recently begun to make use of robots for assembly, and other purposes. A short piece dealing with manufacturing robots is also included.

AN EARLY MOULDING PROCESS

When humankind discovered that metals could be melted, a logical step towards faster manufacture of simple tools and weapons followed. This was the casting or pouring of molten metal into stone, and later, clay moulds. A simple stone mould is shown in FIGURE 1. You can see that the shape of an axe head has been carved out of the stone. When this shape is filled with melted (molten) metal, and the metal is allowed to cool, a simple axehead is produced. The stone mould shown here is one we made in order to show the process. Original moulds of this type are to be viewed in museums. For over 6,000 years, metal objects have been made by pouring molten metal into shaped holes (moulds) in stones, clay/sand, or metal.

FIGURE 1 *Early bronze axeheads were made by casting them in a mould similar to the stone mould shown here. The next development in casting was the two-part clay mould system, which allowed more intricate castings to be made. (Courtesy: the authors)*

FIGURE 2 *The cast axehead would have been tied into a specially chosen branch of a tree. The little outcrop in the casting was to keep the head from falling out of the shaft. (Courtesy: the authors)*

The method shown is similar to that used in Ireland and Britain in the *Bronze Age* to produce axeheads. Weapons and tools were vital to mankind's survival in those early days, but personal objects like brooches and pins were also important. Stone and baked clay moulds have been found in many parts of Ireland and Britain similar to the one shown in **FIGURE 3**, which was found at Dooey in Co. Donegal.

The making of axeheads and brooches, and indeed many other items, are examples of simple metal casting, by which a metal object can be made very quickly. In the present time, there are many methods

of casting, but each method uses the two basic items used in early times:

1 Molten metal.
2 Moulds.

Production by moulding or casting is important for the following reasons:

- **It is the fastest method of changing the raw material into the shape or object required**
- **Very intricate shapes can be produced economically**
- **Methods are available to cast a single item, or many identical items**
- **Shapes may be produced which would be extremely difficult to produce by any other method.**

CASTING METHODS

It is usually the nature of the mould used that gives each process its name. The method to be used in a particular case depends, to some extent, on the metal to be cast.

Casting processes can be broadly divided into:

- **Processes which use moulds which can be used once only, such as sandcasting (using clay/sand moulds)**
- **Processes which use permanent moulds that can be used over and over again. Steel moulds for diecasting can produce many thousands of castings.**

Patterns

No matter what casting process is going to be used to make an article, the first step is to make an accurate full size model of the item to be made. This model is called a *pattern*, and may be made from wood, modelling clay, steel, aluminium, plastic fillers or combinations of different materials, which will hold the desired shape. Patterns are given a slight taper, or *draft*, so that they may be withdrawn from the mould easily.

Because metals are expanded when they are hot, patterns must be made slightly bigger than the

Baked clay mould which was found in Lettermacaward, Co Donegal

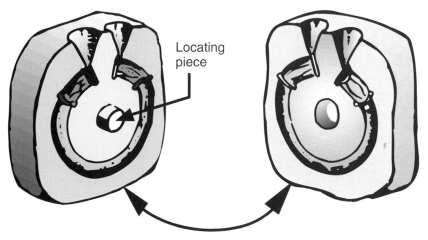

Locating piece

The halves of the mould fit together, with the help of the locating piece on the left half of the mould, and the socket hole on the right half of the mould, as shown

Molten metal poured in here

Molten metal was poured into the closed mould and the whole thing was allowed to cool. When the mould was opened the item was removed

One hole was for pouring and the other was to see when the mould was full

Our impression of what the ring-brooch may have looked like

The diameter of the ring-brooch would have been 35 mm

FIGURE 3   *Baked clay mould.*

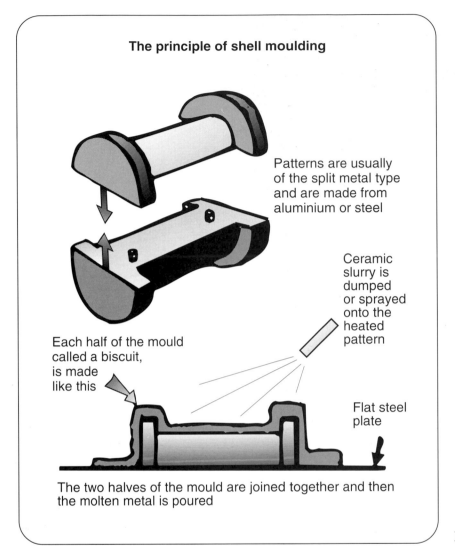

The principle of shell moulding

Patterns are usually of the split metal type and are made from aluminium or steel

Ceramic slurry is dumped or sprayed onto the heated pattern

Each half of the mould called a biscuit, is made like this

Flat steel plate

The two halves of the mould are joined together and then the molten metal is poured

FIGURE 4   *Shell moulding.*

object being cast, so that when the metal cools and contracts, the cast is the size required. A special measuring rule, which is used by patternmakers, allows for the contraction of the metal, and is called a *contraction rule*.

SAND CASTING

Baked clay has already been mentioned as a mould material and indeed, in dry sand moulding, the mould is baked also. This gives the mould the necessary accuracy and strength. *Green Sand* moulding uses a damp *green* sand, usually with a binder added, which helps to stick the mould

together. Patterns for sand casting are normally split patterns.

The mould is made in two parts, one half of the pattern fitting into each part. Sprue pins are used to make holes for pouring the molten metal in, and to allow the operator to see that the mould is full. To allow air and gases to escape, small escape holes, or vents are provided.

Other moulding methods include shell moulding, as shown in **FIGURE 4**, which uses sand-resin moulds, are described in Iron and Steels, under *cast iron*, page 72, where centrifugal casting is also discussed.

FIGURE 5 *Molten iron being poured into moulds in a modern casting process. (Courtesy: Waterford Foundry Ltd)*

A new development in sand casting known as CO_2 (carbon dioxide) casting, has recently been developed. In this method, the mould materials contain a hardening agent that sets under the influence of gaseous carbon dioxide. Moulds produced in this way are stronger and more rigid. These moulds are suitable for producing large castings in which considerable weights of molten metal have to be poured, and for casting items with high length to cross sectional area ratios (long items). **FIGURE 6** shows example castings from the CO_2 process.

INVESTMENT OR 'LOST WAX' CASTING

Greeks and Etruscans used this process to make jewellery over 2500 years ago. In 1554, Cellini, the famous Italian goldsmith, used the *lost wax* process to cast the bronze statue of Perseus which still stands in Florence. This method of casting is still used to make jewellery but it has other important applications including the manufacture of:

- **Aircraft parts**
- **Runners for turbines**
- **Parts for guns**
- **Medical replacement joints, e.g. artificial hip joint**
- **Golf clubs**
- **Pump parts**
- **Scientific instruments**
- **Medical instruments.**

All of the above listed components must be made with great precision and so, the term *precision casting* is often used to describe this process.

FIGURE 6 *CO_2 casting produces very accurate results, as may be seen in this photograph. (Courtesy: Deloro Stellite GmbH)*

Two moulds

The process begins with the making of a model, usually from steel, of the object to be cast. Using the model, a split mould is made, often from a lower melting point metal, such as solder, and this mould is called a die. The die is not used for casting, but for producing wax models of the item to be made, by injecting wax into the die. Wax patterns are stuck onto a runner, to make what is known as a *tree*, so that a number of items can be moulded with each pour.

Investment

The wax model is dipped into a slurry of ceramic slurry/cement mixture, which sticks to the wax and forms a covering around the model. It is the *applying of the covering* that gives the name investment, because investment means applying a covering on something.

Dipping is repeated until the coating is to the required thickness. Then the coating, which becomes the mould, is heated. During the heating two things happen:

1 The wax model melts and the wax runs out of the ceramic mould. This is where the name *lost wax* comes from.
2 The mould is cured and becomes hard. Molten metal can now be poured into the mould and allowed to cool, sometimes for 24 hours. When the metal and mould are cool, the mould is broken away to reveal the casting. It is usual to cast a number of components in the one mould by sticking wax models onto a tree, as explained in **FIGURE 7**. The process is also dealt with under Classification of Carbon and Alloy Steels (page 83).

Process variations

Plastics can be used for mould-making instead of wax. Wax models can also be dissolved out of the moulds, rather than melting them out.

A special investment process uses mercury to make the model. Mercury is run into the die and the whole thing is brought to a low temperature until the mercury solidifies. The solid mercury model is removed from the die, and dipped in a special coating material, to make the mould. When the temperature is raised, the mercury runs out.

FIGURE 7   *Trees are being made up by the operator in this photograph. Separate wax patterns are being mounted onto a central part (runner). In this case, nine patterns per runner are used. If you look at the right hand side of the picture, you can see a tree that has been coated with a ceramic slurry. Once the slurry is dry, it is heated to melt out the wax and to form a ceramic mould. Molten metal is then poured into the upside down trees via the runner.*
(Courtesy: Deloro Stellite GmbH)

FIGURE 8   *Five items produced by investment casting for use in the brewery industry. You can see the good finish and the detail involved. (Courtesy: Roscommon Precision Castings Ltd.)*

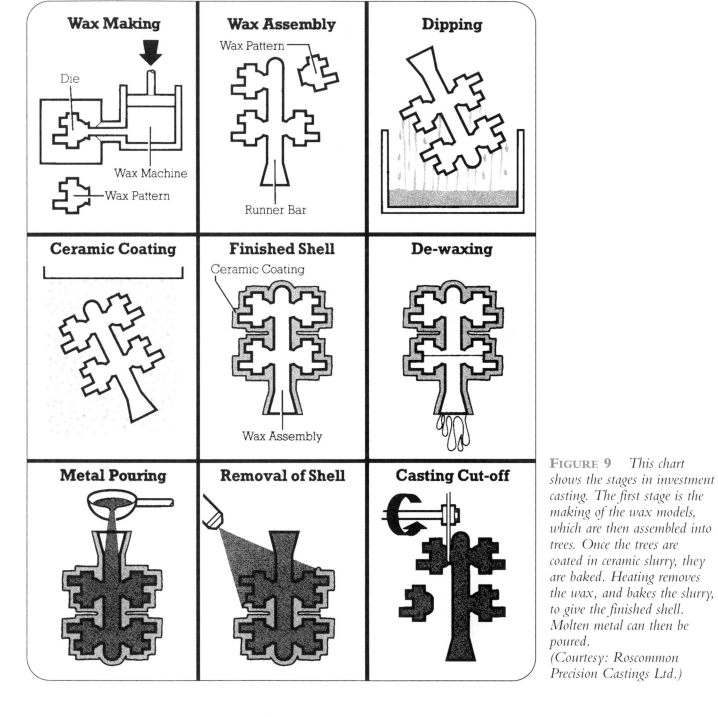

FIGURE 9 *This chart shows the stages in investment casting. The first stage is the making of the wax models, which are then assembled into trees. Once the trees are coated in ceramic slurry, they are baked. Heating removes the wax, and bakes the slurry, to give the finished shell. Molten metal can then be poured. (Courtesy: Roscommon Precision Castings Ltd.)*

Some advantages of investment casting

- Excellent accuracy and finish
- Reduction or elimination of expensive machining
- Intricate shapes can be cast with good detail
- Dies last a long time
- Metals which are difficult to machine can be cast by this process.

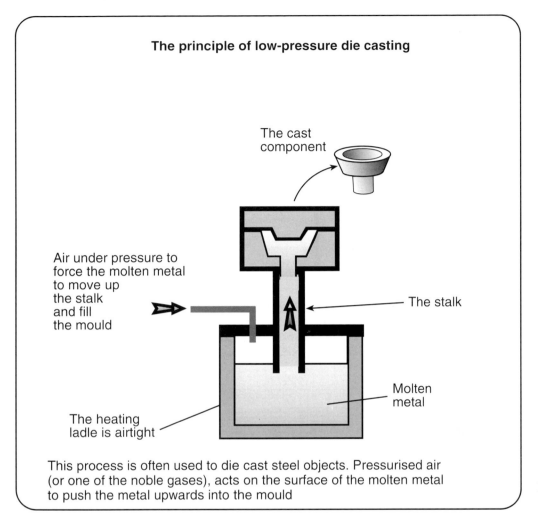

The principle of low-pressure die casting

The cast component

Air under pressure to force the molten metal to move up the stalk and fill the mould

The stalk

Molten metal

The heating ladle is airtight

This process is often used to die cast steel objects. Pressurised air (or one of the noble gases), acts on the surface of the molten metal to push the metal upwards into the mould

FIGURE 10 *Principle of low-pressure die casting.*

DIE CASTING

In sand casting, investment casting and shell moulding, the moulds are used once only, and have to be broken open. Die casting makes use of permanent moulds called dies, which are made from steel or heat-resisting alloys. High cost of dies and equipment means that die casting is mostly used for making large quantities of items (mass production).

Metals which are die cast are: aluminium alloys, brass, bronze, magnesium alloys, zinc-based alloys, such as *mazak*, and stainless steel. The name mazak, was coined by one of the leading firms in die casting – Morris Ashby. Morris Ashby produced a zinc based alloy which they named *Morris Ashby Zinc*

Alloy, which gave the letters MAZA. Somewhere along the line, the K was added, and the word Mazak entered the language.

There are two basic die casting methods:

1 Gravity die casting (or Permanent mould casting).
2 Pressure die casting.

Gravity die casting

Also known as permanent mould casting, is the simplest form of die casting where the molten metal is poured into a mould, or die, just as in sand casting. The die is filled by straightforward pouring (the force of gravity keeps the metal in the mould), and a runner and a riser are used, as in sand casting.

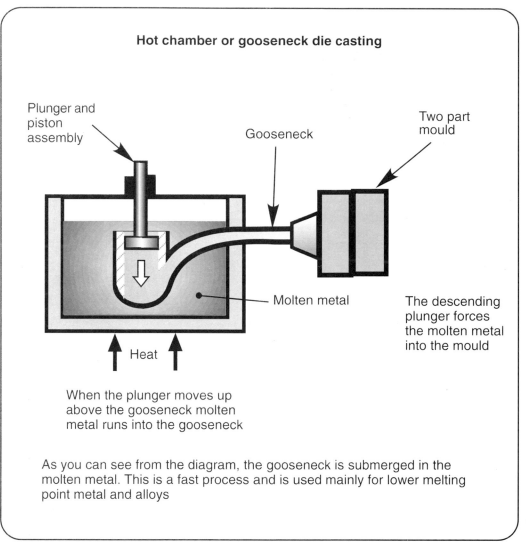

Hot chamber or gooseneck die casting

Plunger and piston assembly

Gooseneck

Two part mould

Molten metal

The descending plunger forces the molten metal into the mould

Heat

When the plunger moves up above the gooseneck molten metal runs into the gooseneck

As you can see from the diagram, the gooseneck is submerged in the molten metal. This is a fast process and is used mainly for lower melting point metal and alloys

FIGURE 11   *Hot chamber die casting.*

Aluminium alloy, and magnesium alloy car wheels are sometimes produced in this way. These alloy wheel rims are much stronger, and safer for driving at high speeds, than conventional wheel rims. They also look 'sporty'.

After each casting, the die, which splits into a number of parts, must be cooled down. A release agent is sprayed onto the die, to prevent the casting from sticking to the die.

Pressure die casting
In pressure die casting, the molten metal is forced into the die under pressure. This results in a very good finish and great accuracy. Many automotive components are produced by die casting. Intricate castings such as engine blocks, carburettors, alternator housings, turbo charger casings, pump housings and impellers, are possible with pressure die casting. Model toys cars were die cast in great numbers in the past in a zinc-based alloy, but most toys are now injection moulded in one of the polymers.

Low-pressure die casting
Sometimes called pressure pouring, is mostly used for casting steel components. Air, or an inert gas is used to force the molten metal up the pipe (stalk) into the graphite mould, see **FIGURE 10**.

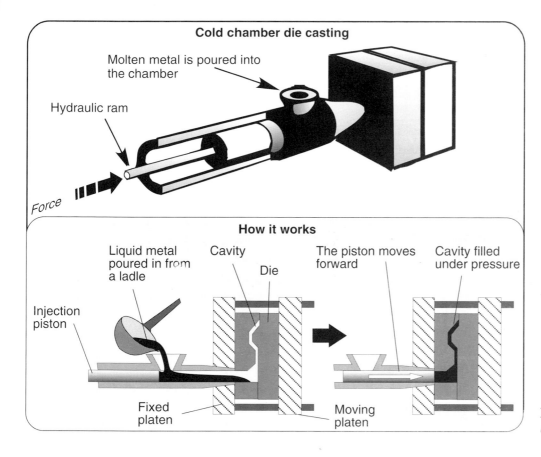

Cold chamber die casting

Molten metal is poured into the chamber

Hydraulic ram

Force

How it works

Liquid metal poured in from a ladle

Cavity

Die

The piston moves forward

Cavity filled under pressure

Injection piston

Fixed platen

Moving platen

FIGURE 12 *Cold chamber die casting.*

The rate of flow of metal into the mould can be controlled by the air, or gas pressure. A vacuum can be used to get all the air out of the mould to make it fill faster and to give higher quality castings.

High-pressure die casting

Two ranges of metals are used:

1 Low melting-point metals such as zinc, tin and lead alloys.
2 High melting-point metals such as brass, aluminium and magnesium.

For low melting-point alloys, the hot chamber process is used. This is generally known as a *Gooseneck die-casting* machine, because of the shape of the nozzle. You can see from **FIGURE 11** that the molten metal is forced into the die via the nozzle pipe by a plunger.

With higher melting point alloys, the iron in the molten metal container causes contamination, and

because of this, the cold-chamber die-casting machine was developed.

The cold-chamber machine has an auxiliary furnace for melting the metal, which is ladled into the plunger chamber as required. The chamber remains relatively cool and so the problem of iron contamination is overcome. **FIGURE 12** shows the cold chamber method.

When the ram of the cold-chamber machine is horizontal, the machine is called a horizontal cold-chamber machine, but if the ram is vertical the machine is a vertical one. Many of these machines are fully automatic, and can produce from 1000 pieces upwards per hour.

Economics of die casting

Compared with the cost of a pattern for sand casting, the cost of a die for die casting is very high indeed. However, when it is remembered that sometimes millions of components can be cast in a die before it wears out, a different picture emerges. Die casting is generally only economic if large numbers of castings are to be made.

Hot chamber and cold chamber dies are similar in construction, but whereas unalloyed steels may be used for cold chamber dies, special heat-resisting alloy steels must be used for hot chamber dies. With the development of these heat-resisting materials came the die casting of metals like grey iron and even alloy steels.

Pressure die casting steps

The pressure die casting process is divided into four main steps:

1 The dies are closed by hydraulic pressure and locked.
2 Molten metal is forced into the die by hydraulic pressure and the pressure is maintained.
3 When the casting is solid, the die is opened.
4 The casting is ejected by special ejector pins in one half of the split die.

THE CONTINUOUS CASTING OF METALS

When molten steel is to be made into plates, sheets, bars, sections, etc., it is first cast into ingots. Then the ingots are rolled into blooms, billets and slabs before going on to various rolling mills. Continuous casting of steel does away with the ingot stage, and the steel is cast directly into blooms, billets and slabs. This means that primary mills, intermediate mills, soaking pits and storage of ingots, are not needed with this process. Consequently, it is a more desirable process, for economic reasons. The steel production industry is very competitive, and any process, such as continuous casting helps to keep costs down.

The fundamental idea of continuous casting was put forward by *Bessemer* over a hundred years ago. However, the realisation of this basic idea made little progress until the late 1930s. Aluminium, with its low melting point and good casting properties, was the first metal for which continuous casting was successfully employed. Whereas the processes for aluminium and copper have been in use for some time, it is only in recent years that the process for steel has been perfected. At present, about 50% of all steel is produced by continuous casting.

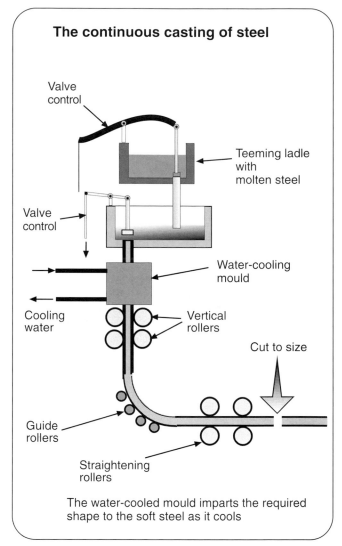

FIGURE 13 *Continuous casting of steel.*

Continuous casting of steel

First, the steel is tapped from the steel-making furnace into a refractory lined ladle, as for ingot casting. Then, it is teemed into a special trough known as a tundish. The reason for this is to ensure an even flow of metal to the casting machine. (**FIGURE 13**)

Originally, continuous casting machines for steel were about 30 metres high, to allow for the billet to be cut into lengths. Now, however, a system which is capable of casting through 90° has been developed.

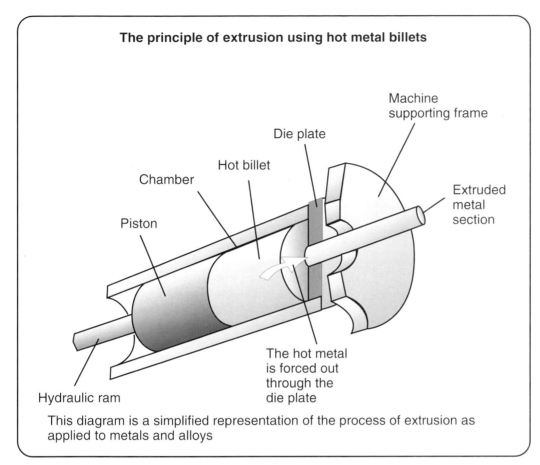

The principle of extrusion using hot metal billets

Machine supporting frame

Die plate

Hot billet

Chamber

Extruded metal section

Piston

Hydraulic ram

The hot metal is forced out through the die plate

This diagram is a simplified representation of the process of extrusion as applied to metals and alloys

FIGURE 14 *The principle of extrusion using hot metal billets.*

Casting control

The molten metal leaves the tundish and flows into a water-cooled copper mould. When the first part of the metal reaches the mould, it cools and solidifies onto a dummy bar. As the mould fills, the dummy bar is pulled slowly out through the withdrawal and straightening rolls. Metal passing through the mould forms a solid skin, but the core stays liquid for a while.

The emerging shape (billet, bloom or slab) is cooled by jets of water and then cut into lengths. Usually, a number of moulds are operated side by side, and, in this way, more than one bar can be produced simultaneously.

EXTRUSION

If a piece of modelling clay is pushed against a metal plate with a square hole in it, then the clay coming through the hole will have a square shape. This is simple extrusion. Metal extrusion is similar, in that metal in a softened condition is squeezed through a specially shaped hole, called a die, and the metal takes on the shape of the hole. (**FIGURE 14**)

Extrusion is used to produce long lengths with constant cross-section for the whole length. Extrusion is a major method of production in the polymer (plastics) industry, and this is discussed in the relevant section of the text (page 208). Metals used for extrusion must have good ductility.

Aluminium is well suited to this process because of its good ductility, which allows a great variety of shapes to be produced. Aluminium windows are fabricated from a selection of extruded bars. Steel is also shaped by the extrusion process. Many plastic or polymer sections are extruded.

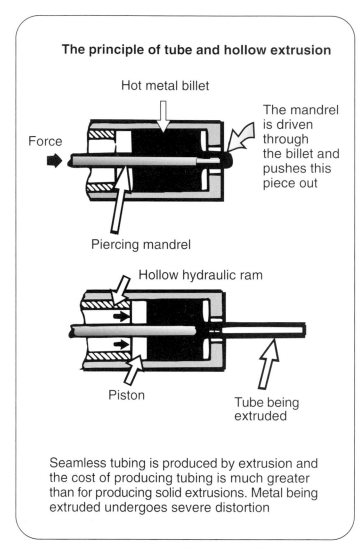

The principle of tube and hollow extrusion

Hot metal billet

Force

The mandrel is driven through the billet and pushes this piece out

Piercing mandrel

Hollow hydraulic ram

Piston

Tube being extruded

Seamless tubing is produced by extrusion and the cost of producing tubing is much greater than for producing solid extrusions. Metal being extruded undergoes severe distortion

FIGURE 15 *The principle of tube and hollow extrusion.*

Tube and hollow extrusion

Aluminium and polymer products are produced by this method. Here, we discuss production of aluminium products using the *piercing mandrel* method: A block of aluminium called a billet is heated and held in the extrusion press. Then, a special piercing mandrel is forced through the billet, as shown in **FIGURE 15**. This produces a solid slug which is later removed. Now, great pressure is applied to the hot billet by the main ram which forces the billet forward over the positioned mandrel and through the ring-shaped hole. This is how tube is extruded.

Port hole tube extrusion

In port hole extrusion, the die used is made up of two parts, the outer part and the *stub mandrel*. The stub mandrel does the same job as the piercing mandrel, but the stub mandrel is fixed in position by radial supports from the inside of the extruding unit. The assembled die is held in position at the front of the press and the hot billet is forced against it. Metal flows through the ports and out over the stub mandrel, thus forming the tube. (**FIGURE 16**)

Cold extrusion

In cold extrusion, very high pressure is used to make the metal flow when it is cold. This high pressure forces the metal into the cavity between the punch and the die. Sometimes this process is called *impact* extrusion and, until recently, was only used for shaping very ductile metals such as aluminium, tin, etc. Cans for beverages are produced in this way, as are toothpaste tubes. Now, however, mild steel components can be shaped by cold extrusion and often with cold heading as well, such as in the manufacture of countersunk rivets. There are two methods of cold or impact extrusion. In forward extrusion, the metal being extruded is driven out through a die, while, in reverse extrusion, the extruded metal is forced to extrude in the opposite direction to the ram movement. See **FIGURE 17**.

DROP FORGING

When steel is heated until it is red hot, it becomes *malleable*, and can be hammered into shape easily. This method, called forging, has been used for centuries to make all sorts of things including tools, utensils, weapons, gates, etc. A further development of hand forging is the use of power hammers to shape the hot metal. The hammers are nowadays replaced by either pneumatic or hydraulic presses.

Open die forging

This is just an extension of the blacksmith's art. Power hammer blows shape the metal with the aid of simple open dies. An open die is one which does not totally enclose the metal being forged.

Closed die forging

This is a widely used process for the mass production of many items such as those shown in **FIGURE 18**. A pair of shaped dies is used between which is placed

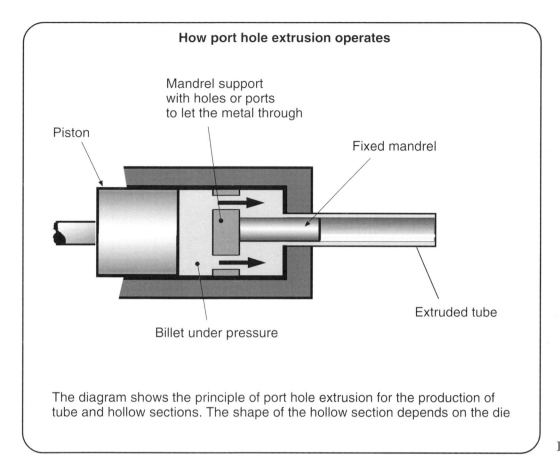

How port hole extrusion operates

Mandrel support with holes or ports to let the metal through

Piston

Fixed mandrel

Extruded tube

Billet under pressure

The diagram shows the principle of port hole extrusion for the production of tube and hollow sections. The shape of the hollow section depends on the die

FIGURE 16 *Port hole.*

the hot 'blank' of metal. A hydraulic ram usually drives the top half of the die down onto the hot metal which is positioned on the stationary bottom half of the die. The size of the blank is such that it is slightly bigger than what is needed and so there is some *flashing*. This is trimmed off later.

Closed die forging is commonly called drop forging and the products are known as drop forgings. Many components are manufactured by drop forging, including crane hooks, camshafts, crankshafts, brackets. Because of the fact that fibre lines in a forging follow the shape of the section, forgings have better mechanical properties. This is especially important in such components as crankshafts and bolt-heads. (**FIGURE 19**)

PRESS FORMING

The shaping of sheet-metal using a power press is really spectacular indeed. A flat sheet of steel goes into the press, down comes the ram with its many tonnes of force, and a mudguard or wing of a car is produced from the flat sheet. A press is a machine with a heavy frame, and a strong base or bed. A hydraulic ram is housed within the frame. There are many types of press, such as blanking press, bending press, coining press, etc.

The main drive mechanisms which are used in presses are direct ram, and rams with toggle mechanisms. Presses, or pressbrakes, as they are sometimes called, are used to produce a very wide variety of components easily and cheaply from sheet metal. Many of the articles which make life easier, such as washing machines, refrigerators, radiators and motor cars are made to a large degree by presswork.

Press tools

Punches and dies are the tools which actually make the parts. The press supplies the force to push the

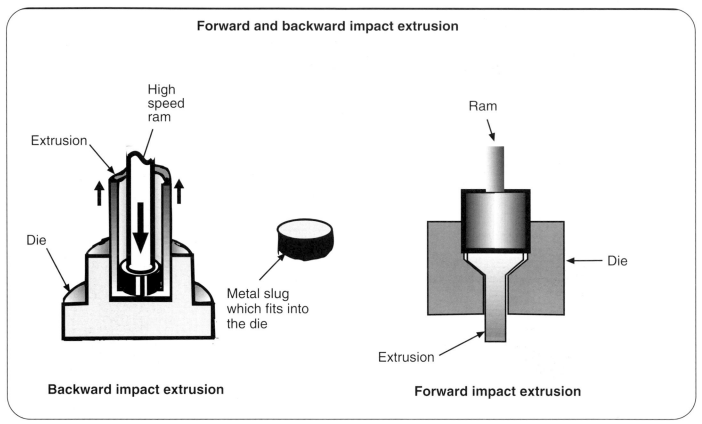

Forward and backward impact extrusion

High speed ram

Extrusion

Die

Metal slug which fits into the die

Backward impact extrusion

Ram

Die

Extrusion

Forward impact extrusion

FIGURE 17 *Forward and backward impact extrusion.*

punch with the metal into or through the die. The top half of the tool is the punch, and is attached to the ram which moves up and down. The die is fixed to a bolster which sits on the bed. *Tooling up*, which is the name given to getting the punches and dies made to do a particular job, is extremely expensive. It is only economical if a very large quantity of the product is going to be manufactured. The job of making the press tools is done by specially-trained toolmakers, who can work to great accuracy. Alloy steels used in making these tools must be hardened by heat treatment.

OPERATIONS

In pressing, mild steel is the most common metal used. It is still fairly cheap, and is usually bought in by the press shop as cold rolled coils. Before going to the press, the steel is straightened by going through straightening rolls.

Blanking
This is the cutting of the metal shape from the sheet metal. Blanks are produced and attention must be given to keeping waste to a minimum. The waste can be reduced by using a strip one and a half times as wide as the original and still produce twice the number of blanks.

Fluid cells are also used to power some presses, which can be very accurately controlled to produce components to a high specification. FIGURE 22 shows a fluid cell press.

Piercing or punching
This is similar to blanking but usually much less metal is removed than when blanking. The metal removed when blanking is used to make something, whereas the metal removed in piercing or punching is scrap. Holes are made in sheet metal by piercing or punching.

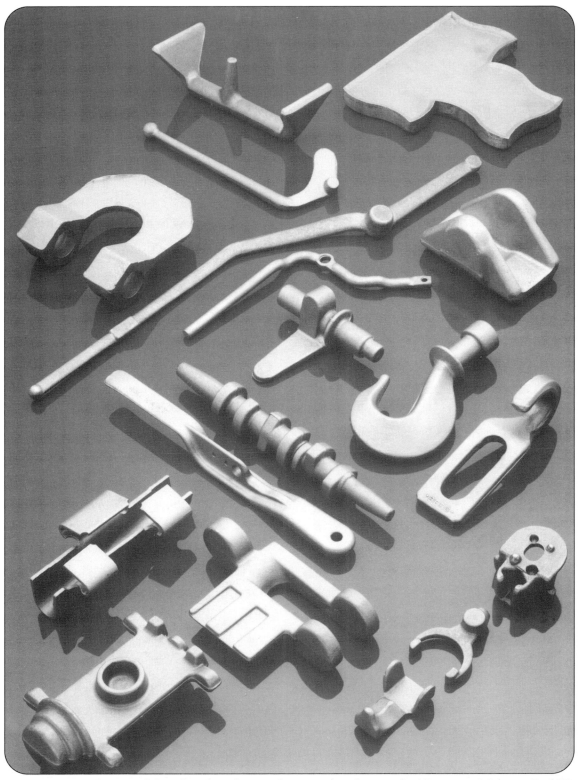

FIGURE 18   *A range of drop forged products is shown in this photograph. (Courtesy: Mylaeus GmbH)*

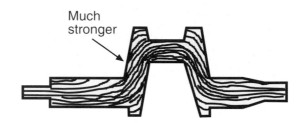

How the direction of the grain in forged parts adds strength

Weak

Much stronger

Grain flow in a machine crankshaft

Grain flow in a forged crankshaft

The forged crankshaft has its grain flow in the general direction of the major stress on the shaft. This is not the case with the machined crankshaft, which is weaker. Forged components have greater resistance to fatigue

FIGURE 19 *Direction of grain.*

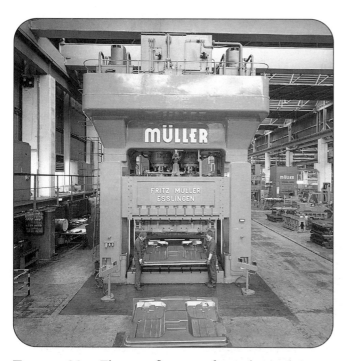

FIGURE 20 *Floors, or floor pans for trucks, are being produced in this photograph, and only some of the press is visible. Several separate pressing operations are needed to make the floor pan. You can see a pressed floor in the foreground of the picture. (Courtesy: Lapple)*

Bending

Bending can be the next operation after blanking and is carried out on a power-assisted flypress or bending press. The direction of the grain in the metal is an important factor in bending. To avoid cracking the metal should be bent at right angles to the grain direction. In bending the metal shape is changed but the metal is not stretched, it does not get thinner at any point.

Drawing

In sheet-metal drawing, the blank is drawn into and through a special die by a moving punch. The gap between the punch and the die is just a little bit more than the thickness of the metal, and so a tube-like component is made with a round end. Not all metals are suitable for drawing. Metals must have excellent ductility to be suitable for this process.

Deep drawing

Extra good ductility is required in a metal to be used in this process. There are variations of the process. To produce steel cylinders for various gases, and cylinders for use as fire extinguishers, which are very deep, a series of ironing rings is used.

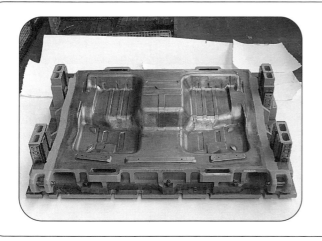 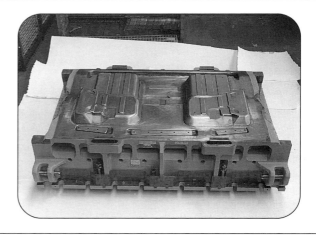

FIGURE 21 *Here, you can see a set of press tools used in the press in* **FIGURE 20***. The tool with the two hollows in it on the left is the die, and the other tool is the punch. (Courtesy: Lapple)*

Blank discs are coated with soap and zinc phosphate for lubrication and the ram pushes the disc through the die arrangement, which is a series of rings. The first ring is called the intake ring and the others are ironing rings, which smooth the metal. Because of the work they have to do, the rings have very hard

inserts which come in contact with sheet-metal being drawn. (**FIGURE 23**)

Complex shapes

Sometimes a particular shape cannot be pressed in one operation and the metal has to go through a

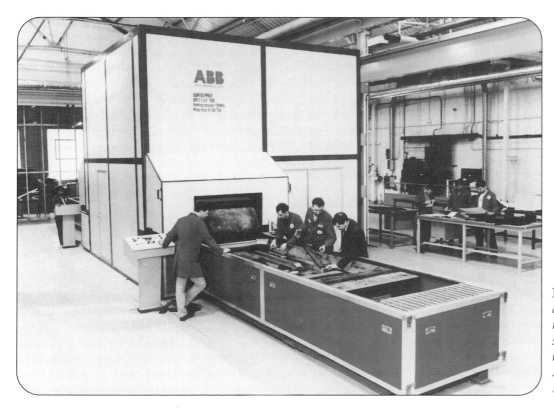

FIGURE 22 *This fluid cell press has a 47,000 tonnes press force, and is seen here producing sheet metal components at British Aerospace. (Courtesy: Asea Brown Boveri)*

FIGURE 23   *A vertical deep drawing press is pictured here. The operator standing in the foreground is holding a deep drawn object, which is about 220 mm in diameter and about 200 mm high. (Courtesy: Asea Brown Boveri)*

series of operations. For small components, a transfer press is used which transfers the metal from one stage to the next, automatically producing up to 20,000 units per hour.

Large pressings

You see large pressings everyday on the roads in motor cars. These are car doors, roofs, front wings, rear wings and other panels which are examples of large pressings. Some of these units are made up of several pressings, which are spot welded together. The automobile or car industries of the world use many manufacturing methods to produce their cars, but the products of the press shop make up the most part of any conventional cars. Most press shops producing motor car panels are now computer controlled. Assembly of cars is achieved, to a large degree, in many factories by the use of *robots*.

ROBOTS IN INDUSTRY

The robots which are used in industry to perform repeated tasks, both simple and complex, do not resemble the robot image to be seen in feature films and on television, where the robot has some resemblance to the human form. An industrial robot tends to look like part of a small earth-moving machine, in that it has an arm structure that can swivel about, as well as move up and down. Most of these robots are really *robot arms*, which can be accurately controlled by programmes run on a computer. Generally, the input keyboard does not resemble the ordinary PC (personal computer) keyboard. Keys have symbols and numbers, for the most part. The control technology is similar to the control systems used in CNC lathes and milling machines, but modern robots also use complex sensing systems. (**FIGURE 24**)

Robot assembly line

In an automated diesel engine assembly line, developed by Asea Brown Boveri in co-operation with the engine manufacturers, there are different flexible conveyor systems, and sixteen six-axis robots with articulated arms. The development of the automation system and the development of the new engine was done at the same time. Two-cylinder, three-cylinder, four-cylinder and six-cylinder

FIGURE 24 *An engine block is shown mounted on a programmable pallet, which is being carried along by the conveyor line. The pallet is programmed where to stop, and when to move on. Each workpiece is accompanied by its relative electronic data, by a data carrier, which stores all the information about the particular engine. Information required at the workstation is read off, and transmitted to the control system. (Courtesy: Asea Brown Boveri)*

engines can be produced. To achieve this, data (information) for each workpiece, or part to be assembled, is attached to the workpiece, so that when it reaches an operation point, the information is read by the control system, which makes the necessary adjustments, and the required operation is carried out.

The system has the information that each operating station needs to do a particular job, stored in memory, for each of the engine types. There are also some manual workstations, at which visual display units (VDU's) give instructions to the operators. Instructions given to an operator might be:

- **The actual operation to be carried out**
- **The order in which the work is to be done**
- **Identification numbers or codes, for each part**
- **Help information which can be called up as needed.**

Multipurpose capabilities

Asea Brown Boveri, who have a branch in Dublin, manufacture robots in Sweden, which are assembled

FIGURE 25 *This is the crankshaft assembly workstation, where the IRB 6000 operates. The inset shows the robot positioning the crankshaft into the engine block. (Courtesy: Asea Brown Boveri)*

in Milton Keynes, for use in the British Isles. It is interesting to note that many of the very special *constant voltage toroidal transformers* for these robots are made by Nuvotem, in Crolly, Co Donegal, and exported to Sweden.

Robots made by ABB and other suppliers may have multipurpose capabilities. This means that they are ideal for assembly line automation, where they can perform tasks such as inserting parts, joining parts, measuring and testing. These robots have high reproducibility, which means they are good at doing what they are supposed to do. The makers say that robots are cost effective, because they can be adapted to changing technologies, and/or product modifications. Robot *cycle times* (the time taken to carry

out a job) are normally about three minutes, which is very similar to the old manual car assembly lines, where the cycle time was from one and a half minutes, to about four minutes.

Worker and robot
Some robots have automatic tool changing facilities, which allows different operations to be carried out at one work station. The crankshaft assembly, in the diesel engine factory, has an IRB 6000 robot and one operator. Both work together simultaneously, which is a good example of the flexibility that has been achieved. To place a crankshaft in an engine block, the robot loosens the crankshaft-bearing screws. The operator removes the bearing cap and places the lower bearing shells in position, and places

FIGURE 26 *Robot-automated station for determining the type of piston, function-testing of the speed sensors, piston rod height, piston assembly position, etc. The different measurements are made possible by automatic changeover of the measuring heads. (Courtesy: Asea Brown Boveri)*

the crankshaft on the pallet (the platforms/trays, that moves along the assembly line). Then, the robot positions the crankshaft in the crankcase and meshes the crank and camshaft gears. The operator puts the upper bearing in place and the robot screws the cap in place. While these operations are going on, the pallet moves to suit. From this brief description, you can appreciate that this is a complex set-up.

PRODUCTION

This is the manufacture of articles from raw or processed materials using hand or machine tools. Production can be said to mean the changing of

materials from an initial form into something that can be sold.

There are three cases to think about:

1 Converting raw materials into usable materials, e.g. smelting iron ore into steel bars.
2 Making components from these usable materials, e.g. making screws from steel bars.
3 Assembling already made components to make a product, e.g. a diesel engine.

The most common types of production in factories are 2 and 3. These are the manufacturing industries.

There are four kinds of production:

Job production

This is a once-only job, for example if you wanted someone to build you a trailer to carry two motor bikes, then this would be a *one-off* job. This type of work is sometimes called *jobbing* and could be applied to repairing houses, etc.

Batch production

Here, we make the distinction between small batch production and large batch production. Small batch production means that the product is needed in small numbers. A factory engaged in small batch production would make a variety of products. Orders for any or all of these products may be repeated. Most engineering manufacturing firms are involved in small batch production.

Mass production or flowline production

These are two names given to large batch production. This is where a large number of identical items are made. There is continuous flow of the same product, sometimes along an assembly line as in car manufacturing, or diesel engine manufacture, where a car, or engine, might come *off the line* every 3 minutes.

Process production

This is continuous production where there is a continuous inflow of raw materials and a continuous outflow of the product. Examples of this type would be the production of steel and the production of chemicals.

QUALITY AND QUALITY CONTROL

A product of the right quality will do the job that it is supposed to do, and thus please the buyer. Determining the quality of any item starts with finding out what the buyer or customer wants. After that, the product is made to that quality.

Quality control

This means making sure that the product is kept up to standard throughout production, and that each unit produced will work properly and be without flaws. It involves inspection at various stages of manufacture.

Materials in: inspection starts with the quality of the material which is used to make the product.

Supposing a factory makes fridges. Pre-painted sheet steel might be *bought* in large quantities, for making the cabinets. It would take a long time to inspect every single sheet, so sample lots are taken, say in lots of 100 sheets. If the inspection of these samples shows a very small rejection, say 1%, then the order is accepted. But if the rejection rate is higher, then 100% inspection might be called for, or the order might be refused and sent back to the suppliers.

During manufacture

At each stage of manufacture, inspection takes place to ensure that the quality of the work up to that stage is acceptable. For example, cars are made of many different parts and quality control is maintained on each part. Gearboxes made for cars are tested by setting them up on a test device that drives the main shaft. Each gear is tried to check for operation, and there should not be excessive noise.

The actual finished product

Final inspection checks that the product has the quality desired. Will it do the job it is supposed to do? A fridge may look beautiful and have a high quality finish, but it is of no use if it does not keep things cool. So fridges are checked to see if they will keep the temperature to a desired level say, 4°C. The freezer compartment, if any, is checked for its ability to freeze goods and keep them frozen. Sometimes, a small certificate of final inspection is attached to the product.

Inspection is an expensive business, and manufacturers use sample inspection, where only some of the products or items are inspected. The system of sampling varies from manufacturer to manufacturer, but a random sampling system might be to take one in five, for inspection.

Sample inspection is not always possible and 100% inspection may be required where every single item or product is inspected. This would be the case where cars come off the assembly line. In the case of cars, each car is driven on a test rolling road system. Engine performance, top speed, braking efficiency, etc. can be tested and the testing inspector will check lights, wipers, washers, radio, doors, windows etc. and paintwork before the car is passed as fit to be sold. If a fault is found, then the car goes to rectification where the fault is put right.

SUMMARY

Casting, or moulding, is a very fast method of manufacture.

A *pattern* is a replica of the object to be cast with allowances made for contraction.

Sand casting. The moulds used are made from a special type of sand with clay-like properties.

Investment, or lost wax casting is a precise form of casting, which makes use of wax patterns to make the required moulds. The process is expensive, and is used to cast metals such as stainless steel and titanium.

Die casting is a process in which permanent steel moulds are used to produce large numbers of components.

Gravity die casting. This is done in much the same way as sand casting, except that a steel mould is used.

Pressure die casting. In this process, the molten metal is forced into the mould, or die, under pressure. A high degree of accuracy is achieved.

Continuous casting allows smelted metal to be cast into special copper moulds, to produce billets, blooms or slabs, without going through the ingot stage.

Extrusion. Used for metals and some non-metals, extrusion is carried out by forcing the material through a shaped hole. The material emerges or is extruded in long lengths to the exact shape of the hole.

Drop forging. Red hot steel is formed between a punch and a die. The punch is forced down onto the die, usually by hydraulic pressure. Crankshafts may be made by this method.

Press forming shapes sheet metal by forcing it to take the shape of a set of press tools, made up of a punch and a die. Presses are extremely large and produce very high pressures.

Industrial robots. An increasingly large number of robots are used in industry for repeated operations, such as assembly and welding.

Quality control is used to make sure that the product reaching the consumer is up to the desired standard.

Manufacturing with Plastics

MANUFACTURING WITH PLASTICS

Converting polymers into useful objects is a very important aspect of manufacturing. Proper application and use of polymers requires that engineers and designers have an understanding of their nature and properties. It is also necessary to know their advantages and limitations. Methods of manufacturing objects from polymers takes into consideration the type of polymer – thermoplastic or thermosetting plastic – and the final shape of the product. Each manufacturing process is designed to suit the polymer to be processed. Some manufacturing processes use powdered polymer as the raw material, others use sheet, while solid bar is machined in a similar way to metal machining. In general, however, the conversion of raw polymer to finished product takes place in a single-operation process.

PROCESSING OF PLASTICS

There are many important techniques used to convert polymers into finished articles. These include:

1 Calendering.
2 Extrusion.
3 Moulding.
4 Heat forming.
5 Foaming.
6 Lamination.
7 Machining.
8 Welding.

1 Calendering

Continuous lengths of sheet are made from a thermoplastic by calendering. The material passes through heated rollers. The sheet is produced in

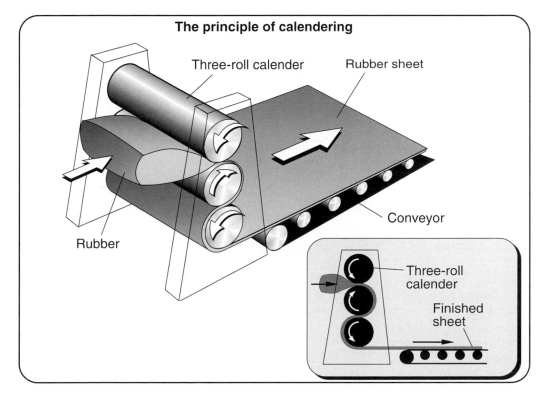

The principle of calendering

Three-roll calender

Rubber sheet

Conveyor

Rubber

Three-roll calender

Finished sheet

FIGURE 1   *Calendering.*

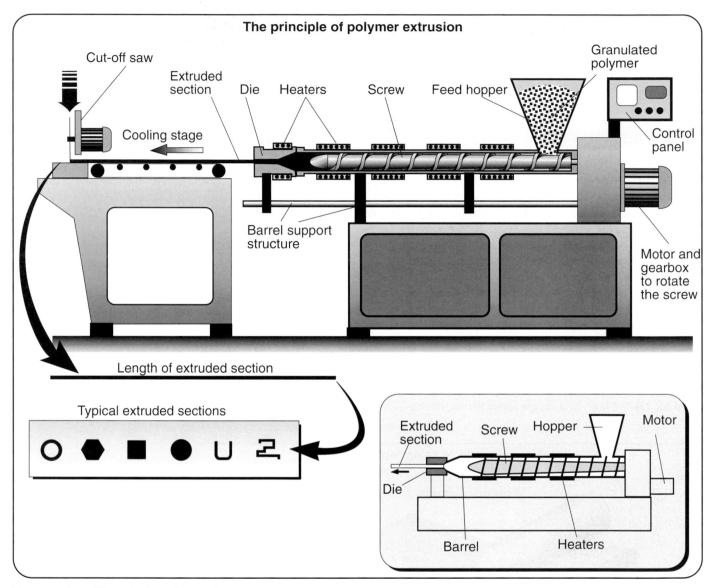

FIGURE 2 *The principle of extrusion.*

much the same way as steel is rolled. This method is used to produce mats and floor coverings. The principle of calendering is shown in **FIGURE 1**

2 Extrusion

Continuous lengths such as tubing or rods are extruded. The thermoplastic material used is in granular form. It is fed through a hopper into a heated chamber. A screw fitted in the chamber forces the softened polymer through a die at the end. The die gives the extrusion its final shape.

Extrusion is suited mainly to thermoplastic materials. You can see the principal parts of an extrusion machine in **FIGURE 2**

3 Moulding

Polymers are usually prepared for moulding as a powder, as chips, or as granules. In order to obtain the finished articles these have to be formed into a solid mass. The conversion usually takes the form of forcing the heated 'raw material' into a mould. If the moulded article is made from a thermoplastic, it is

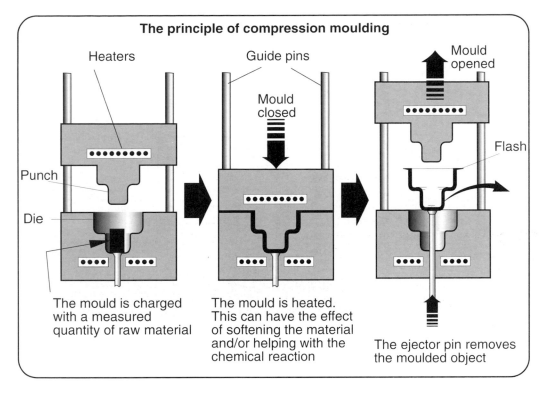

The principle of compression moulding

Heaters

Guide pins

Mould opened

Punch

Mould closed

Flash

Die

The mould is charged with a measured quantity of raw material

The mould is heated. This can have the effect of softening the material and/or helping with the chemical reaction

The ejector pin removes the moulded object

FIGURE 3 *Compression moulding.*

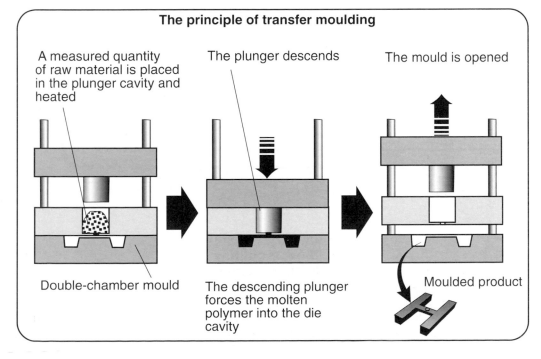

The principle of transfer moulding

A measured quantity of raw material is placed in the plunger cavity and heated

The plunger descends

The mould is opened

Double-chamber mould

The descending plunger forces the molten polymer into the die cavity

Moulded product

FIGURE 4 *Transfer moulding.*

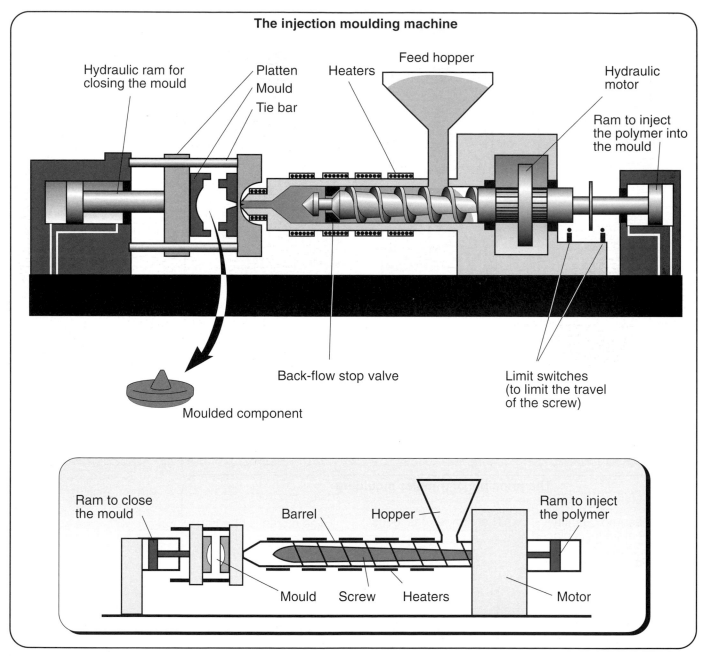

The injection moulding machine

Hydraulic ram for closing the mould

Platten
Mould
Tie bar

Heaters

Feed hopper

Hydraulic motor

Ram to inject the polymer into the mould

Back-flow stop valve

Moulded component

Limit switches (to limit the travel of the screw)

Ram to close the mould

Barrel

Hopper

Ram to inject the polymer

Mould   Screw   Heaters

Motor

FIGURE 5 *Injection moulding.*

cooled immediately after moulding so that it retains the shape given to it by the mould.

The common methods of moulding polymers are:

- **Compression moulding**
- **Transfer moulding**
- **Injection moulding**
- **Blow moulding**
- **Rotational moulding.**

In all types of moulding the polymer is heated and is then forced under pressure into the mould cavity. The plastic takes up the shape of the mould cavity.

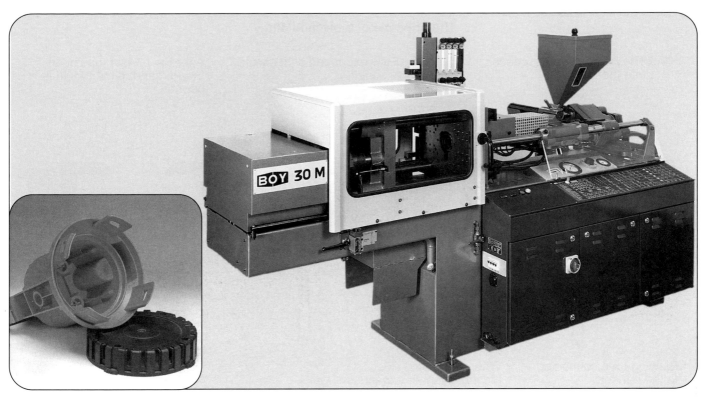

FIGURE 6 *Injection moulding machine. (Courtesy: BOY Ltd.)*
Inset: *Examples of injection moulded products. (Courtesy: Hi-Tech Tools Ltd. Dublin)*

Compression moulding is suited to thermosetting polymers. The process takes place in a split steel mould. The cavity in the mould is the required shape of the finished object. A measured amount of the monomer powder is loaded into the cavity and the mould closes. A punch (which is also shaped to complete the shape of the object) is forced by a hydraulic ram, into the cavity. The heater in the mould causes the powder to melt and as it sets, the cross–linking (curing) takes place. The mould is then opened and the object is removed. In **FIGURE 3** you can see the principle of compression moulding.

Transfer moulding is also suited to thermosetting polymers. The moulding powder is placed in a compartment which is separate from the mould cavity. The plunger forces the molten polymer through feed runners into the cavity. **FIGURE 4** shows the principle of transfer moulding.

Injection moulding is used to produce articles from thermoplastics. The molten material is forced under pressure through a narrow opening into a cooled mould. The plastic solidifies in the mould. The mould is then opened and the finished object is ejected. The principle of injection moulding is shown in **FIGURE 5** and an injection moulding machine is shown in **FIGURE 6**.

There are different types of injection moulding machines. The injection moulding machine shown in **FIGURE 5** is a screw-type. In this type the rotating screw moves the polymer through the heated barrel. The screw is then pushed forward by the hydraulic ram. This forces the molten polymer through the narrow opening into the mould cavity. Other types of injection moulding machines use a piston only.

Blow moulding is a process which is used to manufacture bottles. The first stage is to extrude a thick wall tube down into the mould. This tube is called a *parison*. While the parison is still soft, the mould closes around it and air is blown in. The hot parison is blown into the shape of the mould.

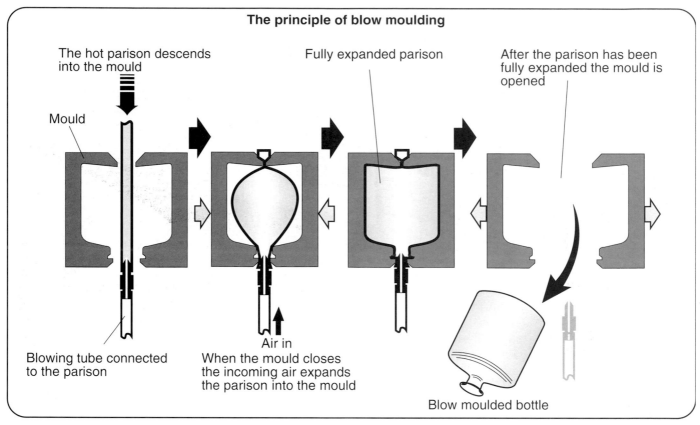

The principle of blow moulding

The hot parison descends into the mould

Mould

Blowing tube connected to the parison

Air in
When the mould closes the incoming air expands the parison into the mould

Fully expanded parison

After the parison has been fully expanded the mould is opened

Blow moulded bottle

FIGURE 7   *Blow moulding.*

FIGURE 7 shows the principle of blow moulding. You can see a milk bottle manufacturing machine in FIGURE 8

Rotational moulding is a process where a measured amount of polymer is placed in the mould. The mould is closed and is then rotated in a very complex motion until the polymer lines the mould cavity. Plastic footballs are made by rotational moulding.

4 Heat forming (thermoforming)
This is used on sheets of polymers. One of the main thermoforming processes is *vacuum forming*. A plastic sheet is clamped around the edges over a pattern. It is then heated uniformly, the heater is removed and

FIGURE 8   *A blow moulding machine manufacturing milk bottles. (Courtesy: Maddens Milk, Parteen, Co. Clare)*

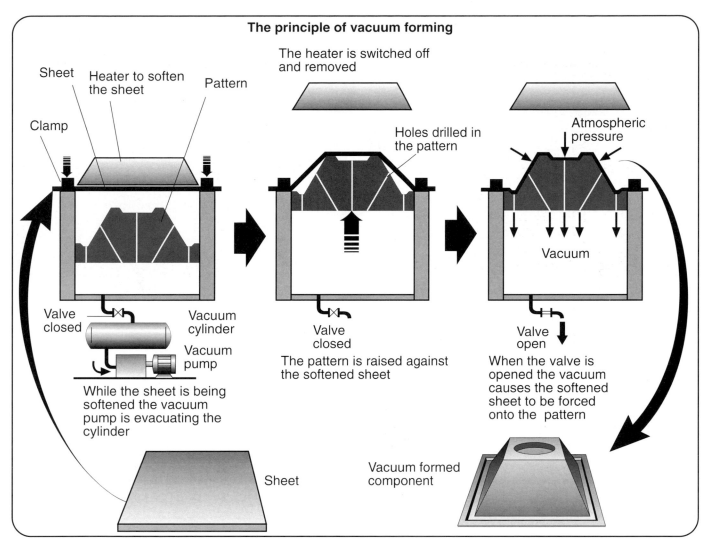

The principle of vacuum forming

Sheet

Heater to soften the sheet

Pattern

Clamp

The heater is switched off and removed

Holes drilled in the pattern

Atmospheric pressure

Valve closed

Vacuum cylinder

Vacuum pump

While the sheet is being softened the vacuum pump is evacuating the cylinder

Valve closed

The pattern is raised against the softened sheet

Vacuum

Valve open

When the valve is opened the vacuum causes the softened sheet to be forced onto the pattern

Sheet

Vacuum formed component

FIGURE 9   *Vacuum forming.*

the pattern is raised. When a vacuum is applied under the pattern, the sudden drop in pressure causes the soft sheet to be forced down over the top of the pattern. See **FIGURE 9**

5   Foaming
Polymers which are converted into sponge-like materials are *foamed* or expanded. A foaming agent is mixed with the resin. This combination is heated during moulding. The products which are produced have very low densities. Both rigid and flexible foams can be produced.

6   Lamination
High strength plastics can be produced by impregnating sheets of paper or cloth with a resin. Layers of this material are bonded by allowing the resin to set into a solid structure. Heat and pressure are often used in this process.

7   Machining
Plastics supplied in the form of rod, tube or sheet can be machined into their final shape. These materials can be machined on metal-working and some wood-working machines, using cutting tools

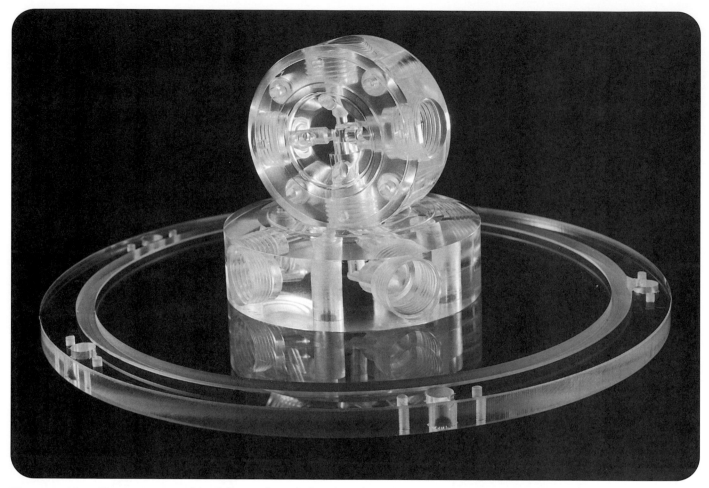

FIGURE 10   *Components machined from polymethylmethacrylate. (Courtesy: HI-TEC Precision Engineering Ltd., Limerick)*

with slightly modified cutting-angles. FIGURE 10 shows a range of components machined from polymethylmethacrylate.

8 Welding

Many parts on the outside of motor vehicles are made from polymers. Bumpers, grilles, lamp surrounds are some of the applications. Polymers will absorb light impacts which would often deform steel parts beyond repair. When the plastic part is cracked or torn it can often be repaired using a hot air welding tool. The welding tool provides sufficient heat to make the plastic 'wet' (molten). A filler rod of the same plastic material is fed through a special nozzle on the welder into the groove.

SUMMARY

The common methods of converting polymers into useful articles are:

1 Calendering – rolling into flat sheets.
2 Extrusion – forcing hot thermoplastic material through a die.
3 Moulding – forcing a hot material to take up the shape of a closed mould. Moulding processes include:
   Compression moulding – suited to thermosetting materials.
   Transfer moulding – suited to thermosetting materials.
   Injection moulding – suited to thermoplastics.

Blow moulding – suitable for making bottles from thermoplastics.

Rotational moulding – a process used to manufacture objects such as plastic footballs from thermoplastics.

4 Heat forming – forming of heated thermoplastics on a mould.

5 Foaming – converting to a sponge-like material.

6 Lamination – manufacture of sheets by impregnating sheets of paper or cloth with resin.

7 Machining – shaping plastics using machine tools.

8 Welding – joining or repair of plastics using a hot air welder.

Heat Treatment

INTRODUCTION

Treating of materials by *controlled heating and controlled cooling* can produce changes in material properties. A treatment may involve one or many processes. *Heat treatment* is an area of technology where almost magical changes can be made in components without changing shape or, in most cases, appearance, by first heating the part and then cooling it.

Heat treatment is a very complex area of *specialised knowledge*. In this book, only simple outlines, with simple explanations, are given to some of the many processes. Although heat treatment is also applied to other materials, such as polymers, ceramics, composites and glass, we briefly consider the heat treatment of *metallic materials*, with an emphasis on *carbon steels*.

PROCESSES

Some of the more common heat treatment processes used in the manufacturing industry, and by specialist heat treatment laboratories are:

- **Annealing**
- **Normalising**
- **Stress relieving**
- **Hardening**
- **Tempering**
- **Case hardening**
- **Age hardening**
- **Quenching.**

As already mentioned, to carry out a heat treatment involves controlled heating and controlled cooling. The general idea behind all heat treatment is to cause some desirable or required property changes in manufactured components. Heat treatment is often the last process a manufactured part goes through. So what are the important factors in any heat treatment process?

The basic steps in a heat treatment process are:

Heating the part to a particular temperature
Soaking or keeping the part at this temperature for a time
Cooling the part in a particular way.

ANNEALING

Full annealing, which is carried out in order make the metal as soft as possible, also improves ductility, refines the grain size and removes *internal stresses*. Internal stresses, or residual stresses, result from cold working, when the metal is bent to shape, or from rapid heating and cooling. The surface of *cold worked* metal may be under tension, while the centre is in compression, or vice versa. This type of situation is undesirable as the material strength and other properties are affected. Corrosion may be speeded up, or fatigue may occur due to residual stresses. It is good practice to remove the internal stresses. During the cold working the grains of the metal are deformed. As annealing is carried out, a whole new set of grains appears, which replace the old grains or crystals. This is known as *recrystallisation*. Recrystallisation in full annealing results in large grains.

In full annealing of steels with less than 0.83% carbon (which are called hypoeutectoid steels), components are heated to 25°C-50°C above the *upper critical temperature*, **FIGURE 1**.

In the case of steels which contain more than 0.83% carbon (hypereutectoid steels), heating is continued to 25°C-50°C above the *lower critical temperature*.

Once the desired temperature is reached, the steel is *soaked* to ensure uniform heating. Cooling is controlled by reducing the temperature of the furnace gradually. Switching the furnace off and allowing it to cool naturally often provides a suitable cooling rate. Furnaces tend to cool very slowly,

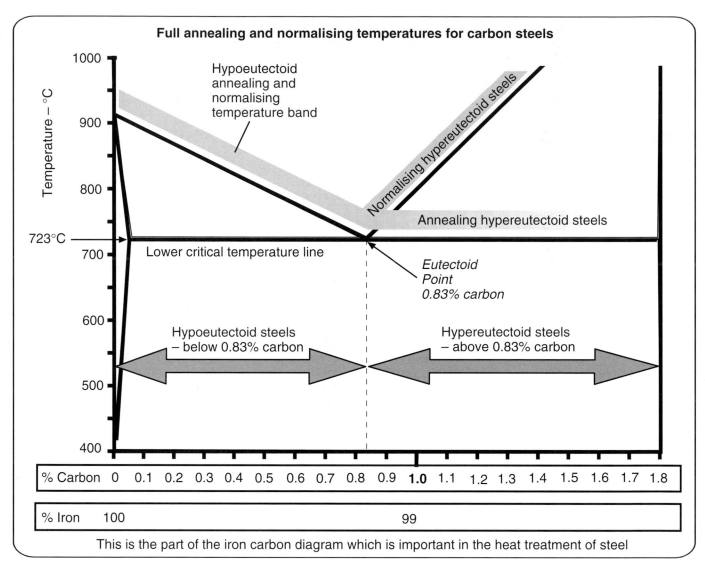

FIGURE 1 *Full annealing and normalising.*

because of a high degree of insulation in the furnace walls. The very slow cooling of the steel results in ferrite, and pearlite with thicker than normal slices of ferrite in it. Since ferrite is soft, full annealing makes a component *as soft as possible*.

Annealing 0.4% carbon steel

In **FIGURE 2**, the full annealing of 0.4% carbon steel is considered, in a simplified way. Above the upper critical temperature, the steel is in solid solution (grains look like a pure metal – see solid solution

alloys, page 221), called austenite, with the carbon completely dissolved. In cooling to below the lower critical temperature, the carbon in the austenite appears as iron carbide or cementite, which is a hard intermetallic compound. The cementite is present in grains of pearlite, which consist of layers of ferrite and layers of cementite. However, the very slow cooling that takes place in the full annealing of 0.4% carbon steel, generates coarse pearlite with thick layers of ferrite and thin layers of cementite. The coarser the pearlite, the softer the structure will be.

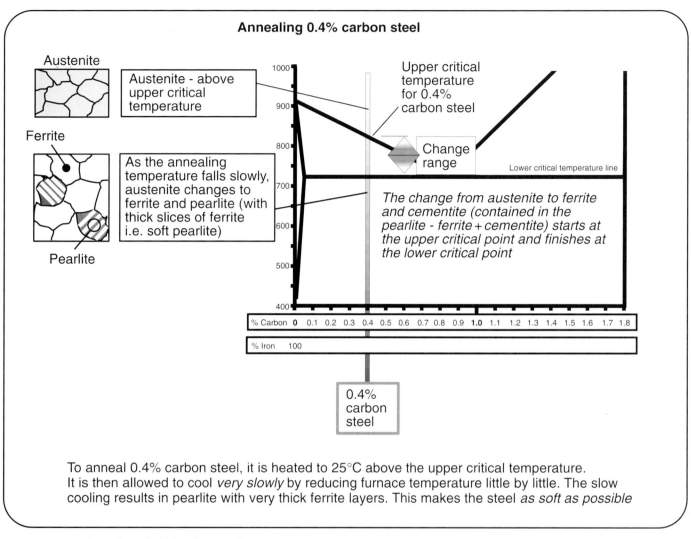

Annealing 0.4% carbon steel

Austenite

Austenite - above upper critical temperature

Ferrite

As the annealing temperature falls slowly, austenite changes to ferrite and pearlite (with thick slices of ferrite i.e. soft pearlite)

Pearlite

Upper critical temperature for 0.4% carbon steel

Change range

Lower critical temperature line

The change from austenite to ferrite and cementite (contained in the pearlite - ferrite + cementite) starts at the upper critical point and finishes at the lower critical point

| % Carbon | **0** | 0.1 | 0.2 | 0.3 | 0.4 | 0.5 | 0.6 | 0.7 | 0.8 | 0.9 | **1.0** | 1.1 | 1.2 | 1.3 | 1.4 | 1.5 | 1.6 | 1.7 | 1.8 |

| % Iron | 100 |

0.4% carbon steel

To anneal 0.4% carbon steel, it is heated to 25°C above the upper critical temperature. It is then allowed to cool *very slowly* by reducing furnace temperature little by little. The slow cooling results in pearlite with very thick ferrite layers. This makes the steel *as soft as possible*

FIGURE 2   *Annealing 0.4% carbon steel.*

Process annealing

Process annealing is used when components made from up to 0.25% carbon steel are going through a manufacturing process which involves cold working. During such cold work, the steel gets harder (strain hardening), and the process cannot continue. Process annealing is not as costly as full annealing because the temperatures required are not as high. To process anneal carbon steel containing up to 0.25% carbon, it is heated to a temperature of about 80°C to 180°C below the *lower critical temperature,* allowed to soak for a time, and then normally cooled in air. Recrystallisation takes place, in a similar manner to that in full annealing, but, because the temperature is

lower, the new grains are much smaller. Process annealing temperature bands are shown in **FIGURE 3**.

Higher carbon steels are heated to 30° below the lower critical temperature, and put through a process annealing procedure, known as *spheroidising*. This improves the machinability of the steels.

NORMALISING

When a material is formed by cold rolling, hot rolling, forging, etc., stresses are set up in the

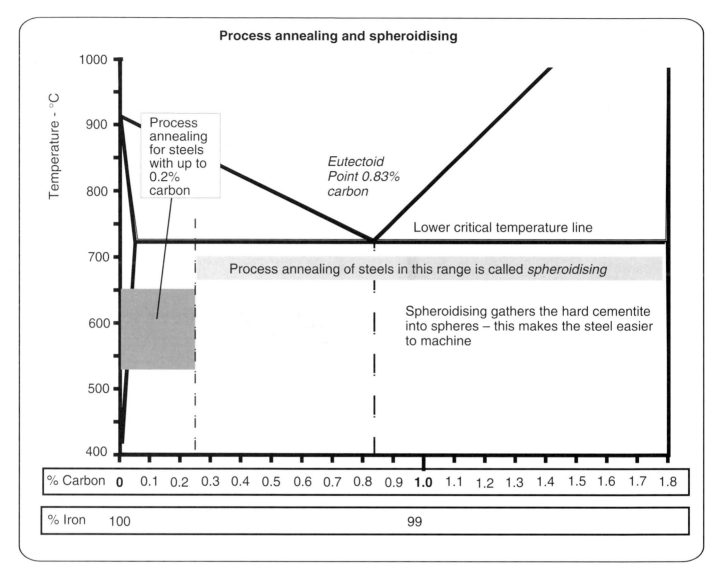

Process annealing and spheroidising

Temperature - °C

Process annealing for steels with up to 0.2% carbon

Eutectoid Point 0.83% carbon

Lower critical temperature line

Process annealing of steels in this range is called *spheroidising*

Spheroidising gathers the hard cementite into spheres – this makes the steel easier to machine

| % Carbon | 0 | 0.1 | 0.2 | 0.3 | 0.4 | 0.5 | 0.6 | 0.7 | 0.8 | 0.9 | 1.0 | 1.1 | 1.2 | 1.3 | 1.4 | 1.5 | 1.6 | 1.7 | 1.8 |

| % Iron | 100 | 99 |

FIGURE 3 *Process annealing and spheroidising.*

material, as explained earlier. Normalising, very similar to full annealing, is a process which removes these internal stresses. For *hypoeutectoid* steels (below 0.83% carbon content), the metal is heated to the same temperature as for full annealing, and allowed to soak until it is heated evenly throughout. Hypereutectoid steels (steels with more than 0.83% carbon content), are heated in the band shown in **FIGURE 1**. In both cases, the steel is then allowed to cool in air. The cooling rate is slightly faster than in annealing. This gives a fine grain structure, which is free from internal stresses, and has improved machinability. Normalised steel has higher strength, and lower ductility than fully annealed steel.

STRESS RELIEVING

This is a process in which the component is reheated and held at a slightly elevated temperature, for a period of time and then cooled slowly. (Exact temperatures and times depend on the condition of the component.)

HARDENING

Heating carbon steel (with a carbon content in the range of 0.4% to 0.2%) until it is red hot, and then quenching it in water produces a remarkable change in the steel. This fairly simple operation makes the steel extremely hard and brittle. The iron-carbon thermal equilibrium diagram is used extensively to provide information about the various heat treatments for carbon steels. FIGURE 1, FIGURE 2 and FIGURE 3 give an indication of the usefulness of the iron-carbon diagram. The information about hardening is also obtained from the diagram.

Carbon content

The extent to which steel can be hardened will depend on its composition.

The amount of carbon in the steel is most important. Another important factor in hardening is the rate at which the hot steel is cooled. Alloy steels contain other metals such as chromium and vanadium. These will also affect the hardening behaviour of the steel. To understand how the carbon content and the cooling rate affect the properties of a steel, it is necessary to examine its structure. The structure of a material is the way in which the various elements are arranged in it. Plain carbon steel, as we have seen, is an alloy of iron and carbon. The maximum amount of carbon which plain carbon steel can usefully contain is 1.7%. The structure of steel with a very low carbon content contains large areas of ferrite and small areas of pearlite. As the carbon content is increased, the structure will comprise larger areas of pearlite (a mixture of ferrite and cementite) and smaller concentrations of pure ferrite. At 0.83%, carbon (the eutectoid composition), the structure is purely pearlitic. Before any heating of a plain carbon steel takes place, the structure consists of ferrite and pearlite. If the carbon content is low, there will be areas of pure ferrite intermingled with areas of pearlite. When the temperature of the steel is raised to 723°C, important changes occur.

- **The BCC arrangement, ferrite, changes to an FCC structure (austenite)**
- **Because of this change, more spaces exist between the atoms.**

Austenite is named after Sir William C. Roberts-Austen, a most distinguished metallurgist, who was Professor of metallurgy at the Royal College of Science. His book, entitled *An Introduction to the study of Metallurgy*, which was written in 1890, was a milestone in metallurgical information.

The carbon atoms then begin to move into the spaces between the iron atoms. This movement or diffusion of the carbon into the austenite, is often referred to as *going into solid solution*.

Hardening of 0.6% carbon steel

We have chosen to consider the hardening of 0.6% carbon steel, FIGURE 4, in an effort to study the changes which take place during hardening. Carbon steel containing 0.6% carbon is a hypoeutectoid steel.

From the iron-carbon equilibrium diagram, FIGURE 4, the upper critical temperature is seen to be about 780°C. However, it is safer to harden from a slightly higher temperature, to be certain that all of the carbon has the chance dissolve in the FCC austenite (in solid solution). Quenching the steel in oil or water cools it very quickly indeed. There is not enough time for equilibrium to take place. If the cooling was slow, then the austenite would change to two separate types of grain: one, BCC ferrite, and the other pearlite. During the fast cooling in hardening, the FCC structure tries to change to a BCC structure, but does not manage to do so. A different structure altogether is generated, called *martensite*, which is extremely hard and strong. The structure of martensite is a topic that required a lot of investigation before it was fully understood. It is neither FCC, nor BCC, but a body centred tetragonal (BCT) structure. It looks as if dark grey needles have been mixed through each grain. This type of structure is not confined to iron-carbon systems.

It is the martensitic structure which produces the extreme hardness, mentioned earlier. However, with the hardness comes brittleness. In fact, the hard brittle steel is not of much use, and to make it useful, another heat treatment, called *tempering*, is required.

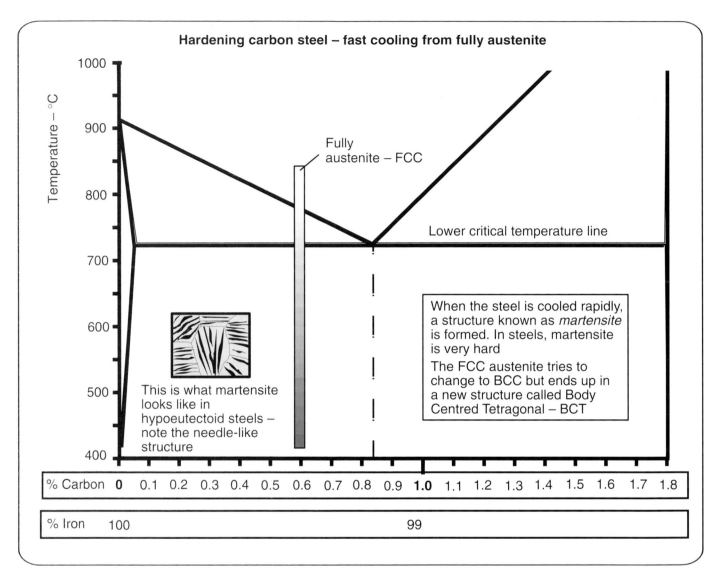

Hardening carbon steel – fast cooling from fully austenite

Fully austenite – FCC

Lower critical temperature line

This is what martensite looks like in hypoeutectoid steels – note the needle-like structure

When the steel is cooled rapidly, a structure known as *martensite* is formed. In steels, martensite is very hard

The FCC austenite tries to change to BCC but ends up in a new structure called Body Centred Tetragonal – BCT

| % Carbon | 0 | 0.1 | 0.2 | 0.3 | 0.4 | 0.5 | 0.6 | 0.7 | 0.8 | 0.9 | **1.0** | 1.1 | 1.2 | 1.3 | 1.4 | 1.5 | 1.6 | 1.7 | 1.8 |

| % Iron | 100 | | | | | | | | | 99 | | | | | | | | | |

FIGURE 4   *Hardening carbon steel.*

TEMPERING

To remove some of the brittleness, the steel is heated to a temperature below the lower critical temperature – 723°C, usually in the range: 230°C to 300°C. This heating at low temperature removes the *quenched-in stresses*, but also allows some of the martensite to change to ferrite pearlite, which has the effect of reducing hardness, brittleness and strength. The result is a steel hard enough to do the job required and tough enough to withstand the wear and tear. When tools made from steel have been machined, or forged into their final shape, they invariably have to be heat treated. You can, for example, forge a steel bar into the shape of a chisel, but before you can use it, you must make it harder than the steel you intend it to cut, and tough enough so that it will not break in use.

Tempering temperatures
The tempering temperature will depend on what the compromise between toughness and hardness should be. A cutting tool should be hard, and so the

tempering temperature required is low. A cold chisel must be tough, so the tempering temperature is higher.

USES OF THE IRON-CARBON EQUILIBRIUM DIAGRAM

We have referred to the iron-carbon diagram earlier in this chapter, and a basic analysis of the structure of the diagram is given under Thermal Equilibrium Diagrams, page 39. The temperature at which alpha iron (ferrite) changes completely to gamma iron (austenite) depends on the amount of carbon in the steel. If you examine FIGURE 4, you should notice that when there is a greater percentage of carbon in the steel, the change from ferrite + pearlite to austenite takes place over a shorter temperature range. By taking a variety of steels with different carbon contents you can plot the points at which the complete changes in structure occur.

If you know the amount of carbon in a particular carbon steel, then the iron-carbon equilibrium diagram provides the following information:

The annealing temperatures for full annealing, and process annealing
The normalising temperature
The hardening temperature
The temperature at which the structure begins to change from ferrite + pearlite to austenite
The temperature at which the steel is fully austenite.

QUENCHING MEDIA IN HEAT TREATMENT

The most commonly used quenching media are:

- **Oil**
- **Water**
- **Air.**

The rate at which any quenching medium conducts heat from a heated component depends on the heat transfer conditions. Water can conduct heat from a heated component approximately twice as fast as oil. If more rapid quenching is required, iced brine (water and salt solution) can be used. It is important to remember that rapid cooling of a component can lead to cracking and/or distortion.

CASE HARDENING

To harden a carbon steel component by the method described in this chapter, it must contain enough carbon. If it does not contain enough carbon (normally greater than 0.3% carbon for plain carbon steel), then heating and quenching will have little effect on the material. It is possible to add additional carbon to the outer surface of a steel component which has a low carbon content. The treated outer surface, or case, as it is known, can then be heat treated in the normal way giving a hard outer skin, and a softer tough core. The process is known as *case hardening*.

The addition of carbon to the outer skin is known as *carburising*. Carburising can be carried out by:

- **The pack method**
- **Salt bath carburising**
- **Gas carburising.**

The pack method of carburising

The component is packed in a box surrounded by a carbon rich material, such as powdered charcoal, and placed in the furnace at 920°C. This temperature is above the upper critical point which allows the carbon to diffuse into the austenite, FIGURE 5.

The depth of penetration of carbon into the surface depends on the temperature and the time spent in the furnace. To carburise to a depth of, say 1 mm, the component needs to be left in the furnace for up to 12 hours (depending on the carbon-rich material used). Because the component is so long in the furnace, grain growth occurs in the steel. The high carbon case has a very coarse crystaline structure, which is prone to cracking. A process known as grain refining is necessary.

After cooling, the component is immersed in a bath of molten salt. The salt is kept at a temperature of 780°C. The component remains immersed for half an hour, and it is then quenched in water. The salt used in this process will not add, or remove, carbon from the surface. It is a neutral salt. Molten salt is used because it provides uniform heating over the entire surface of a complicated shape.

Case hardening of low carbon steel by carburising

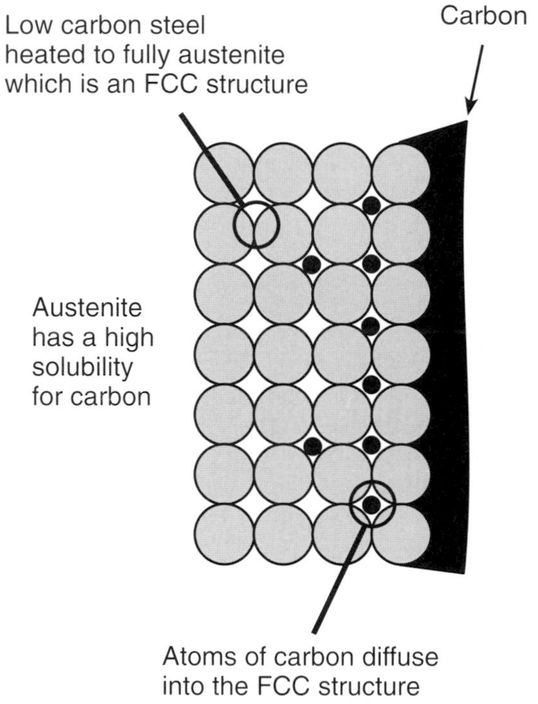

Low carbon steel heated to fully austenite which is an FCC structure

Carbon

Austenite has a high solubility for carbon

Atoms of carbon diffuse into the FCC structure

Carbon is diffused into the surface of the steel and when the steel is quenched from the fully austenite temperature, a skin of martensite is formed which is very hard. The depth of the skin is called the *case depth*

FIGURE 5 *Case hardening by carburising.*

Salt-bath carburising

Case hardening without causing coarse structures is possible using salt-bath carburising. The molten salt bath contains a mixture of sodium cyanide, sodium carbonate and sodium chloride.

The component is placed in the salt bath at 900°C for one hour. This gives a thin carbon case, and not too much grain growth. The component is then quenched in water to harden the surface.

Gas carburising

Gas carburising is carried out in a special sealed furnace. The carburising agent is a carbon-rich gas, usually carbon monoxide, circulating in the furnace chamber. This is a faster method of carburising than the pack method, and greater control over the process is possible.

Nitriding

This is also a case hardening process, but it is more expensive, and is only used where high quality is required. It is used for alloys which contain elements such as chromium, molybdenum, vanadium and aluminium. During heating, these elements form *nitrides* at the surface of the component. A nitride is a binary compound of nitrogen, e.g. aluminium nitride. Nitrides are ultra-hard, and consequently, the cases formed, although thin, are extremely hard. Nitriding is carried out in a furnace in which ammonia gas is circulated. Heating the ammonia gas produces the nitrogen. The temperature of the furnace is 500°C and the process can take up to 100 hours, depending on the case depth required. Nitriding can be used to case harden parts which are finish machined. Because no quenching is necessary, no distortion of the component is likely. Nitriding steels contain 0.2% to 0.5% carbon, alloyed with chromium and aluminium.

Carbonitriding

Carbonitriding is carried out in a gas atmosphere in a special furnace. The gas atmosphere is a mixture of ammonia and carbon monoxide. This results in an atmosphere which can produce carbon and nitrogen, and both of these elements diffuse into the steel being treated. The presence of carbon and nitrogen lead to the formation of iron carbides and iron nitrides, which are very hard, at the surface of the component. The component is quenched after the required case depth is achieved. A period of 30 minutes can produce a case depth of approximately 0.01 mm.

INDUCTION HARDENING

It is sometimes necessary to heat treat a component in such a way that it has a very hard outer surface and a softer core. An example of this would be slideways on a lathe. You will often see an *induction hardened* label on the bed of a lathe.

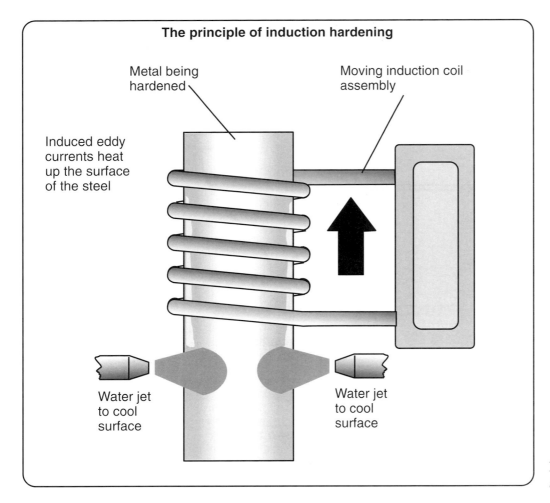

The principle of induction hardening

Metal being hardened

Moving induction coil assembly

Induced eddy currents heat up the surface of the steel

Water jet to cool surface

Water jet to cool surface

FIGURE 6 *Principle of induction hardening.*

This is a technique of heating the component very quickly in small areas using a high frequency electric current, principle shown in **FIGURE 6**.

Current at high frequency passing through the coil induces eddy currents in the component. These cause a rapid rise in temperature in the outer layers. Water is then sprayed on to the surface by a number of jets or nozzles, to quench the component.

FLAME HARDENING

This process, which is very similar to induction hardening, uses a flame of a hydrocarbon gas with oxygen. The flame is hot enough to raise the temperature of the outer surface above the upper critical temperature, before the core becomes heated by conduction. Water jets then quench the component.

AGE HARDENING OR PRECIPITATION HARDENING

In 1906, research metallurgist A. Wilm discovered that he could harden certain aluminium alloys. Following quenching from high temperature, the aluminium-copper alloy was allowed to stand at room temperature. Over a period of a few days the material increased in hardness. The phenomenon is known as *age hardening*. It was later discovered that ferrous alloys as well as non-ferrous alloys could be age hardened. Three separate stages are involved in age hardening:

1 *Solution treatment:* the metal being treated is heated above the solvus temperature, and soaked for a while.
2 *Fast cooling:* the alloy is quenched in water or oil.

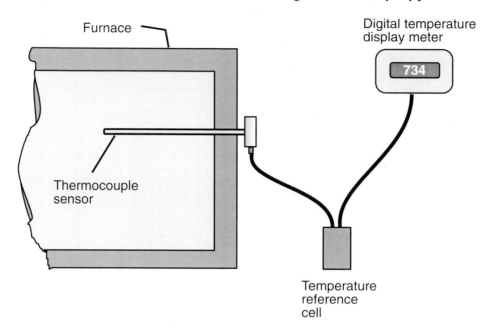

Temperature measurement in furnaces using a thermocouple pyrometer

Furnace

Digital temperature display meter

734

Thermocouple sensor

Temperature reference cell

A typical set-up for a K-type thermocouple is shown below

Nickel-chromium (*Chromel*) wire

Reference junction

Ouput voltage in μV

Nickel-aluminium (*Alumel*)

The temperature measuring range of this type of thermocouple is 0 to 1100°C

Output per degree averages 40 microvolts (μV) e.g. Reading is 1203 μV at 30°C

In many cases, the output is first amplified with a special amplifier such as the AD 597, which has a built-in reference point, and then interfaced to a computer for reading and control

FIGURE 7 *Temperature measurement in furnaces.*

3 *Ageing:* originally carried out at room temperature, components are now heated to higher temperatures, to speed up the ageing.

Duralumin, an aluminium alloy containing about 4% copper, can be age-hardened. It is used in the space industry because of its light weight and high strength. It is also possible to age-harden certain steels.

MEASUREMENT OF FURNACE TEMPERATURE

The measurement and control of the temperature in a heat treatment furnace is of extreme importance. There are a number of methods which can be used to measure the temperature.

Pyrometers
Modern heat treatment furnaces use pyrometers to measure the temperatures. Because the temperatures involved can be quite high, perhaps up to 1100°C, ordinary thermometers are of no use. Common methods in use include:

- **The thermo-electric or thermocouple pyrometer**
- **The optical pyrometer.**

Thermo-electric temperature measurement
If one end of a thin wire is heated, heat will flow from the hot end to the cool end. This movement of electrons will produce a very small voltage in the wire; a thermo-electric effect. The voltage depends on the material in the wire, and the temperature difference between the ends. If a couple of different types of wire of the same length are joined at each end, FIGURE 7, a useful output can be obtained for measuring temperature. This was first done in 1821, by T. J. Seebeck, a Russian scientist, who lived in Berlin, and is often called the *Seebeck effect.* Seebeck used a strip of copper and a strip of bismuth, and joined the ends to make a loop. He put a galvanometer into the bismuth strip. When he heated one end of the loop by holding it in his hand, the galvanometer showed that a current flowed. Georg Simon Ohm (of Ohm's law fame), the son of a Bavarian locksmith, used the Seebeck effect in many of his experiments.

The hot junction, or *measuring junction,* known as the thermocouple, is placed in the furnace, and the other junction, *the reference junction,* is kept at a set temperature, or reference temperature. The common reference temperature is 0°C. Output is measured across the the two wires (see FIGURE 7).

The current flowing in the circuit may be measured by a sensitive meter, or amplified and interfaced to a computer. Computer controlled furnaces are fast becoming the standard.

Optical pyrometer
This pyrometer compares the intensity of the light coming from the furnace with the light coming from the filament of a lamp. The current flowing in the lamp is varied, until the light matches the light coming from the furnace. A variable resistance, which is used to vary the current flowing in the lamp, is graduated in °C. The light from the lamp and the furnace match when the filament of the lamp disappears.

SUMMARY

Heat treatment is the combined controlled heating and controlled cooling of materials to produce property changes.
Soaking is the keeping of a component at a certain raised temperature for a specified length of time.
Recrystallisation occurs in some heat treatment processes, when a whole new set of grains replaces the old grains.
Full annealing is a process used to make a material as soft as possible.
Process annealing is a low-temperature process used for steels containing less than 0.25% carbon.
Normalising removes internal stresses set up in materials normally by cold working.
Hardening of steel may be achieved by heating it to a specific temperature and quenching it in water or oil.
Tempering of hardened steel removes some of the brittleness, hardness and strength.
Case hardening is the formation of a hardened skin or case on the surfaces of low carbon content steels.
Induction hardening is an electrical induction method of hardening the surfaces of items such as lathe beds.
Age hardening, which is also known as precipitation hardening, occurs in aluminium alloys with 4% copper. It can also occur in other material.
Pyrometer is a name given to an instrument which measures high temperatures, such as those in heat treatment furnaces.

Corrosion of Metals and Allied Technology

INTRODUCTION

Many of the objects used by us are made from mild steel. It is the most commonly used engineering material, but it has one major drawback, and that is that it rusts. Rust, which is the corrosion of carbon steels, occurs when these metals are exposed to the environment, unless special protection measures are taken. One hears of steel bridges which have to be painted continuously (i.e. when the painters have finished, they just start all over again) to keep the *rogue rust* at bay! Everyone is familiar with rust, because there are so many examples of it to be seen in everyday life. Steel gates, car bodies, sheet-steel roofs, are all examples of what we may see rusting. However, there are some cases of rusting which are not normally to be seen. Most domestic and industrial central heating systems suffer from rusting from within the system. We refer to this as a special case, later in the chapter. Corrosion of steel is common, but what about other metals? Other metals and alloys corrode also, and the amount of corrosion depends on certain factors, some of which are examined in this chapter.

OXIDATION

Metals have a chemical attraction for oxygen. When moisture is present, the metals can combine with oxygen in the atmosphere to form surface oxides. This is called oxidation. Copper, brass, aluminium and lead are common metals that oxidise fairly easily. It is interesting to note that silver does not oxidise easily, and has a high resistance to corrosion. Silver, however, combines with sulphur, which turns the metal yellow. Keeping silver shining means that the yellow coating, or *tarnish*, must be removed at regular intervals.

FIGURE 1 *This photograph clearly shows the result of the corrosion of steel. It is in fact, the corner of a steel trailer. Water lodging in the corner and crevices have accelerated the corrosion in this case. (Courtesy: the authors)*

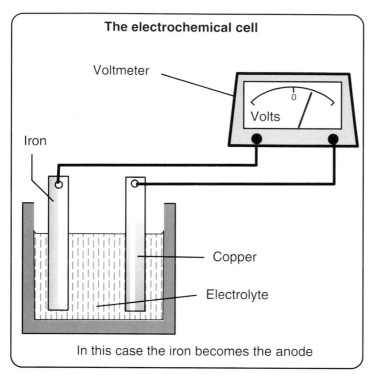

The electrochemical cell

Voltmeter

Volts

Iron

Copper

Electrolyte

In this case the iron becomes the anode

FIGURE 2   *The electrochemical cell.*

In the case of mild steel, the oxide formed is red and is known as rust. The process is speeded up if the atmosphere is polluted. When sulphur bearing fuels are burned, sulphur dioxide is formed and this contributes a lot to the corrosion of steel.

ELECTRO-CHEMICAL CORROSION

When two different metals (e.g. copper and zinc) are placed in a jar of electrolyte (e.g. dilute sulphuric acid, or salt water, or even in tap-water), an electric current is produced. This current, which is small, is caused by *electro-chemical action*. This type of corrosion is sometimes referred to as *wet corrosion*. See **FIGURE 2**.

This same electro-chemical action can cause corrosion if:

- **Two different metals are involved**
- **The metals are touching**
- **There is sufficient combined potential**
- **There is an electrolyte present.**

The simple cell is set up with the water acting as the electrolyte. One of the two metals will be *eaten away* or corroded. The further apart two metals are in the table, **FIGURE 3**, the greater will be the electric current between them in the presence of an electrolyte.

Consider steel and you will see that any of the metals above it in the table, will corrode, instead of the steel in the two different metal situation (see sacrificial protection).

WHICH METAL WILL CORRODE?

In the two different metals situation, the metal which will corrode depends on the potential difference between the two metals. The relative positions of the two metals in the electrochemical series, can be a fair guide to the expected corrosion. If the two metals in contact have a potential of 0.6 Volts, or over, the corrosion that takes place will be serious.

In the event that any two of the metals shown in **FIGURE 3**, *are in contact with an electrolyte present, the metal which is higher on the list is the one that will become the anode, and corrode.*

Electrochemical series	
Metal	Electrode potential (Volts)
Magnesium	- 2.38
Titanium	- 1.75
Aluminium	- 1.68
Zinc	- 0.76
Chromium	- 0.56
Steel (Iron)	- 0.44
Cadmium	- 0.40
Nickel	- 0.22
Tin	- 0.14
Lead	- 0.13
Copper	+ 0.34

If any two of the listed metals are in an electro-chemical cell, the metal nearest the top of the table becomes anodic and corrodes

FIGURE 3   *Electrochemical series.*

If the metals copper and zinc are considered, the electrode potential may be found using figures from **FIGURE 3**, as follows:

Copper (+ 0.34) V - zinc (− 0.76) V

= + 0.34 + 0.76

= **1. 1 Volts potential**

If these two metals touch in the presence of water, then the zinc corrodes away very quickly indeed. Metals at the top of the table are said to be more *reactive* than those below. Electrolytic action is responsible for most of the corrosion which takes place at ambient temperatures. The metal which goes into solution (corrodes) is said to be *anodic* towards the other metal, which becomes cathodic. For this reason, this kind of corrosion action may be known as *galvanic action*.

IMPORTANT CASES OF ELECTRO-CHEMICAL CORROSION

You should now know why it is not a good idea to have two different metals in contact with an electrolyte present. Moisture in the atmosphere or rain can both act as electrolytes.

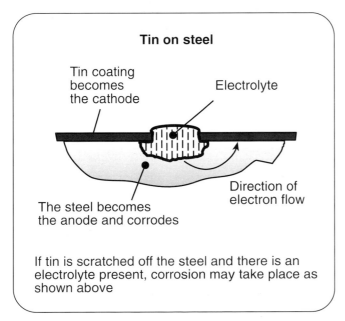

Tin on steel

Tin coating becomes the cathode

Electrolyte

Direction of electron flow

The steel becomes the anode and corrodes

If tin is scratched off the steel and there is an electrolyte present, corrosion may take place as shown above

FIGURE 4   *Tin on steel.*

Metal trims on cars

In the immediate past, bright strips of metal were added to the bodywork of cars to enhance their appearance, but they sometimes cause corrosion. Stainless steel is an example of a metal used for these 'decorative strips' or *trims*. Supposing the paint under a stainless steel trim chips off, then the trim will be in contact with the mild steel body of the car. To set up electrolytic action, all that is needed is a shower of rain, or some condensation. Then an electrolytic cell starts up, and the result is that the steel in the body of the car corrodes.

Tinplate

Tinplate is thin sheet steel covered with a coating of tin. It is widely used in the tinned food industry. The tin is only a mechanical protection for the steel because, if any of the tin coat is removed, and moisture is present, electrolytic action can start. Study of **FIGURE 3**, will show you that the steel in the tinplate case will actually corrode faster, if some of the tin is scraped off, than if the steel did not have a tin coating. It is not difficult to carry out a simple test to demonstrate this fact.

Copper and steel case

In many central heating installations, both domestic and commercial, the metals copper and steel are used in various combinations. Consider the case of a steel oil burner or steel back boiler, and copper pipes. It is also usual to use brass fittings. You will notice from **FIGURE 3**, that the copper and steel situation may result in the corrosion of the steel. Fortunately, these metals are used in the indirect part of heating systems. This means that the water in contact with the two metals is not changed, and so corrosion may not be excessive. It is normal practice to add rust inhibitor to help to reduce corrosion.

Sacrificial or cathodic protection

This is where one metal is *sacrificed* to save another from corrosion. One of the best examples of cathodic protection is the protection of propellers on wooden boats. Most propellers on trawlers are made from bronze. Sea water attacks and corrodes the bronze propellers, which are very expensive to replace.

So, a slab of zinc, aluminium, or magnesium, is screwed to the wooden hull near the propeller,

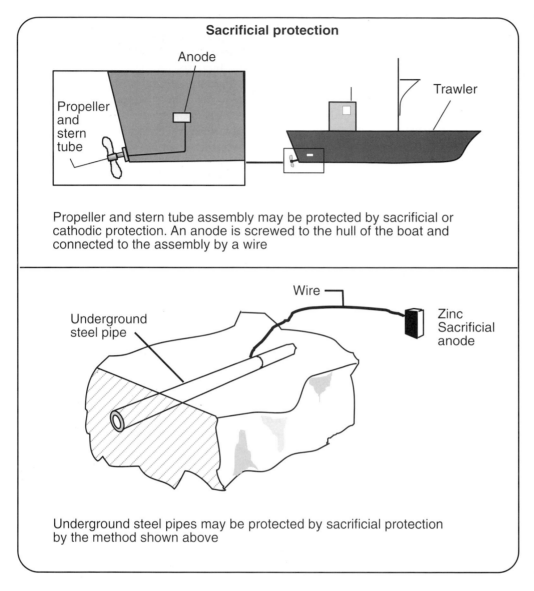

Sacrificial protection

Anode

Propeller and stern tube

Trawler

Propeller and stern tube assembly may be protected by sacrificial or cathodic protection. An anode is screwed to the hull of the boat and connected to the assembly by a wire

Wire

Underground steel pipe

Zinc Sacrificial anode

Underground steel pipes may be protected by sacrificial protection by the method shown above

FIGURE 5 *Sacrificial protection.*

making the anode in the electro-chemical action. Zinc anodes are most common. The propeller and stern tube assembly is made the *cathode* in this case of cathodic protection, and the zinc anode must be replaced on a regular basis.

Galvanised steel uses the zinc coating for mechanical protection, and the zinc also will provide sacrificial protection if some of the zinc is scraped away from the surface of the steel. See **FIGURE 5**

Stress corrosion
When a mild steel component is cold worked, as in pressing, or bending operations, the worked parts become internally stressed. These stressed parts may be where there is a channel at the edge of a sheetmetal component, such as the wing of a car. Because of internal microstructure changes, the stressed parts may have a different electro potential than the rest of the component. The effect of this is one area of the component becomes anodic to the rest of the metal, and if an electrolyte is present, the anodic part will corrode. This is known as a *stress cell*. Uneven cooling in hot, worked metal, can set up a similar situation. See **FIGURE 6**

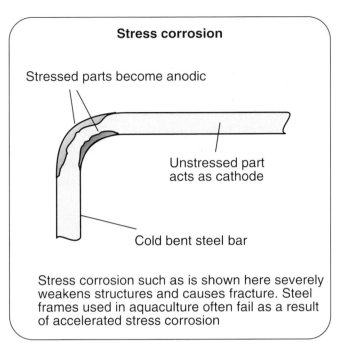

FIGURE 6 *Stress corrosion.*

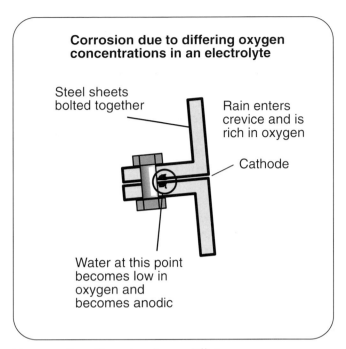

FIGURE 7 *Corrosion due to differing oxygen concentrations in an electrolyte.*

Electrolyte oxygen contents

Examples of what may happen when water as an electrolyte contains differing amounts of oxygen are shown in **FIGURE 7**. Crevice corrosion can take place on a sheet of painted mild steel, such as that used on a vehicle, where the paint has chipped. It may also take place between two sheets of metal. Water makes its way under the paint, or between the two metal sheets, and remains there for a long time. The amount of dissolved oxygen in the water at the point nearest to the open atmosphere, becomes greater than the amount of oxygen in the *hidden* water. The metal in contact with the water *low in oxygen* becomes the anode and corrodes. Crevice corrosion is often present under nuts and washers.

ENVIRONMENTAL CORROSION TESTS

Tests to find out how much metals and alloys will corrode when subjected to atmospheric corrosion, are carried out by specialised laboratories. The method of measuring the rate of corrosion is to expose *weighed samples* to the weather, for a certain length of time, remove the corrosion product, and measure the loss in weight. Cleaning methods vary according to the metal. Metals do not corrode evenly, and they may be pitted, or preferentially attacked at grain boundaries. It is usually advisable to make a metallographic section to check the evenness of the corrosion attack.

Exposing of corrosion test samples

The exposure racks usually face South (in the Northern hemisphere), and are inclined at between 30° to 45° to the horizontal. The specimens are mounted on insulators to avoid galvanic effects due to electrical contact with dissimilar metals, and the positioning has to be worked out so that one metal is not exposed to drips from a different metal that would affect the results. For instance, aluminium is kept well away from copper. There may be differences in rate of corrosion between the upper and lower surfaces of the specimens due to differences in wetting and drying. To overcome this problem, automatic controls that slide the specimens under cover when it begins to rain, are used. Specimens are also sprayed with distilled water. The idea of this is to distinguish between the effect of pollutants that arrive already dissolved in rain and those that are taken up from the air by wet or damp surfaces. Louvered boxes similar to those used to screen thermometers are also used to keep out direct rain while allowing dew, moist air, dust, etc., to have their effects.

The corrosion measurements usually give only an average rate over a fairly long time interval, because it is not very convenient to use large numbers of specimens to get short-term results. This makes it difficult to define the *time-dependence* of the rate of corrosion and answer the questions like *do rust scales protect steel as they grow?*

Corrosion and pollutants

Equations to predict rates of corrosion from measurements of atmospheric pollution and climate, so that the cost of corrosion can be compared with the cost of measures to reduce atmospheric pollution, are being developed. The total corrosion over a period of time depends on the sum of a series of isolated events, since there is very little corrosion when the metal is not wet. The equation for total corrosion must, therefore, contain parameters for pollutant contents and a term related to wetness which might be the number of times the specimen gets wet, the number of hours it spends wet, the average relative humidity, etc. The influence of the various factors may be understood by using *continuous monitoring.*

Continuous monitoring

Continuous monitors usually rely on the gain in weight when a metal is converted to hydrated oxide. Weighing is carried out by using electronic micro-balances. Another method used is to check the loss of cross-section in a wire or a thin foil, using electrical resistance. As the cross-section decreases, the electrical resistance, measured in Ohms, increases. Another method is to use a small galvanic cell made from alternate sheets of two metals (for instance, steel and copper) separated by thin sheets of insulator, set in a block of plastic and ground down on one face, to expose the metals. When the surface gets wet, the moisture film bridges across the insulator and sets up a galvanic current between the dissimilar metals. The current can be recorded in an external circuit, and used as an indicator of the rate of corrosion.

PROTECTION AGAINST CORROSION

Corrosion Resistance

Some metals are very resistant to corrosion. This is because they form strong oxides on their surfaces. If you cut or scrape a piece of lead with a knife, you will notice that the surface is very shiny. If you leave the scraped lead for some time, a dull grey oxide forms. This same oxide protects the lead from further oxidation. Aluminium, copper, and zinc are three other metals which have high resistance to corrosion in the same way that lead has.

Anodising of aluminium

This is an electrolytic process for increasing the thickness of the oxide film on aluminium. A hard, dense protective oxide film is produced. The thickness of the film can be controlled to suit the application of the aluminium being anodised. If the aluminium is to be exposed to the atmosphere, then a film of about 25 micrometres is used. An example of the use of anodising is to be seen on aluminium extrusions for making windows and doors. Sulphuric acid electrolytes will give films which are good enough for indoor uses. However, special organic acid electrolytes are necessary to produce harder films, which can incorporate dyes to give the films colour. You may have noticed aluminium window frames with a similar colour to mahogany.

Corrosion resistance of steel

When chromium is added to steel, an alloy called stainless steel is formed. The chromium, which may make up 18% of the alloy, forms a protective oxide on the surface of the steel.

Protective coatings

Protection against corrosion in the case of steel can be achieved by the application of a protective coating. This is an area where large sums of money are spent in the battle against corrosion. Coatings used can be divided into:

- **Paint and plastic coatings**
- **Metal coatings.**

Painting

Although paint coatings are widely used to protect steel they do not last very long and must be renewed. Many so-called rust stopping paints are on the market and some are very good but only for a limited time. The best preparations contain a lot of zinc, or aluminium, as metal flakes, and the protection may be partly sacrificial.

Plastic Coatings

These range from brush-on preparations to electrostatic spraying of plastic powder onto heated metal. Plastic coating may also be applied by hot dipping which is dipping the metal into a hot liquid bath of plastic or by dip coating in a fluidised bath. Some plastic coated steel is very well protected against corrosion, such as the cladding used to build factories. One of the most widely used plastic coatings is a nylon known as polyamide 11, which is made from castor oil. Electrostatic spraying is very useful for parts of a thin nature, such as supermarket shopping baskets. The process makes use of electrostatic charges to attract the spray to the items being coated.

Metal coatings

Metal coatings give the best protection to steel as they give excellent covering and are more durable than other finishes (e.g. paint).

Methods used to apply protective metal coatings include:

- **Hot dipping**
- **Powder cementation**
- **Metal spraying**
- **Metal cladding**
- **Electro-plating.**

Hot dipping

In the hot dipping process, the steel is dipped into a molten bath of the coating metal. The two most common coating metals are tin for tinplating, and zinc for hot-dip galvanising.

As already mentioned, the zinc gives both mechanical, and cathodic protection to the steel. When the steel is immersed in the bath of molten zinc, it is left there until its temperature reaches that of the molten zinc. Alloys of zinc and iron form the coating, which bonds well to the steel. Coatings of about $550 \ g/m^2$ give very good protection in normal circumstances, and may provide thirty years protection. It is interesting to note that the thin

coating of zinc would not last too long in a totally sacrificial situation. When cathodic action takes place, the zinc forms what is sometimes known as *white rust*, which gives added protection. The white rust is, in fact, made up of insoluble zinc salts and zinc oxide, which form a protective layer, and keeps air and moisture away from the metal. It is important however, to take the type of exposure environment into consideration. The more hostile the environment, the greater is the protection needed. A very general classification of environmental sites is listed:

- **Rural**
- **Urban**
- **Marine**
- **Industrial.**

Powder cementation

Normally zinc is used in this process. The steel to be coated is heated along with the powdered metal until the coating metal bonds to the steel. The process is called *sherardising* (named after Sherard Cowper-Cotes), and the steel is heated to about $370°C$, which is just below the melting point of zinc ($419°C$). The heating is done in closed drums, so usually only *small items* like nuts and bolts are sherardised. Sherardising produces a dull grey finish.

Metal spraying

Metal coatings can be applied by metal spraying, which consists of a method of melting the metal to be sprayed and blowing it onto a prepared surface. A pistol-like spray unit is used, which looks a bit like a paint spray gun. The metal used for the coating is fed into the back of the unit and is then melted inside the unit. Then, the molten metal is carried from the spray unit to the prepared surface by a jet of compressed air. Heat for melting the spray metal may be produced by an oxy-acetylene flame, or by an electric arc.

As well as having wide applications in protection against corrosion, metal spraying is extensively used to reclaim worn shafts. Zinc and aluminium may hot-sprayed onto steel to provide protection against corrosion.

Metal cladding

This is a method applied only to sheet or plate steel. A *sandwich* of the steel between two thin sheets of

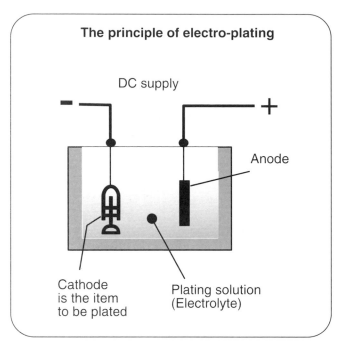

FIGURE 8   *Electro-plating.*

the cladding metal, is rolled in a rolling machine. During the rolling, the thickness of the steel and the cladding metal is reduced. Aluminium alloys, zinc, copper and lead are used as cladding metals.

Electro-plating

Electro-plating uses the chemical effect of electric current to deposit protective and/or decorative metal coatings on metal objects. The item to be *plated* is made the cathode as shown in **FIGURE 8**. Electrolytes containing salts of the plating metal must be used. In nickel plating, a solution of nickel sulphate can be the electrolyte.

Metals commonly electroplated include:

Cadmium – used on steel with a tin undercoat as a protection against corrosion. It is now mainly used where thin coatings will do.

Chromium – widely used for its decorative finish, chromium is usually plated over an undercoat of copper or nickel. The thickness of the coating is about 0.1-0.2 mm. Another use of chromium plating is to obtain a hard surface with good wear resistance.

Copper – copper plating is mainly used as an undercoat for nickel-chromium plating on steel.

Gold – gold plating is used extensively on jewellery where the coating is very thin (about 0.002 mm). It also has electronic applications, and is used in such applications as digital telephone exchange hardware. Coloured gold alloys can be plated in red, white and pink.

Lead – lead plating has good chemical resistance against sulphuric acid, etc.

Nickel – nickel plating is decorative in its own right and is used on small articles for this reason. However, the main use is as an undercoat for chromium, brass and gold. Many bath solutions are available which will give a variety of finishes from bright to black. Platinum – used for a long time to plate jewellery. Platinum has now been replaced by rhodium for this purpose. However, there is a number of electrical and protective applications.

Silver – the jewellery industry makes extensive use of silver plating. Some domestic articles are also silver plated. Because of its high electrical conductivity, silver is used to plate electrical contacts in some specialised applications.

Tin – because of its non-toxicity, tinplating on steel is used in the tinned food industry. It is also widely used in electronics because of its good solderability, (i.e. on component terminals).

Zinc – zinc is about the most common plated coating. It is plated extensively on ferrous metals as a protection against corrosion. Zinc plating has an advantage over hot dip galvanising and zinc spraying, because the coating thickness can be closely controlled. However, where thick coatings (1 mm and over) are required, hot dipping is cheaper.

CORROSION PREVENTION FACTORS

In order to cut corrosion to a minimum, it is important to take the following points into consideration:
Dissimilar metals can set up a cell situation (one metal will corrode faster)
Avoid crevices where water can be trapped to start crevice corrosion
Allow for drainage and ventilation in areas where water or moisture might collect
Metals of special composition resist corrosion, e.g. stainless steel
Provide adequate protective coating
Avoid contact with corrosive fluids, such as acids.

SUMMARY

Most of the corrosion of steel is by electro-chemical corrosion, or wet corrosion, as it is also known.

Sacrificial or cathodic protection is a very good method of protecting a metal from corrosion, by sacrificing an anode of another metal.

Stress corrosion can take place in steel as a result of working such as bending. The stressed parts normally have a different electro-potential to the unstressed parts.

In situations where there are different concentrations of oxygen present in water in contact with steel, crevice corrosion may take place.

Environmental corrosion tests are difficult to carry out accurately, and take a long time to complete.

Plastic coatings may be applied to steel by hot dipping and other methods, to provide protection against corrosion.

One of the most common methods of protecting steel from corrosion, is by painting.

Metal coatings may be applied to metals to increase resistance to corrosion.

Galvanising. Steel is dipped into a molten bath of zinc, and the steel is coated with zinc. The zinc coating gives excellent corrosion resistance to the steel.

Some metals have high resistance to corrosion because of the formation of oxides on their surfaces. Aluminium and lead are examples of metals with corrosion resistant oxides.

Protection against corrosion may also be achieved by electro-plating. This is the deposition of metal by electrolysis.

ENGINEERING TECHNOLOGY

5

The Centre Lathe

INTRODUCTION

The centre lathe, now more commonly known as a lathe, is a machine tool for producing cylindrical and conical shaped parts. It can also produce flat surfaces on the ends of a workpiece. The tool cuts away unwanted material from the workpiece in a precisely controlled way until the desired shape and size is achieved. Machining parts on the lathe is normally called turning. A cutting tool with a single cutting edge is usually used. **FIGURE 1** shows a standard centre lathe and examples of the work which can be done on it.

FIGURE 1 *A lathe and examples of turned parts. (Courtesy: T.S. Harrison & Sons Ltd.)*
Inset: *Parts made on the lathe. (Courtesy: Sandvik Coromant)*

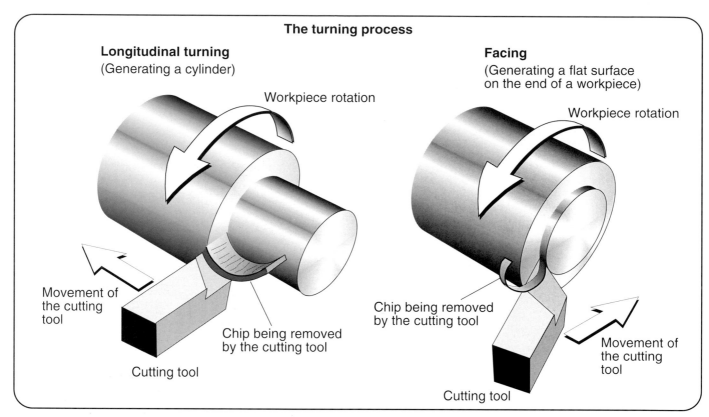

FIGURE 2 *The turning process.*

THE TURNING PROCESS

The principal movement on the lathe is the rotation of the work. The tool is fed along the work at a constant rate. The constant rotation of the work and the constant feed motion of the tool combine to *generate* a new surface on the workpiece. The two basic operations in the turning process are:

1 Turning – generating cylindrical shapes.
2 Facing – generating a flat surface on the end of the workpiece.

You can see these in **FIGURE 2**.

If you study **FIGURE 2** you can see how cylindrical surfaces are generated. The work rotates at a constant speed against the tool which itself is fed at constant feed rate parallel to the work axis. In facing, the tool is fed at right angles to the axis of the rotating work. Feeding the tool at any other

angle (other than parallel, or at right angles, to the work axis) will generate a tapered or conical shaped workpiece. See page 250 for more information on taper turning.

The forerunner of the lathe dates back to around 3500 BC. The first generation lathe was powered by a bow-type mechanism. The 'bow-lathe' did not run continuously in one direction – it rotated backwards and forwards.

It was not until the fourteenth century that a lathe capable of running in one direction was invented. These lathes were hand or foot operated. A French lathe constructed of wood in 1568 was the first screwcutting lathe. Probably the most important contribution to the development of the lathe was made by Henry Maudsley in 1800. He invented a screwcutting lathe which was an improvement on the French lathe.

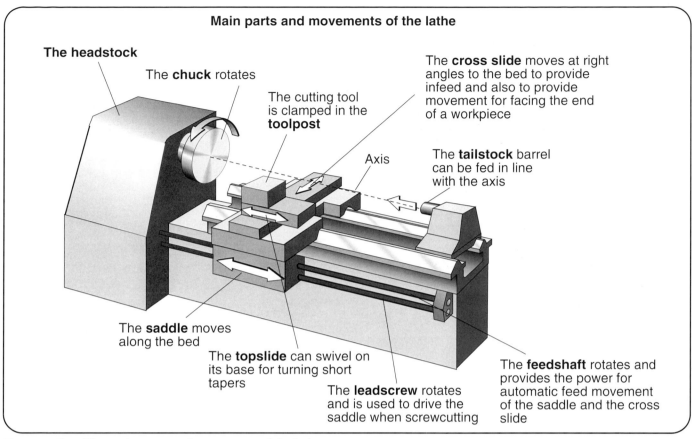

Main parts and movements of the lathe

The headstock

The **chuck** rotates

The cutting tool is clamped in the **toolpost**

The **cross slide** moves at right angles to the bed to provide infeed and also to provide movement for facing the end of a workpiece

Axis

The **tailstock** barrel can be fed in line with the axis

The **saddle** moves along the bed

The **topslide** can swivel on its base for turning short tapers

The **leadscrew** rotates and is used to drive the saddle when screwcutting

The **feedshaft** rotates and provides the power for automatic feed movement of the saddle and the cross slide

FIGURE 3   *The main parts and movements of the lathe.*

CONSTRUCTION OF THE LATHE

The lathe comprises a number of parts and important features. These are designed and arranged so that the lathe can generate and form many workpiece shapes. The main parts and their possible movements are shown in **FIGURE 3**

The bed
This is a very strong horizontal platform made from cast iron. The reasons it is made from cast iron include:

- **It can be cast as a ribbed hollow structure in a single piece. This makes it very rigid, strong and relatively light-weight**
- **Cast iron prevents vibrations building up during machining. This means it has good damping properties**

- **Cast iron is a good bearing material. This is desirable because there are many sliding parts.**

Precision slideways are machined on top of the bed. These slideways support the carriage and the tailstock and ensure that they are correctly *aligned* at all times. **FIGURE 4** gives details of the bed.

The headstock
The headstock is a hollow casting which supports the main spindle in high quality bearings. It is fixed to the left-hand end of the bed. It contains a set of gears which enable you to set the spindle rotating at any one of a number of speeds. Different speeds are necessary so that workpieces can be rotated at speeds which are correct for the material and the diameter. (This will be discussed in greater detail under cutting data on page 252) **FIGURE 5** shows external features of the lathe headstock.

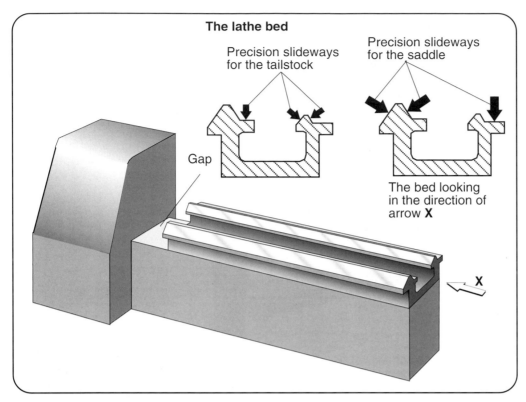

The lathe bed

Precision slideways
for the tailstock

Precision slideways
for the saddle

Gap

The bed looking
in the direction of
arrow **X**

X

FIGURE 4   *The lathe bed.*

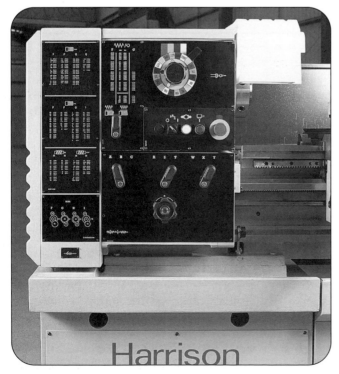

Harrison

FIGURE 5   *The headstock of a lathe.*
(Courtesy: T.S. Harrison & Sons Ltd.)

The headstock has a second gearbox, the feed gearbox, which drives the leadscrew and the feedshaft.

The spindle
The purpose of the spindle is to carry the chuck and other workholding equipment. It is rotated by the motor at the desired speed (depending on the material being machined). The spindle is hollow so that long work can be passed through it. Its axis is parallel to the bed. The *nose* of the spindle has two important features:

- **The bore is specially machined to take a centre (this centre is known as a *live centre*).**
- **The outside is machined to take a chuck or other workholding device.**

The feed gearbox
The feed gearbox is situated at the base of the headstock.

The feedshaft and the leadscrew protrude from the

FIGURE 6 *The end gear train.*
(Courtesy: 1600 Group)

gearbox and extend across the front of the bed. The feed shaft provides the power to the apron for the automatic carriage feed and for the automatic cross slide feed. The leadscrew is used to move the carriage when screw threads are being cut on the workpiece. Screwcutting is treated in detail on page 259.

This gearbox provides a wide range of speeds for both the feedshaft and the leadscrew. The input to the gearbox is from the spindle via the end gear train which you can see in **FIGURE 6**. While the gearbox itself has a large range of speeds, you can sometimes further increase the range by changing the sizes of the gears on the end gear train.

The feedshaft and the leadscrew normally rotate simultaneously. Because the leadscrew is not used as much as the feedshaft, the leadscrew is often fitted with a *dog-clutch*. By disengaging this dog-clutch you will stop the leadscrew rotating with the feedshaft. This prevents unnecessary wear of the leadscrew bearings.

The direction of rotation of the feedshaft and the leadscrew can be changed by operating a special reversing lever on the headstock.

The tailstock

The tailstock, shown in **FIGURE 7**, stands on the bed opposite the headstock. It can be clamped to the bed at any point. The body is made from cast iron. The *barrel* is a very accurately made cylindrical part which slides in the body when you turn the handwheel. The barrel can be locked in any position.

The tailstock is used to hold cutting tools such as drills and reamers. A centre can be fitted into the barrel and used to support long workpieces. The centre of the barrel is on the axis of the lathe. You can, however, move the tailstock from side to side on its base. This feature is used for taper turning.

The carriage

The main purpose of the carriage is to hold and completely control the movement of the cutting tool. The carriage can be moved manually by rotating the handwheel, or by using the power feed. It is made up of a number of components. The important parts of the carriage are shown in **FIGURE 8**.

These are:

The *saddle* is the horizontal portion which spans the bed. Precision slideways are machined on its underside to match the slideways on the bed.

The *apron* is suspended from the saddle in front of the bed. It is in reality a gearbox containing all of the gears and controls necessary to move the carriage along the bed.

The *cross slide* will move the tool at right angles to the axis. It is located on top of the saddle. Its movement is controlled by a leadscrew. The cross slide can be operated manually by rotating the handwheel or it can be operated automatically by a power feed.

The *compound slide*, sometimes called the *topslide*, allows you to move the cutting tool at any angle to the lathe axis. It has a swivel base and it is located on the cross slide. Its movement is controlled by a

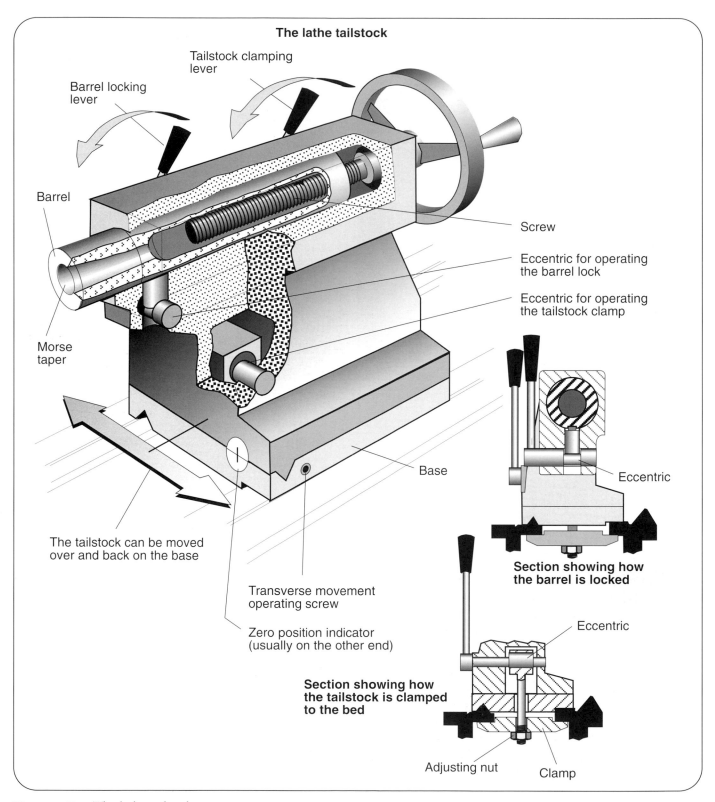

The lathe tailstock

Tailstock clamping lever

Barrel locking lever

Barrel

Morse taper

The tailstock can be moved over and back on the base

Transverse movement operating screw

Zero position indicator (usually on the other end)

Screw

Eccentric for operating the barrel lock

Eccentric for operating the tailstock clamp

Base

Eccentric

Section showing how the barrel is locked

Eccentric

Section showing how the tailstock is clamped to the bed

Adjusting nut

Clamp

FIGURE 7 *The lathe tailstock.*

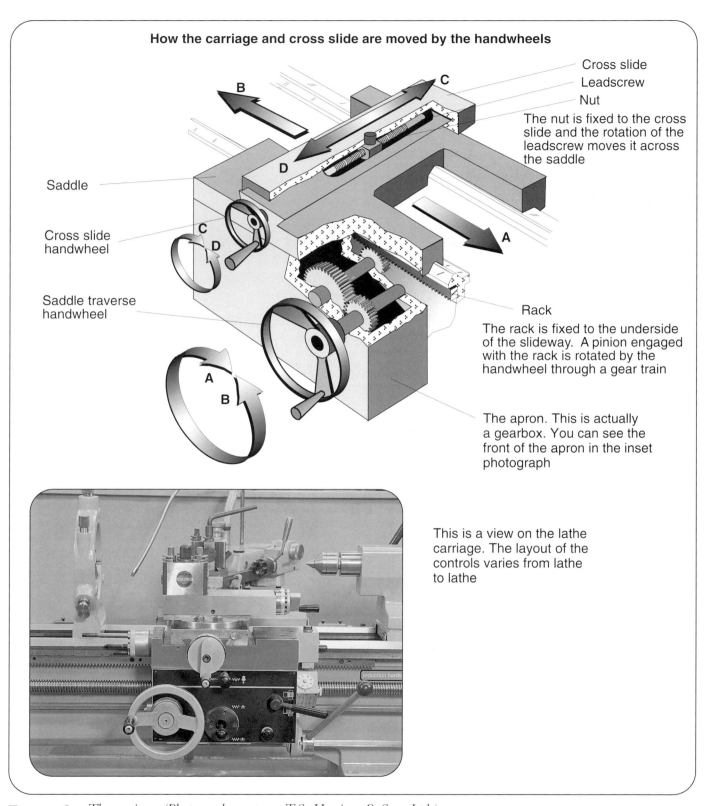

How the carriage and cross slide are moved by the handwheels

Cross slide

Leadscrew

Nut

The nut is fixed to the cross slide and the rotation of the leadscrew moves it across the saddle

Saddle

Cross slide handwheel

Saddle traverse handwheel

Rack

The rack is fixed to the underside of the slideway. A pinion engaged with the rack is rotated by the handwheel through a gear train

The apron. This is actually a gearbox. You can see the front of the apron in the inset photograph

This is a view on the lathe carriage. The layout of the controls varies from lathe to lathe

FIGURE 8   *The carriage. (Photograph courtesy: T.S. Harrison & Sons Ltd.)*

FIGURE 9   *Two types of lathe toolpost. On the left is shown a four-way toolpost and on the right is shown a quick-change type. (Courtesy: T.S. Harrison & Sons, Ltd)*

leadscrew similar to the cross slide. It can be operated by hand only – it does not have a power feed facility.

The *toolpost* is fitted on the topslide. Its purpose is to hold the cutting tool during machining. Some of the more common toolposts in use are shown in **FIGURE 9**.

On the left you can see the four-way toolpost. It is useful if you require a number of different tools to complete a workpiece. You can set up four tools and bring each into use in turn by unlocking and rotating the toolpost. When the tool is in the correct position you re-lock the toolpost.

The quick-change toolpost shown on the right is even faster to operate. You clamp the tool into a special tool holder. This part is then secured to the toolpost by operating a cam. You can set up as many tool holders as you like. Changing the tool holder is simple and very fast. This type of toolpost is frequently used in industry.

ALIGNMENTS AND MOVEMENTS

Machine tools are constructed in such a way that certain parts are always in line with each other, and even when some of the parts move, they remain in line. This is called the *alignment* of the parts.

The bed is parallel to the axis in the horizontal plane and also in the vertical plane. If you move the carriage along the bed, therefore, the distance between any point on the carriage and the axis will not change.

The centre of the tailstock barrel normally coincides with the lathe axis but even when the tailstock is offset (moved to one side on its base) its barrel remains parallel to the axis.

TURNING OPERATIONS

Some of the more common turning operations are illustrated in **FIGURE 10**. These include:

1 Parallel turning (external turning).
2 Facing.
3 Form turning.
4 Drilling/Reaming.
5 Parting-off/Grooving.
6 Boring (internal turning).
7 Taper turning.
8 Knurling.

Screwcutting is another very important turning operation. You will find screwcutting on page 259.

1 Parallel turning
This is the most common turning operation. The

Turning

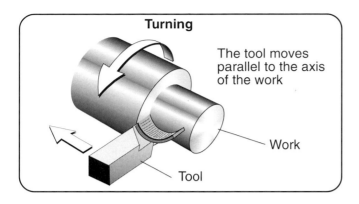

The tool moves parallel to the axis of the work

Work

Tool

Parting-off

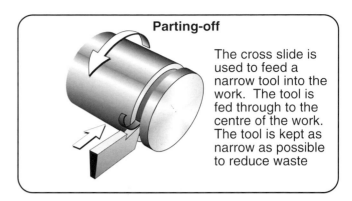

The cross slide is used to feed a narrow tool into the work. The tool is fed through to the centre of the work. The tool is kept as narrow as possible to reduce waste

Facing

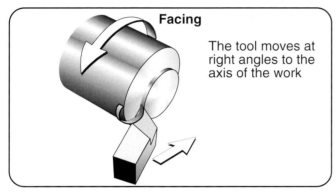

The tool moves at right angles to the axis of the work

Boring

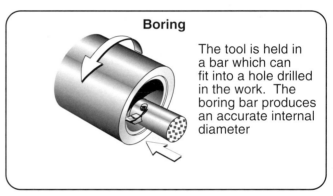

The tool is held in a bar which can fit into a hole drilled in the work. The boring bar produces an accurate internal diameter

Form turning

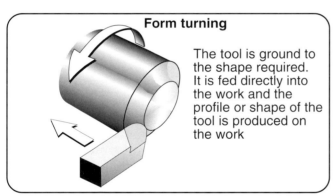

The tool is ground to the shape required. It is fed directly into the work and the profile or shape of the tool is produced on the work

Taper turning

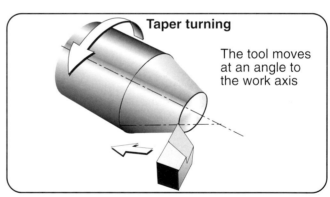

The tool moves at an angle to the work axis

Drilling/reaming

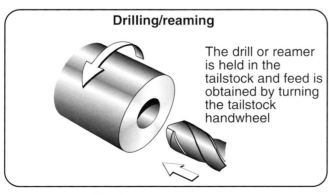

The drill or reamer is held in the tailstock and feed is obtained by turning the tailstock handwheel

Knurling

The wheels of the knurling tool are pressed into the work by the cross slide. The teeth on the wheels form the knurl

Knurl

Knurling tool

FIGURE 10   *Turning operations.*

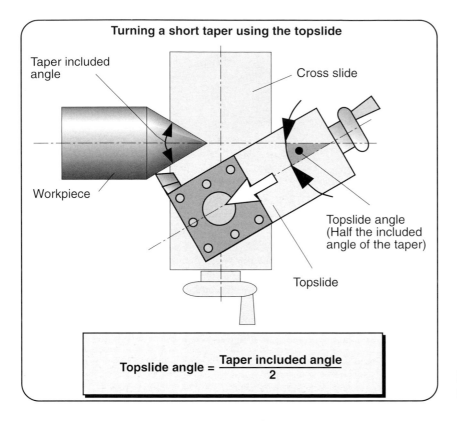

Turning a short taper using the topslide

Taper included angle

Cross slide

Workpiece

Topslide angle
(Half the included angle of the taper)

Topslide

$$\text{Topslide angle} = \frac{\text{Taper included angle}}{2}$$

FIGURE 11 *Turning a short taper using the topslide.*

tool moves parallel to the workpiece axis, removing a chip and producing a smaller diameter.

2 Facing
Facing generates a flat surface on the end of the workpiece perpendicular to its axis.

3 Form turning
In form turning, a tool which is the same shape as the form you require on the work is used. The tool is ground to the shape required. It is then fed directly into the work and the surface produced is a reflection of the tool shape.

4 Drilling/Reaming
The two operations can be performed by fitting the drill or reamer in the tailstock barrel. You then feed the drill into the work by rotating the tailstock handwheel.

5 Parting-off
This is an operation in which a bar is cut off by a parting-off tool. This tool is fed into the work by the cross slide movement.

Grooving is similar to parting-off but the workpiece is not cut through.

6 Boring
Boring is a very accurate method of machining internal diameters. The hole can be finished to any size you require and it will be concentric with the outside diameter. The tool is fitted in a boring bar which in turn is clamped in the tool post. Boring bars required for deep holes can be very "springy" because they are long. This can lead to vibration and bad finish on the machined surface. Light cuts are often the only way to solve this problem. "Tuned" boring bars have been developed to overcome vibrations and chatter. They are often used in industry.

7 Taper turning
Taper turning is a result of turning with the basic alignments of the lathe altered. For turning short tapers the topslide can be swivelled on its base and its axis set at some angle to the lathe axis. You can see this in **FIGURE 11**. The length of the taper produced by operating the top slide is normally confined to less than the full travel of the slide.

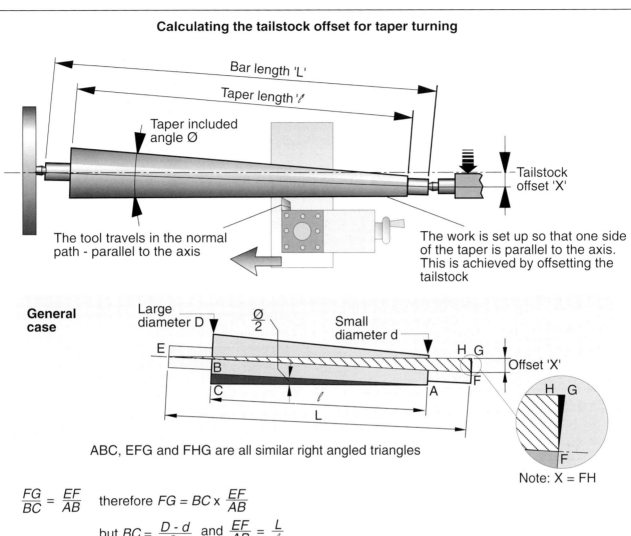

Calculating the tailstock offset for taper turning

Bar length 'L'

Taper length 'ℓ'

Taper included angle Ø

Tailstock offset 'X'

The tool travels in the normal path - parallel to the axis

The work is set up so that one side of the taper is parallel to the axis. This is achieved by offsetting the tailstock

General case

Large diameter D

$\dfrac{\varnothing}{2}$

Small diameter d

Offset 'X'

Note: X = FH

ABC, EFG and FHG are all similar right angled triangles

$$\frac{FG}{BC} = \frac{EF}{AB} \quad \text{therefore } FG = BC \times \frac{EF}{AB}$$

$$\text{but } BC = \frac{D-d}{2} \quad \text{and} \quad \frac{EF}{AB} = \frac{L}{\ell}$$

$$FG = \frac{D-d}{2} \times \frac{L}{\ell} \quad \text{But } X = FH = FG \cos \frac{\varnothing}{2}$$

$$\text{Tailstock offset 'X'} = \left(\frac{D-d}{2} \times \frac{L}{\ell} \right) \cos \frac{\varnothing}{2}$$

where D = the large diameter of the taper
d = the small diameter of the taper
L = the overall length of the bar
ℓ = the length of the tapered section
$\varnothing$ = the included angle of the taper

FIGURE 12 *Calculating the tailstock offset for taper turning.*

Longer tapers would require repositioning of the tool on the taper. This can be inaccurate and unsatisfactory.

Long tapers can be turned by supporting the work on centres and off-setting the tailstock. Off-setting entails shifting the tailstock axis, by a calculated amount, off the lathe axis. The work axis will then be at the desired angle to turn the taper required. The method of calculating the amount by which the tailstock should be offset is shown in **FIGURE 12**. Another example is given in **FIGURE 13**. Here the entire workpiece is tapered. (Special procedures would be required to turn this type of workpiece.)

Another method of turning long tapers is by using the taper turning attachment, see **FIGURE 14**. This device causes the cross slide to move at the same time as the carriage is moving along the bed. The combined movement of the two slides causes the cutting tool to move at an angle to the lathe axis producing a tapered workpiece.

8 Knurling

This usually consists of deforming the surface of the workpiece to produce a rough surface in order to improve the grip on it. A knurling tool has two wheels, each with teeth cut at an angle to the axis. A high force is exerted by the knurling wheels on the workpiece. The teeth form the knurl on the surface of the work. The result is typically a diamond shaped pattern. Long workpieces must be well supported on the tailstock centre.

CUTTING DATA

It is very important that the work rotates at the correct speed. The speed is determined from a recommended cutting speed for the tool, the workpiece material and also its diameter. The cutting speed, spindle speed, feedrate and depth of cut are known collectively as the cutting data.

- **Cutting speed (Surface speed)**
- **Spindle speed (the speed at which the work rotates)**
- **Cutting depth**
- **Feed rate.**

Cutting speed

This is the 'distance' the rotating surface of the workpiece travels in one minute. Here it is given the symbol **S**. It represents the 'length of surface' of the workpiece passing over the cutting edge each minute as the work rotates. A workpiece often consists of several different diameters. If the workpiece rotates at constant spindle speed the surface speed of the work will vary with the diameters.

The surface speed should be kept constant, even when the diameter is reducing, and this will mean increasing the speed of the spindle. **FIGURE 15** shows the effect of reducing diameter on the spindle speed as the surface or cutting speed is kept constant. Cutting speed is expressed in metres per minute (S m/min).

Spindle speed

This is the number of revolutions through which the workpiece rotates per minute. Here it is given the symbol **N**.

The lathe has a range of fixed spindle speeds to suit different workpiece diameters and different workpiece materials. It is expressed in revolutions per minute (N rev/min).

The work speed, which is also the spindle speed, can be calculated from the recommended cutting speed for the material and the diameter being turned. **TABLE 1** gives a selection of workpiece materials and the recommended cutting speeds and tool angles for high speed steel.

The cutting speed is very important in turning. It affects

- **The metal removal rate**
- **The working life of the tool**
- **The power consumed.**

The problem of having to change speeds at certain intervals as the diameter reduces to keep the surface speed of the work constant has been solved by computer numerical control (CNC) lathes. On these machines the spindle speed is infinitely variable. When the lathe is programmed for constant cutting speed, the speed of the spindle increases

To turn a taper using the tailstock offset method

Example 1 Calculate the tailstock offset required to turn a tapered bar if its overall length is 380 mm, its large diameter is 50 mm and its small diameter is 42 mm

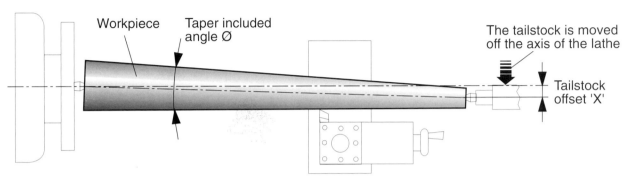

Solution

$$\text{Tailstock offset 'X'} = \left(\frac{D-d}{2} \times \frac{L}{\ell} \right) \text{Cos} \frac{\emptyset}{2}$$

where D = the large diameter of the taper
d = the small diameter of the taper
L = the overall length of the bar
ℓ = the length of the tapered section
$\emptyset$ = the included angle of the taper

therefore $X = \dfrac{D-d}{2} \times \text{Cos} \dfrac{\emptyset}{2}$ $\left(\dfrac{L}{\ell} = 1 \right)$

$X = \dfrac{50 - 42}{2} \times \text{Cos} \dfrac{\emptyset}{2}$

$X = 4 \times \text{Cos} \dfrac{\emptyset}{2}$

To find $\dfrac{\emptyset}{2}$ $\text{Tan} \dfrac{\emptyset}{2} = \dfrac{\frac{D-d}{2}}{\ell} = \dfrac{4}{380}$

$\dfrac{\emptyset}{2} = 0° \, 36'$

$X = 4 \times \text{Cos} \, 0° \, 36'$

X = 3.999 mm

This is the tailstock offset. Notice how little the offset is affected by the Cos of the angle of the taper. Because it is so small you will sometimes find that this element is not used in the formula

Example 2 Calculate the tailstock offset required to turn a taper on a bar if the overall length of the bar is 280 mm, the length of its tapered portion is 200 mm, the large diameter of the taper is 40 mm and its small diameter is 30 mm

FIGURE 13   *To turn a taper using the tailstock offset method.*

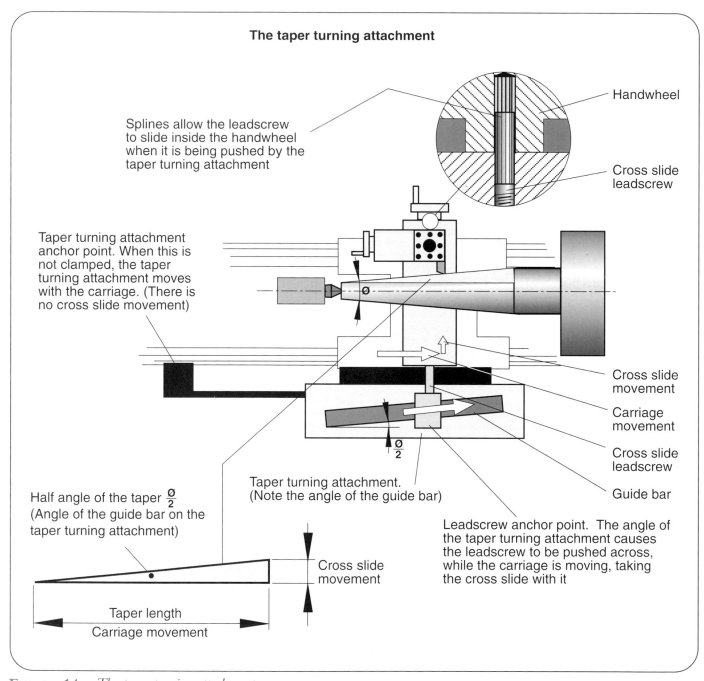

The taper turning attachment

Splines allow the leadscrew to slide inside the handwheel when it is being pushed by the taper turning attachment

Handwheel

Cross slide leadscrew

Taper turning attachment anchor point. When this is not clamped, the taper turning attachment moves with the carriage. (There is no cross slide movement)

Cross slide movement

Carriage movement

Cross slide leadscrew

Guide bar

Half angle of the taper $\frac{\emptyset}{2}$ (Angle of the guide bar on the taper turning attachment)

Taper turning attachment. (Note the angle of the guide bar)

Leadscrew anchor point. The angle of the taper turning attachment causes the leadscrew to be pushed across, while the carriage is moving, taking the cross slide with it

Cross slide movement

Taper length
Carriage movement

FIGURE 14   *The taper turning attachment.*

automatically each time the tool moves towards the axis to machine smaller diameters.

The constant surface speed (CSS) lathe is similar to the standard lathe in appearance. The main difference is that, like the CNC lathe, it also has an infinitely variable spindle speed feature. It allows exactly the right speed for every diameter. The spindle speed is automatically increased as the cross slide moves in and decreased as it moves out. This

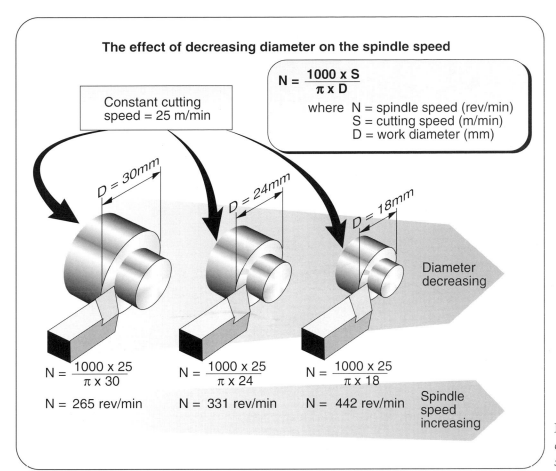

The effect of decreasing diameter on the spindle speed

Constant cutting speed = 25 m/min

$$N = \frac{1000 \times S}{\pi \times D}$$

where N = spindle speed (rev/min)
S = cutting speed (m/min)
D = work diameter (mm)

D = 30mm

D = 24mm

D = 18mm

Diameter decreasing

$$N = \frac{1000 \times 25}{\pi \times 30}$$

$$N = \frac{1000 \times 25}{\pi \times 24}$$

$$N = \frac{1000 \times 25}{\pi \times 18}$$

N = 265 rev/min   N = 331 rev/min   N = 442 rev/min

Spindle speed increasing

FIGURE 15 *The effect of reducing diameter on spindle speed.*

Cutting speeds and tool angles for turning with high speed steel			
Material	**Cutting speed** (m/min)	**Side rake angle** (degrees)	**Clearance angle** (degrees)
High carbon steel	10-15	5-10	6
Low carbon steel	25-30	15-18	6
Grey cast iron	22-30	3-6	6
Free-cutting steel	25-40	15-20	6
Bronze (low tensile)	30-60	8-12	6
Copper	50-90	20-30	6
Brass (soft)	50-120	3-6	6
Aluminium	60-150	20-30	6-10

TABLE 1 *Cutting speeds.*

FIGURE 16 *Constant surface speed lathe. (Courtesy: T.S. Harrison & Sons, Ltd)*

lathe maintains ideal cutting conditions irrespective of diameter change. **FIGURE 16** shows a CSS lathe.

Cutting depth

This is the depth to which the tool is engaged in the workpiece. It is normally the radial distance between the uncut surface and the new surface of the workpiece. Here it is given the symbol **d**. The depth of cut usually depends on:

• **The type of machining operation – roughing cuts which may be deep or finishing cuts which are usually light**

Example

Calculate the spindle speed of the lathe if the recommended cutting speed for the workpiece material is 30 m/min and the diameter is 25 mm

Solution

$$N = \frac{1000 \times S}{\pi \times D}$$

where N is the spindle speed (rev/min)
S is the cutting speed (m/min)
D is the work diameter (mm)

$$N = \frac{1000 \times 30}{\pi \times 25}$$

N = 381.97 rev/min

Select the closest available speed on the lathe

Say **380 rev/min**

CALCULATION 1 *Cutting speeds.*

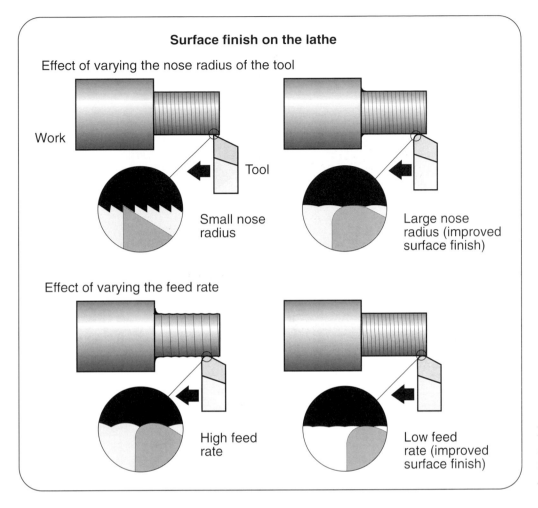

Surface finish on the lathe

Effect of varying the nose radius of the tool

Work

Tool

Small nose radius

Large nose radius (improved surface finish)

Effect of varying the feed rate

High feed rate

Low feed rate (improved surface finish)

FIGURE 17 *The effect of the nose radius of the tool, and varying the feed rate on the surface finish.*

- **The type of cutting tool – the tool material and its geometric shape**
- **The condition of the machine – you may have to take light cuts on worn machines**
- **The power of the electric motor driving the lathe. Deep cuts require more power from the motor than light cuts.**

Feed rate

This is the distance the tool moves during each revolution of the workpiece. Here it is given the symbol **f**. The thickness of the chip depends on the feed rate. It is expressed in millimetres per revolution (f mm/rev).

The smaller feed rate gives you a smoother surface – better surface finish. You can see this in **FIGURE 17**.

THE LATHE CUTTING TOOL

As with any machining operation, very careful attention must be given to the cutting tool. High speed steel tools must be carefully ground to the required angles. The tool must be set correctly in the tool holder.

Preparing the tool

A lathe tool is usually ground from a solid square section bar of high speed steel. This material has special properties which help it to remain very hard even when it reaches high temperatures during machining. High speed steel is discussed in detail in Cutting Tool Materials, page 333.

After grinding, the cutting edge will be in the form of minute peaks and valleys left by the abrasive on the

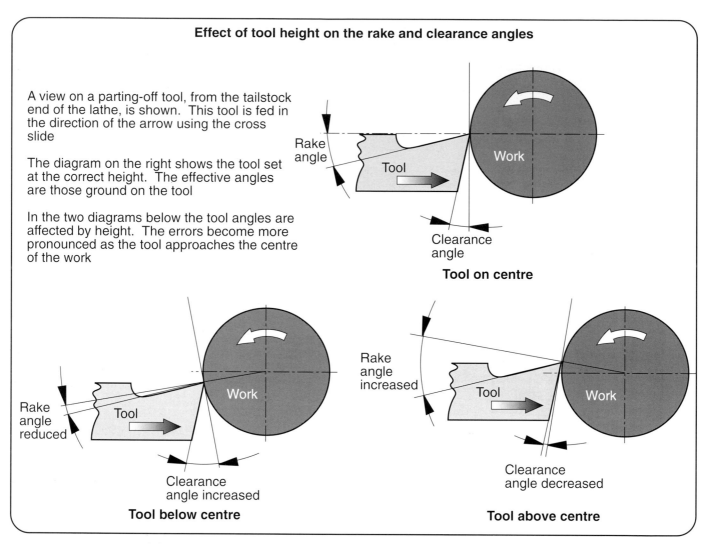

FIGURE 18 *Setting of the cutting tool.*

face of the grinding wheel. If you use the tool in this condition the peaks will wear down very quickly and this will lead to bad surface finish on the workpiece.

This problem is solved by honing the cutting edge. Honing is basically a type of very fine grinding or polishing on an oil stone. A well honed tool has the advantage that the entire length of the cutting edge can contact the workpiece. This has the effect of distributing the wearing tendency over all the cutting edge and so the tool will last longer. The time you take to hone the tool will be well worth while in terms of the extra time the tool will last in use.

Setting the tool

Correct setting of the tool is essential if it is to cut properly. There are two aspects of setting which are very important:

- **The point of the tool should be at the same height as the work axis**
- **The tool holder should be very rigid.**

When a tool is set correctly, the point touches the workpiece at the same height as the lathe axis. The top rake angle is formed between a line drawn from the axis through the tip of the tool, and the rake face of the tool, see **FIGURE 18**. The front clearance angle is formed between the tangent to the work-piece at the tool point and the end face of the tool.

When the tool is set too high the effective rake angle increases and the effective clearance angle decreases. There is the likelihood that the cutting tool will rub the workpiece below the cutting edge thereby preventing the cutting edge from contacting the work. When the tool is set too low the effective rake angle decreases and the effective clearance angle increases.

Often, the only method by which you can alter the height of a lathe tool is to insert packing strips underneath the tool holder. You will need a variety of thicknesses so that by using different combinations you can obtain a good range of heights. The packing pieces you use should extend across the entire width of the toolpost but not beyond.

The distance between the point of the tool and the toolpost must be kept to a minimum. The more you increase this overhang the greater is the likelihood that the tool will deflect when you are taking a cut off the workpiece. Deflection may turn to a continuous up and down springing motion, giving rise to the problem of chatter. Indications of chatter are:

- **A high pitched whine (sound) coming from the tool**
- **A regular pattern of tiny marks on the surface of the workpiece.**

SCREWCUTTING IN THE LATHE

Screwcutting in the lathe is a special process which combines parallel turning and form turning.

- **The screw or *helix* is generated by the rotation of the work and the feed movement of the tool**
- **The thread profile is formed by the shape of the tool.**

A helix can be defined as the path traced by a point moving around a cylinder at a constant rate, while at the same time moving along the cylinder at a constant rate.

To cut a screw thread accurately you have to set the lathe so that there is a definite relationship between the rotation of the workpiece and the movement of the carriage. This relationship is that for each revolution of the workpiece, the tool (carriage) moves a distance of 1 pitch or lead of the thread. See **FIGURE 19**.

The carriage is moved by the leadscrew and the leadscrew is rotated by the spindle. It is possible to change the speed of the leadscrew relative to the spindle speed by repositioning the levers on the feed gearbox. This gearbox has a range of pitches and by moving the levers you can set the leadscrew rotating to give you the correct pitch. The chart indicates the position of the levers for any desired pitch.

The longitudinal movement of the carriage is engaged by closing a *half nut* on the leadscrew. The half nut is housed behind the apron and it is operated by a special lever on the front. For most screwcutting you need to engage the half nut at some definite point on the leadscrew so that the tool will re-enter the thread on the workpiece. A special indicator dial called a chasing dial is fitted to the apron. This dial, shown in **FIGURE 20**, is driven by a gearwheel which is in constant mesh with the leadscrew.

When the leadscrew is rotating and the carriage is parked on the bed, the dial will be rotated by the leadscrew. When a specified line on the dial reaches the zero mark you can engage the half nut. The carriage then moves and the dial will remain stationary until the half nut is disengaged and the carriage stops.

There is a number of possible "points of engagement" specified for every screw thread pitch that can be cut on the lathe. There is also a complete set of chasing dial gears to cover this range of pitches. For any desired thread pitch to be cut, the correct gear must be used to drive the dial and the points of engagement on the dial must be specified. If either is ignored the tool may not re-enter the thread properly and may cause it to be destroyed. A chart on the dial gives information about the correct gear to use and the possible points of engagement for the thread. The basic profile of the ISO metric screw thread is shown in **FIGURE 21**.

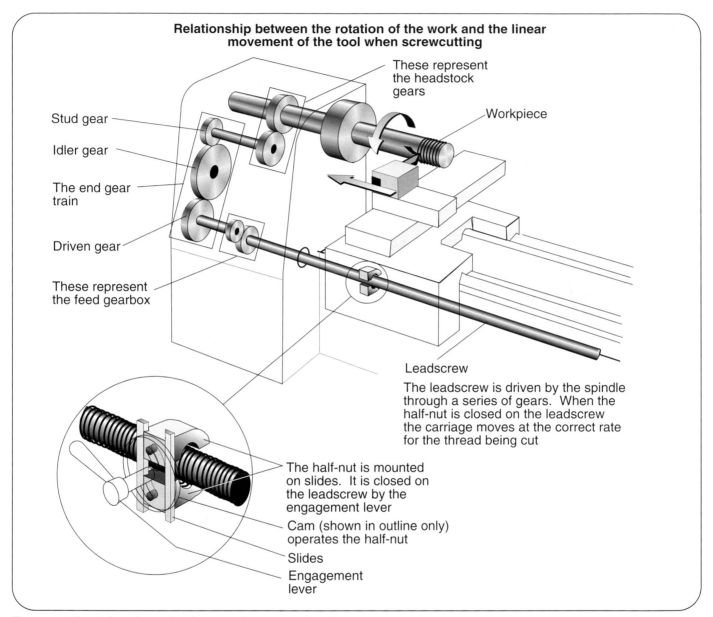

Relationship between the rotation of the work and the linear movement of the tool when screwcutting

These represent the headstock gears

Workpiece

Stud gear

Idler gear

The end gear train

Driven gear

These represent the feed gearbox

Leadscrew

The leadscrew is driven by the spindle through a series of gears. When the half-nut is closed on the leadscrew the carriage moves at the correct rate for the thread being cut

The half-nut is mounted on slides. It is closed on the leadscrew by the engagement lever

Cam (shown in outline only) operates the half-nut

Slides

Engagement lever

FIGURE 19   *The relationship between the work and tool.*

Left-hand threads

When the leadscrew is made to rotate in the opposite direction to that required for right-hand threads, a left-hand thread can be cut. Remember the work must rotate in the same direction. By operating the reversing lever for the feed gear box, the leadscrew will change direction and the carriage will travel towards the tailstock when the half-nut is engaged.

Multistart threads

These threads have more than one helix. They are used where fast movement of a nut along a screw is required. It is important to remember the difference between a single start thread and a multistart thread.

- **In a single start thread the lead and the pitch are the same**

FIGURE 20 *The chasing dial.*
(Courtesy: T.S. Harrison & Sons Ltd.)

- **In a two start thread the lead = pitch x 2**
- **In a three start thread the lead = pitch x 3 and so on.**

Therefore lead = pitch x number of starts.

There is a difference between cutting a multistart thread and cutting a single start thread on the lathe. This difference is in setting up the lathe. The lead is used to set the correct carriage movement (this is the pitch x number of starts) and the relative position of the tool and work must be altered so the starts must be equally spaced.

To cut a four start 2 mm pitch thread, for example, the leadscrew is set as if to cut an 8 mm pitch thread. Four separate threads (starts) are then cut beside each other, the tool position having to be changed for each start.

The first start is cut, its depth calculated on the basis of a 2 mm pitch thread. When the first start is complete the tool is moved 2 mm parallel to the axis of the lathe and the second start is cut. When this is

complete the tool is moved again and the third start is cut. The final movement of 2 mm will position the tool to cut the fourth start.

Grinding and setting the tool

The screwcutting tool is ground to the same form as the thread. The form is checked on a screwcutting gauge. It should have the same cutting geometry as a plain turning tool in addition to its thread form.

The tool is set in the correct position by seating it in the screwcutting gauge which in turn is resting against the work. See **FIGURE 22**.

Cutting threads in the lathe

The tool is normally fed into the work in such a way that the chip is removed off one flank of the thread only.

This can be achieved by setting the topslide to half the included angle of the thread. You then in-feed the tool using the topslide only. The accuracy of the thread can be improved by using a pre-shaped screwcutting tool. These tools are normally made of tungsten carbide and there is a separate tool for each pitch.

POWER DISTRIBUTION IN THE LATHE

An important consideration in any metal cutting operation is the power which is required to cut the material. The rotation of the electric motor driving the lathe is transmitted to the spindle through a gearbox. During machining, the power is used in:

- **Cutting the metal (removing the chip)**
- **Friction in the bearings**
- **Friction between the gear teeth**
- **Friction between the bed and the carriage**
- **Heat losses at various points.**

FIGURE 23 shows how the power is distributed in the lathe. The power distribution is similar in other machine tools. The power required to cut the metal is affected by:

- **The cutting data (cutting speed, depth of cut and the feed rate)**
- **The hardness of the workpiece material.**

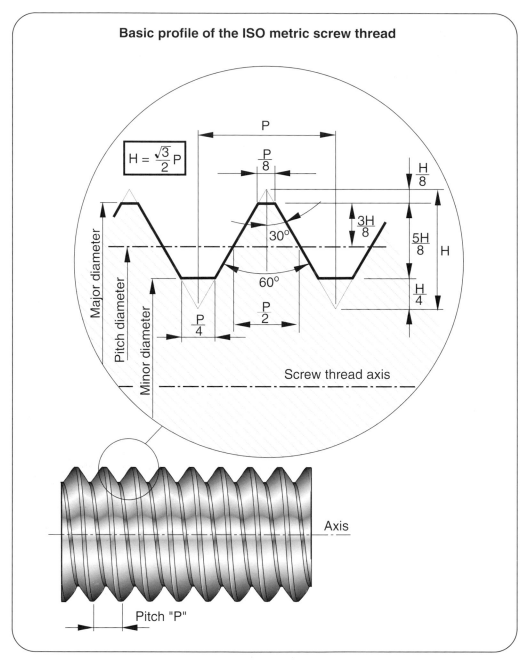

Basic profile of the ISO metric screw thread

$$H = \frac{\sqrt{3}}{2}P$$

FIGURE 21 *The ISO metric screw thread.*

As a general rule, the higher the values of the cutting data and the harder the workpiece material, the more power is required.

THE CAPACITY OF THE LATHE

There are at least three very important dimensions which determine the capacity of a lathe:

1 The distance between centres.
2 The swing over the bed.
3 The swing in the gap.

You may also be given the swing over the cross slide. The swing of the lathe, as you can see in **FIGURE 24**, is the maximum diameter which you can accommodate on the machine. Sometimes this

Setting up the lathe to cut a screw thread

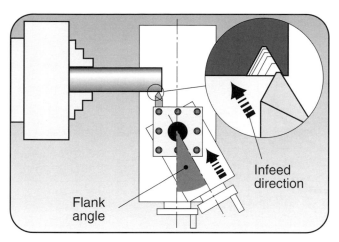

Flank
angle

Infeed
direction

Setting the topslide

The topslide is swivelled until it makes an angle with the cross slide equal to half the thread angle (the flank angle). This ensures that with each infeed increment the tool will remove a chip from one flank only

Setting the tool

The correctly ground tool should fit neatly into the screwcutting gauge. The gauge is in turn, correctly positioned by placing it against the work. This ensures that the tool form is at right angles to the work axis

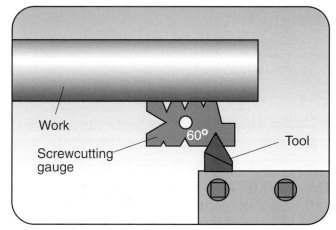

Work

Screwcutting
gauge

60°

Tool

FIGURE 22 *Setting the tool for cutting a screw thread.*

information is given as the height of the centres over the bed, the gap and the cross slide respectively. For example, a centre height of 200 mm over the bed would be a swing of 400 mm over the bed.

WORKHOLDING IN THE LATHE

There is a great variety of methods for holding and driving the workpiece on the lathe. The work-holding device is mounted on the spindle. The most important means of holding workpieces are:

* **The three-jaw self-centring chuck. (There is also a six-jaw self-centring chuck)**

* **The four-jaw independent chuck**
* **The collet chuck**
* **The faceplate**
* **Mandrels**
* **Between centres.**

The three-jaw chuck
A self-centring chuck is designed to hold *cylindrical* shaped workpieces. It can also hold polygon shapes where the number of sides is a multiple of the number of jaws in the chuck (a three-jaw chuck can grip a hexagon). The jaws move simultaneously as the *chuck key* is rotated. There are two sets of jaws supplied with the three-jaw chuck. One set is for

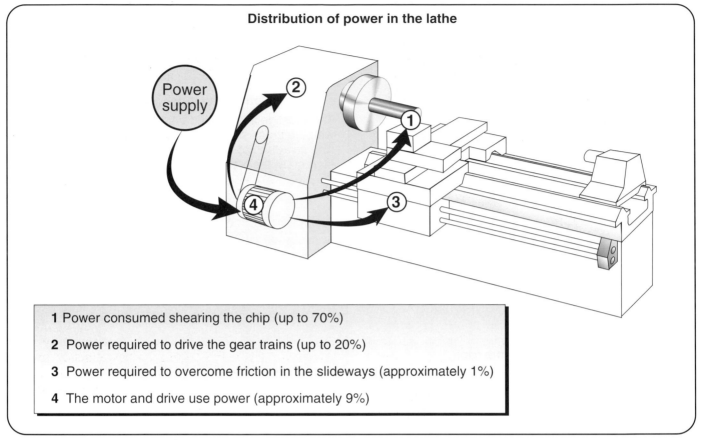

Distribution of power in the lathe

1 Power consumed shearing the chip (up to 70%)

2 Power required to drive the gear trains (up to 20%)

3 Power required to overcome friction in the slideways (approximately 1%)

4 The motor and drive use power (approximately 9%)

FIGURE 23   *Distribution of power in the lathe.*

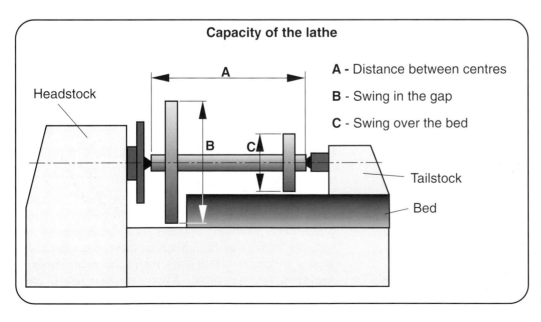

Capacity of the lathe

A - Distance between centres

B - Swing in the gap

C - Swing over the bed

Headstock

Tailstock

Bed

FIGURE 24   *The capacity of the lathe.*

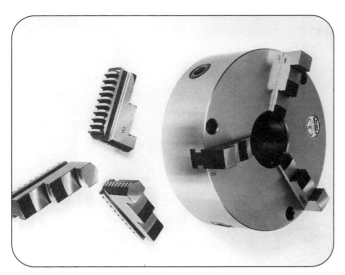

FIGURE 25 *A three-jaw self-centring chuck.* *(Courtesy: Pratt Burnerd International)*

FIGURE 26 *A six-jaw self-centring chuck.* *(Courtesy: Pratt Burnerd International)*

gripping external diameters and the other set is for gripping internal diameters. You can see a three-jaw chuck in **FIGURE 25**.

The six-jaw chuck
A six-jaw self-centring chuck is shown in **FIGURE 26**. It works on the same principle as the three-jaw. Six jaws improve the gripping power of the chuck, especially on workpieces which might tend to collapse as the chuck is tightened.

The four-jaw chuck
The four-jaw independent chuck has four jaws each of which can be moved independently of the other three. It is an ideal chuck for gripping irregular shaped workpieces. Each jaw is operated by means of a screw located at the back of the jaw. It is possible, therefore, to reverse each jaw in its slot so only one set of jaws is supplied with the chuck. The screw is rotated by the chuck key. To assist in setting work on the axis of the chuck, concentric rings are cut on its face. These rings can be used to roughly position the jaws before setting up accurately with a dial gauge. The four-jaw chuck is shown in **FIGURE 28**.

Centrifugal force versus gripping force
A problem that most chucks suffer from is the loss of gripping force as the spindle speed is increased. This

loss of gripping force is due to centrifugal force on the jaws. Centrifugal force is the tendency for the jaws to be thrown outwards from the rotating chuck (similar to the way a tyre throws water outwards when the wheel is rotating at speed).

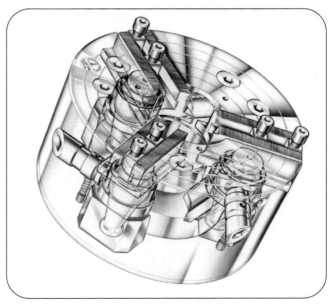

FIGURE 27 *A high speed power chuck. (This chuck is counterbalanced against loss of grip due to centrifugal force).* *(Courtesy: Pratt Burnerd International)*

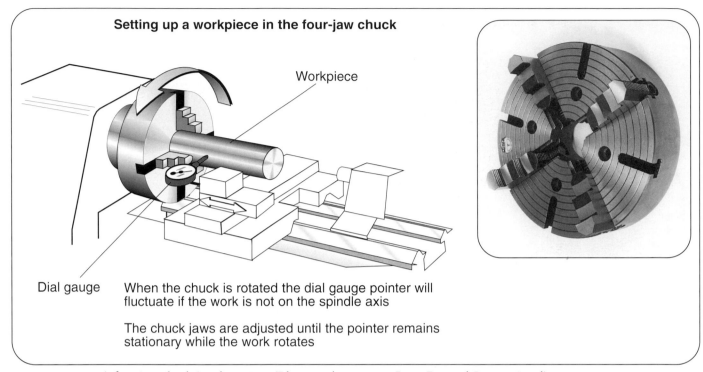

Setting up a workpiece in the four-jaw chuck

Workpiece

Dial gauge

When the chuck is rotated the dial gauge pointer will fluctuate if the work is not on the spindle axis

The chuck jaws are adjusted until the pointer remains stationary while the work rotates

FIGURE 28   *A four-jaw chuck/work setting. (Photograph courtesy: Pratt Bernard International)*

Modern high-speed chucks are centrifugally counter-balanced to retain the gripping force on the work and increase safety at high speeds.

Workholding in a collet

The collet, shown in **FIGURE 29**, is very compact. It has very good gripping power. Because there is a large area of contact between the collet and the workpiece, it is very suitable for gripping thin wall cylinders which might distort under the pressure of three jaws acting on separate points on the cylinder. Collets have almost 100% circumferential contact with the work so distortion is not a problem. Neither is centrifugal force a problem. The main disadvantage with collets is that a separate collet is needed for every workpiece diameter. Also the workpiece should have a good surface finish where it is to be gripped by the collet.

The faceplate

This method of workholding is used on workpieces whose shapes do not permit gripping in a chuck.

The workpiece is bolted to the faceplate or to a fixture on the faceplate. It is important to counter-balance the workpiece to prevent vibration during the machining operation.

Turning between centres

This is a suitable method of holding very long shafts. Machining the shaft which is supported on centres ensures that the diameters will be concentric with the centres. The shaft is driven by a carrier and a driving plate.

Mandrels

This method is used to hold and drive workpieces which have a finished bore but need to be machined completely on the outside. One type of mandrel is tapered. This taper is usually not more than 1.5 mm per metre length. The workpiece is pushed onto the mandrel until it is held firmly on the taper. The mandrel is then mounted between centres and driven by a carrier and driving plate. You can see this method of workholding in **FIGURE 30**.

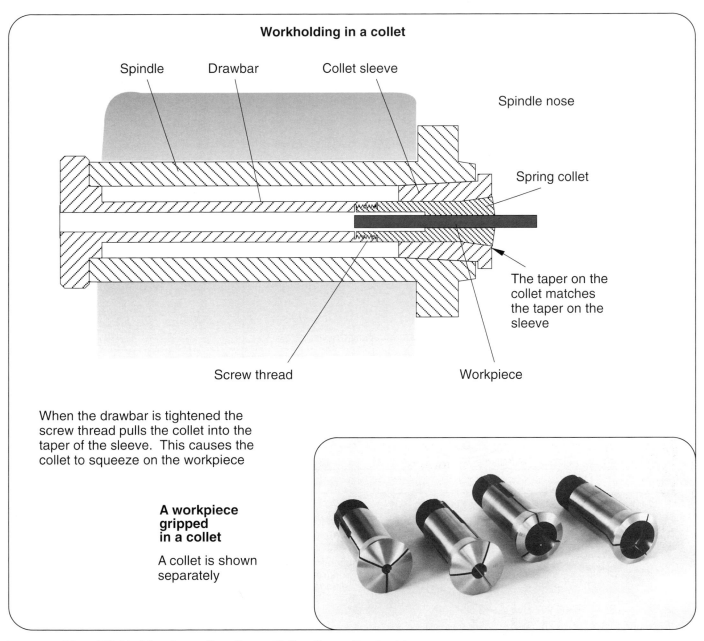

FIGURE 29 *Workholding in a collet. (Inset: Collets for a collet chuck)*

Lathe steadies

Long shafts tend to deflect away from the cutting tool. To prevent this, a travelling steady can be used. The travelling steady supports the workpiece at the point where the cutting tool is removing the chip. This steady is bolted to the saddle and is shown in **FIGURE 31**.

A fixed steady is normally used to support long shafts which need to be machined on the end. The fixed steady is clamped to the bed of the lathe. You can see a fixed steady in **FIGURE 32**. The fingers of the steady are adjustable to suit different workpiece diameters.

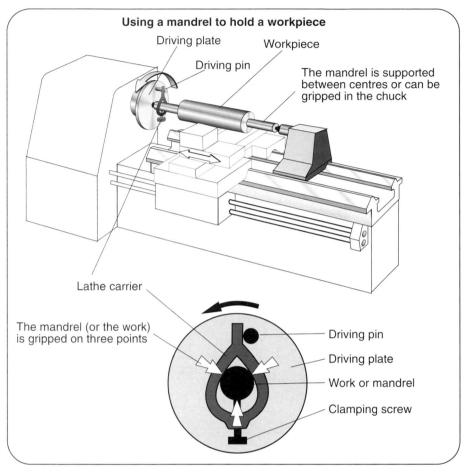

Using a mandrel to hold a workpiece

Driving plate

Workpiece

Driving pin

The mandrel is supported between centres or can be gripped in the chuck

Lathe carrier

The mandrel (or the work) is gripped on three points

Driving pin

Driving plate

Work or mandrel

Clamping screw

FIGURE 30 *Using a mandrel to hold a workpiece.*

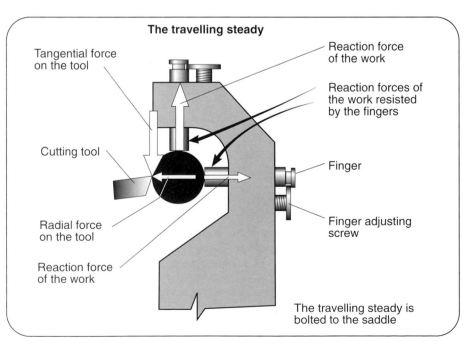

The travelling steady

Tangential force on the tool

Reaction force of the work

Reaction forces of the work resisted by the fingers

Cutting tool

Finger

Radial force on the tool

Finger adjusting screw

Reaction force of the work

The travelling steady is bolted to the saddle

FIGURE 31 *Travelling steady.*

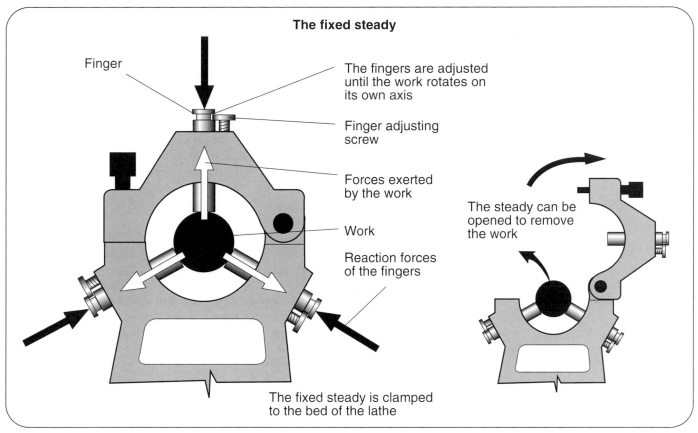

The fixed steady

Finger

The fingers are adjusted until the work rotates on its own axis

Finger adjusting screw

Forces exerted by the work

Work

Reaction forces of the fingers

The steady can be opened to remove the work

The fixed steady is clamped to the bed of the lathe

FIGURE 32   *Fixed steady.*

SUMMARY

The lathe is a machine tool for producing cylindrical components. The process is known as turning. It can also produce flat surfaces on the ends of workpieces. This is known as facing. The principal movement of the lathe is the rotation of the work. The single point tool is fed at a constant rate along the work to remove a chip.

The lathe is usually made from cast iron. This material has strength and rigidity, it is a good bearing material (the lathe has many sliding parts) and it is a good material to damp out vibrations. The lathe spindle is supported in bearings in the headstock. The headstock itself contains the gears necessary to rotate the spindle at many different speeds. The lathe tool is fitted in a holder which in turn is secured in the tool post. The tool post is mounted on top of a series of slides which allow the

tool to be moved in different directions. The movements are controlled by handwheels. Some movements have an automatic feed facility.

There are many different turning operations. These include:

- **Parallel turning**
- **Facing**
- **Form turning**
- **Drilling/Reaming**
- **Parting-off/Grooving**
- **Boring**
- **Taper turning**
- **Knurling**
- **Screwcutting.**

Cutting data is the name given to speed, feed and depth of cut. Cutting speed refers to the surface speed of the work. This is used to calculate the speed of the spindle because surface speed must take the diameter of the work into consideration. Surface speed is important and must be kept constant. To keep the surface speed constant as the diameter reduces, the spindle speed must be increased, This problem is solved with modern "constant surface speed" lathes. On these machines the speed of the spindle automatically increases as the cross slide moves in towards the centre of the work. On the regular centre lathe, the spindle speed will have to be increased periodically as the diameter of the work becomes smaller.

The feed rate is given on the lathe as the distance travelled by the tool per revolution of the spindle (work).

The lathe tool can be ground from a small high speed steel bar or it can be a preshaped tool clamped to a special holder (see Cutting Tool Materials, page 333). The tip of the tool should be set at the height of the work axis. It should be well supported to avoid vibration. Vibration will result in chatter on the work.

Screw threads can be cut on the lathe. Screwcutting is performed with a specially shaped tool (the same shape as the thread profile). The tool is fed along the work by the leadscrew. The leadscrew is set to rotate at a speed which will cause the tool to give the thread pitch required. Left-hand threads can be cut by reversing the rotation of the leadscrew but leaving the work rotate in the same direction as for right-hand threads.

Multistart threads are cut by setting the leadscrew for the lead of the thread. The lead is equal to the pitch multiplied by the number of starts in the screw.

Power from the lathe motor is mainly used in removing the chip from the work. Other areas where power is used include:

- **Bearing friction**
- **Slideway friction**
- **Heat losses at various points of the machine.**

Workholding is an important consideration in turning. Special workholding devices may be needed to hold special work shapes. The usual workholding device is a self-centring three-jaw chuck. This can hold round, triangular, hexagonal or any workpiece which is a regular polygon with a multiple of three sides.

The four-jaw independent chuck is very versatile as it can grip almost any shape.

Collets are very precise but must be used on work which is the same diameter as the inside of the collet. A set of different size collets is normally required.

The faceplate is a useful workholding device as the work can be bolted directly to it. When the work is bolted in position, the assembly should be checked for balance and, if necessary, balanced before it is used. Out-of-balance forces will cause the lathe to vibrate. This is potentially dangerous and may also cause bad surface finish.

Long work can be turned between centres and driven with a driving plate/lathe carrier. Long workpieces may need the support of lathe steadies. There are two types, a fixed steady and a travelling steady. The fixed steady is clamped the lathe bed while the travelling steady is clamped to the saddle and supports the work close to where the tool is cutting. Hollow work can be turned on a mandrel.

The Milling Machine

INTRODUCTION

The milling machine is one of the most important machine tools. It is capable of generating flat and contoured surfaces, drilling and boring. The milling machine has a set of special accessories which extend its range of possible milling operations. In FIGURE 1 you can see a milling machine.

Milling is a metal cutting process in which a surface is generated on a workpiece by the action of a revolving cutting tool. The work is held rigidly on the machine table and it is fed into the cutting tool. On some milling machines the cutting tool is fed into the work. The cutting tool used in milling is known as a milling cutter. Milling cutters have a number of cutting edges or teeth, each of which removes a chip from the workpiece. Each tooth contacts the work only briefly as the cutter rotates, so the cutting process is *intermittent*. This will be obvious if you study FIGURE 2. (In turning the cutting process is continuous.)

Another important point is that the chip does not have a uniform thickness due to the combined rotary movement of the cutter and the linear feed of the work.

There are two main categories of milling:

1 Peripheral milling.
2 Face milling.

A French engineer Jacques de Vaucanson is often given credit for making the first milling cutter. This was about 1782, eight years before Henry Maudslay used a revolving cutter to mill a slot in a part for a lock. Maudslay mounted the cutter on an arbor and set it up between centres on the lathe. The milling machine first appeared in America about 1818 and it was made by an English gunsmith, Robert Johnson. This milling machine was constructed in much the same way as a lathe. The cutter was mounted on an arbor between centres as Maudslay had done and the workpiece was clamped to a cross-slide. The milling machine in its present form began to take shape in 1820, when a machine was built at the Whitney Works in America. This machine had the centre lathe arrangement for driving the cutter but the bed and cross-slide were replaced by a table which was similar to modern milling machines. Until the middle of the 19th century, milling machines tended to be modifications of the lathe. In 1862 Joseph Brown designed a universal milling machine to mill the flutes in twist drills.

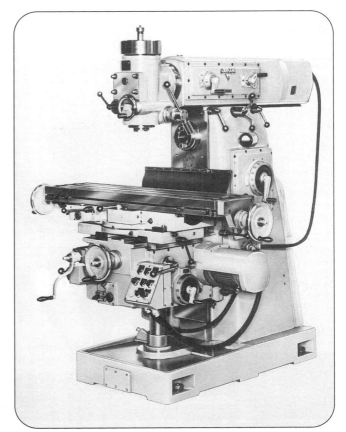

FIGURE 1   *A universal milling machine.*
(Courtesy: Värnamo Sweden)

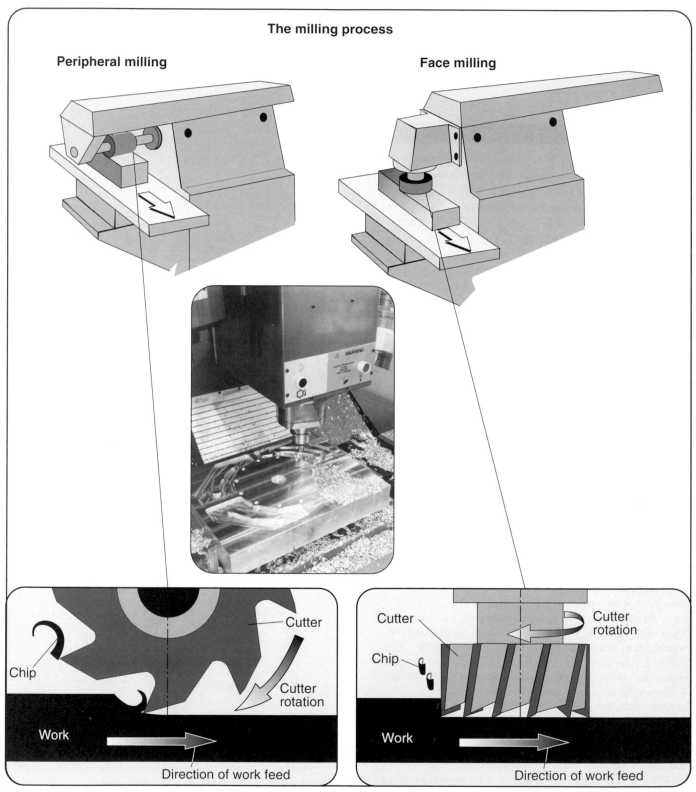

FIGURE 2 *The milling process. Inset shows a milling operation. (Photograph courtesy: Bridgeport Machines Ltd.)*

In peripheral milling the surface is generated on the workpiece by the cutting action of teeth on the periphery of the milling cutter. Peripheral milling with a long cylindrical cutter is sometimes called *slab milling*.

In face milling the milling cutter generates a surface at right angles to the axis of the cutter. The end or face of the milling cutter provides the finished surface on the workpiece. You can see the two types of milling in **FIGURE 2**.

MILLING MACHINES

There are many different types of milling machines. The general purpose milling machines used in manufacturing can be set up for various types of milling operations. Special milling machines can be designed and built for certain applications. There are also milling machines which are controlled by computer.

The main categories of milling machine include:

1 Column-and-knee type
2 Bed type
3 Planer type.

1 Column-and-knee milling machines include:

- **Horizontal milling machines**
  In this type the main spindle is mounted horizontally near the top of the column.

- **Vertical milling machines**
  These machines have the spindle mounted vertically in a head at the top of the column.

- **Universal milling machines**
  On these milling machines the table can swivel on its base. This extends the range of work for which the machine can be used.

- **Turret milling machines**
  The head of the turret milling machine is mounted on a beam. This beam can swivel on the top of the column about a vertical axis. The head itself can swivel about a horizontal axis on the beam and it can tilt forward and backward. This makes turret milling machines very flexible and

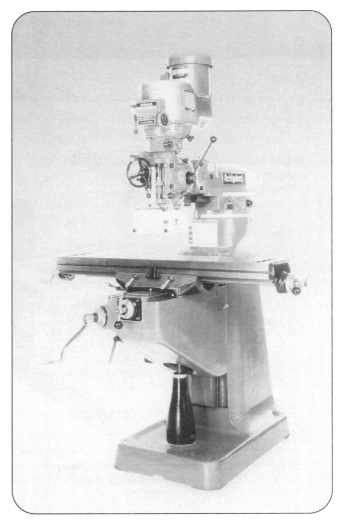

FIGURE 3 *Turret milling machine. (Courtesy: Bridgeport Machines Ltd.)*

versatile. They are, however, usually confined to light milling operations. You can see a turret milling machine in **FIGURE 3**.

Construction of the milling machine
On column-and-knee type milling machines the column is mounted on a heavy rigid base. All the main parts of the machine are supported on the column. The drive mechanism for the spindle is (with the exception of the turret type) contained within the column. The drive mechanism on the turret machine is on the head. **FIGURE 4** shows the main parts of a milling machine.

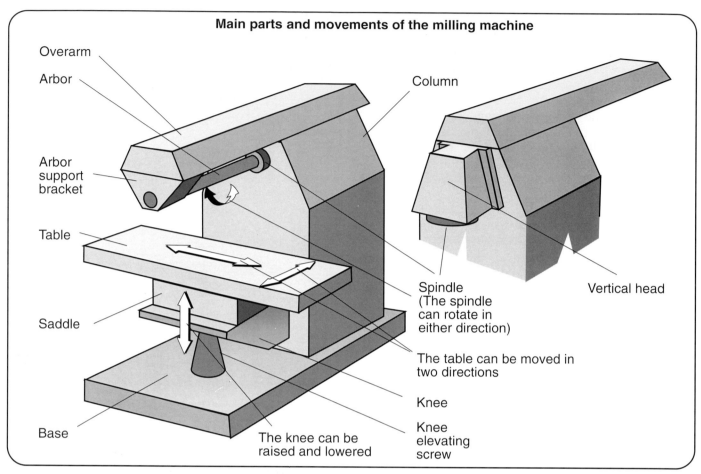

Main parts and movements of the milling machine

Overarm

Arbor

Arbor support bracket

Table

Saddle

Base

Column

Spindle (The spindle can rotate in either direction)

The table can be moved in two directions

Knee

Knee elevating screw

The knee can be raised and lowered

Vertical head

FIGURE 4 *Main parts and movements of the milling machine.*

The main elements of these milling machines are:

The base
This is made from cast iron. Cast iron is used because it is very strong and rigid and does not tend to vibrate. The base is hollow and is used for storing the cutting fluid. A pump, fitted into the base, pumps the cutting fluid up to the cutter.

The column
The column is a hollow casting and it is mounted on the base. All of the gears necessary to rotate the spindle at a range of speeds are contained in the column.

The knee
This is a very robust support for the machine table. It can be moved vertically on guideways on the front of the column. It is supported from the base by a vertical leadscrew similar to a screwjack. The knee is raised and lowered by means of a handwheel. When you rotate this handwheel you rotate the vertical leadscrew between the knee and the base. Working in the same way as a screwjack, this leadscrew moves the knee up and down. The slideways on the column ensure that the knee cannot move in any other direction. You can lock the knee at any height.

The saddle
The saddle is mounted on a slideway on top of the knee. You can move the saddle on its slideways by rotating a handwheel. It is also provided with power feed. You can lock the saddle to the knee in any position.

The table

The table is supported by the saddle. The top surface is accurately machined. Tee slots running the length of the table make it possible to bolt on workpieces or attachments for holding workpieces. You can move the table by rotating a handwheel at either end. The table is provided with power feed. You can lock the table in any position.

The spindle

The spindle of the milling machine supports and drives the cutter holding device. On a horizontal milling machine the spindle is mounted horizontally in precision bearings near the top of the column. Vertical milling machines have a vertically mounted spindle in a head attached to the top of the column.

On some milling machines, particularly the turret type, the spindle is mounted in a very robust quill similar to a drilling machine. The quill allows the spindle axial travel over a limited distance. It is operated by a handwheel or lever and can sometimes be provided with a power feed. The quill can be locked in any position.

The nose of the spindle has an internal taper. Each cutter holding device suited to the machine has a matching taper. This taper is normally an International Standard Taper (IST) whose angle is 16° 0" 36'. Other forms of taper can be used on small milling machines.

To secure the cutter holding device in the spindle, a drawbolt is passed through the spindle from the back (on a horizontal spindle) or the top (on a vertical spindle) and screwed into the device. This pulls the tapers firmly together and ensures perfect alignment with the spindle axis. The drive is transmitted from the spindle through tenons.

Cutter holding devices include arbors and chucks. All of these have tapers to match the spindle taper.

Arbors

Long arbors with collars are usually used on horizontal milling machines. The collars can be placed so that the cutter can be located in any position on the arbor. A key in the arbor drives the cutter. The arbor is supported on its outer end by a bracket secured to the overarm. Stub arbors are very short and are used for special cutters.

Chucks

Chucks for holding milling cutters are very precise in that they ensure that the axis of the cutter is perfectly on the spindle axis.

The overarm

This is a rigid casting which is located in dovetail slides on the top of the column. Its purpose is to carry the arbor support bracket. An arbor support bracket is needed to prevent the long arbor from bending when the cutter contacts the work.

The overarm can slide on the column and it can be locked in any position. A special bearing is fitted on the arbor assembly and this bearing runs in the arbor support bracket.

Alignment and movements

The table must be flat and level in both its length and its width.

- **The movement of the table in its two horizontal directions must be parallel to its surface.**
- **The spindle axis in a horizontal milling machine is parallel to the table surface.**
- **The spindle axis in a vertical milling machine is at right angles to the table surface.**
- **The centre tee-slot must be parallel to the longitudinal movement of the table.**
- **The vertical movement of the knee must be perpendicular to the surface of the table.**
- **The cross traverse moves parallel to the spindle axis on a horizontal milling machine.**

2 Bed type milling machines

These milling machines are heavy and robust. The table is mounted directly on the bed. These machines can have two or three heads which can be moved vertically for adjustment. They are normally clamped in position and the only movement during milling is the table longitudinal movement.

3 Planer type milling machines

These milling machines have several spindles. The cutters can remove large amounts of swarf with each

FIGURE 5 *Slab milling.
(Courtesy: Bridgeport
Machines Ltd.)*

FIGURE 6 *Gang milling.
(Courtesy: Bridgeport
Machines Ltd.)*

pass. A variety of cutter shapes and sizes can be used at the same time. The slideways on the bed of a lathe, for example, could be milled in a single pass on this type of milling machine.

MILLING CUTTERS

There is a large variety of milling cutters available. Most milling cutters belong to one or other of two categories:

1 Cutters which are mounted on an arbor.
2 Cutters which are held in a special chuck.

Arbor-mounted milling cutters

These cutters have a hole through the centre. The arbor passes through the hole and the cutter is secured by means of a screw or a nut. These cutters are usually large in diameter. The main types are:

- **Cylindrical cutters**
- **Side and face cutters**
- **Slitting saws**
- **Angle cutters**
- **Form cutters.**

Cylindrical milling cutters are often referred to as slab mills and are used to generate flat surfaces on large workpieces. These cutters can have straight or helical teeth running along their length. Helical tooth cutters have an advantage over straight tooth cutters in that they usually have more than one tooth cutting at a time. The teeth contact the work gradually and this reduces the tendency to cause vibration or chatter. A slab milling operation is shown in **FIGURE 5**.

Side and face milling cutters have cutting edges on the periphery and on the sides. Their main purpose is to produce steps and grooves. A number of side and face cutters can be assembled on an arbor. This is known as *gang milling* and is shown in **FIGURE 6**

Slitting saws are thin milling cutters. They can range from 1 mm to 5 mm in thickness. They are used for producing very deep narrow slots and for cutting-off. The teeth on a slitting saw are usually small.

FIGURE 7 *Slitting saw. (Courtesy: Värnamo Sweden)*

FIGURE 7 shows a narrow groove being milled with a slitting saw.

Angle cutters are used for milling edges and corners to desired angles. The two types of angle cutters are single-angle and double-angle.

Form cutters have their teeth ground to special shapes. For example, the shape could be that of the space between two gear teeth or the space between two teeth on a bicycle sprocket wheel. Both gear wheels and sprockets can be milled using form cutters. Other form cutters are used for milling the flutes in twist drills.

Chuck-mounted cutters

These cutters have a small shank which has a thread on the end. The shank fits into a *collet* which in turn

FIGURE 8 *Variety of chuck mounted cutters.*
(Courtesy: Clarkson Osbourne Ltd.)

is gripped in the chuck. The main types, shown in **FIGURE 8**, are:

- **End mills**
- **Slot drills**
- **Special shapes.**

End mills have helical cutting edges running along their length. There are also cutting edges on the end. This cutter can be used for general milling operations. An end mill cannot be fed into the work along its axis because the teeth on the end do not reach into the centre of the cutter.

Slot drills have only two cutting edges which are also helical. They also have two cutting edges on the end. One of these cutting edges reaches in to the centre of the cutter. This gives the slot drill the

ability to cut if it is fed into the work along its axis (in the same way as a drill). The slot drill is a versatile cutter as you can mill and drill with it.

Special cutter shapes are used to mill special profiles on workpieces. Examples of some of the more common types are shown in **FIGURE 9**.

Angle cutters are used for milling chamfers on the corners of workpieces. The more usual angles available are 30°, 45° and 60°.

Ball-nosed slot drills are used for milling slots with a radius. They can also be used for milling a radius on an internal corner.

Corner-rounding cutters are for removing sharp external corners from the workpiece.

Dovetail cutters are used for milling dovetail slideways on machine parts. The angles are usually 60° and 45°.

Woodruff key-seat cutters. Woodruff keys are often used where components have to be fitted to a taper shaft. You would see examples on small engines of the type used on lawn mowers. Woodruff key-seat cutters are used to cut the keyways for these keys.

Tee-slot cutters are used for milling tee-slots in machine tables. The slot is first milled with an end mill and then followed by a tee-slot cutter.

Shell end mills are mounted on a special arbor and kept in place with a screw. The range of sizes can go up to 60 mm diameter.

Inserted-tooth milling cutters. In this type of cutter each cutting edge is a separate *insert* clamped into a solid steel body. The insert may be high speed steel or it may be tungsten carbide. When the cutting edges become worn the insert is taken out and indexed to give a new cutting edge. **FIGURE 10** shows a face mill with inserted teeth.

Milling cutter geometry
Each tooth on a milling cutter has a rake and clearance angle in the same way as a lathe tool. The teeth on most milling cutters are coarse (large) as

End mill

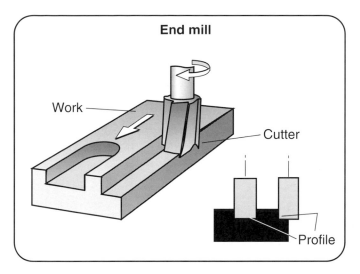

Work

Cutter

Profile

Slot drill

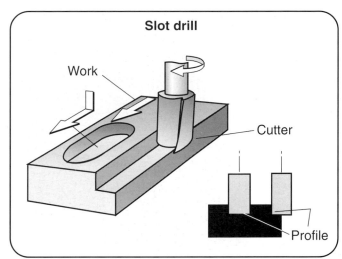

Work

Cutter

Profile

Angle cutter

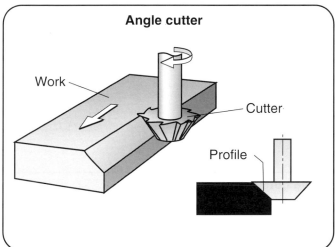

Work

Cutter

Profile

Ball-nosed slot drill

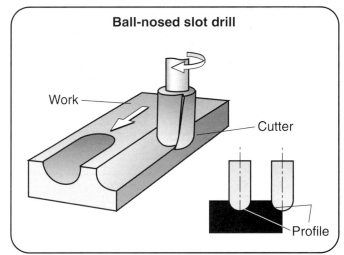

Work

Cutter

Profile

Corner rounding cutter

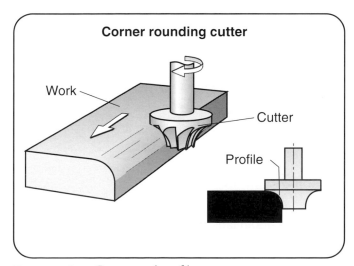

Work

Cutter

Profile

Dovetail cutter

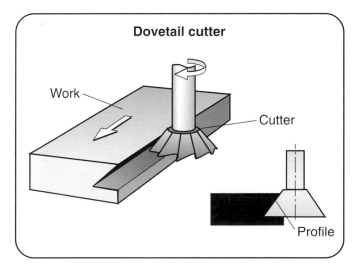

Work

Cutter

Profile

FIGURE 9 *Cutters and profiles.*

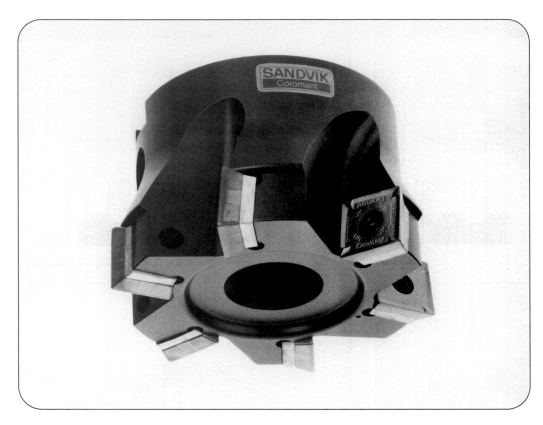

FIGURE 10 *Inserted tooth milling cutter. (Courtesy: Sanvik Coromant)*

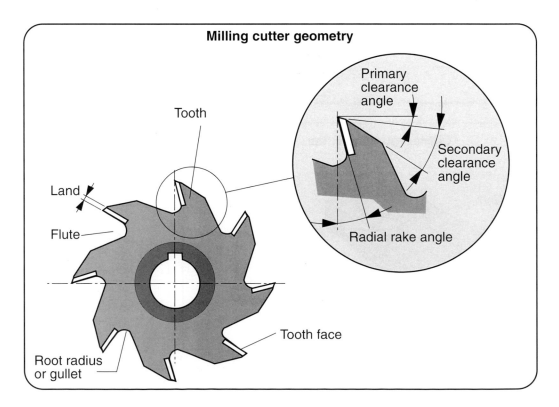

Milling cutter geometry

Tooth

Land

Flute

Root radius or gullet

Tooth face

Primary clearance angle

Secondary clearance angle

Radial rake angle

FIGURE 11 *Cutter geometry.*

280

they are more efficient for removing metal than fine teeth. A coarse-tooth cutter has more clearance space for swarf and has a freer cutting action. Fine-tooth cutters are usually in the form of slitting saws. Typical cutter geometry is shown in **FIGURE 11**.

CUTTING DATA

Cutting data is a collective term given to the following:

- **Spindle speed**
- **Cutting speed**
- **Depth of cut**
- **Feed rate.**

Spindle speed

Spindle speed is the number of revolutions the cutter makes per minute. It is given the symbol 'N'. The milling machine has a range of spindle speeds to suit various cutter diameters and different workpiece materials. (Turret milling machines usually have a variable spindle speed.)

Cutting speed

This is the 'distance' one cutting edge rotates in one minute. It is given the symbol 'S'. It represents the actual speed at which a cutting edge removes a chip in metres per minute. The cutting speed is calculated in the same way as the cutting speed is calculated in turning. There is a difference, however, in that the diameter 'D' is that of the cutter and not the workpiece. The most important factors you must consider when selecting a cutting speed are the type and hardness of the workpiece material, and the type and hardness of the cutting tool.

Depth of cut

The depth of cut is the depth at which the cutter is set below the unmachined surface – the depth of material to be removed.

Feed rate

In milling there are three feed types taken into account:

- **Feed per tooth**
- **Feed per minute**
- **Feed per revolution.**

Feed per tooth

This is the linear distance moved by the cutter during the engagement of one tooth. Although the milling cutter has a number of teeth, it is the capacity of one single tooth which must be considered. If the feed per tooth is excessive there may not be enough space in the flute of the cutter for the entire chip. See **FIGURE 11**. Remember the chip is trapped in the flute until the tooth disengages from the work. Another consideration is that the tooth might not be strong enough to take a large chip.

If the feed per tooth is not large enough then the cutting edge may not engage the workpiece properly. There will be an increase in rubbing before the tooth begins to cut the chip. This will cause a lot of heat to be generated through friction and the edge may suffer as a result.

Feed per minute

This is the actual distance travelled by the table in millimetres per minute. It is given the symbol 'F'. The feed per minute is set on the machine by placing the feed control levers at the correct position. The setting is determined by calculation.

Feed per revolution

This tells how far the work advances in one revolution of the cutter. It is given the symbol 'f'. The feed per revolution is important as it is influenced by the number of teeth in the cutter. In general terms the greater the number of teeth the higher the possible feed per revolution. The feed per revolution is also important when you are concerned with surface finish. The surface finish will be affected by the distance between each edge contact with the surface.

It is worth remembering that feed on the lathe is given in millimetres per revolution of the spindle. The feed rate is directly linked to the speed of the spindle. In milling the feed is independent of the spindle. This is necessary because of the vast range of milling cutter types. For example, even if two cutters are the same diameter, the feed rate will have to be different if they do not have the same number of teeth.

Example 1

Calculate the spindle speed of the milling machine if the recommended cutting speed for the workpiece material is 28 m/min and the cutter diameter is 20 mm

$$N = \frac{1000 \times S}{\pi \times D}$$

where   N is the spindle speed (rev/min)

S is the cutting speed (m/min)

D is the cutter diameter (mm)

$$N = \frac{1000 \times 28}{\pi \times 20}$$

$N = 445.6$ rev/min

Select the closest available speed on the milling machine

Say **440 rev/min**

Example 2

Calculate the feedrate for the milling operation above if the milling cutter used has 4 teeth and the feed is 0.1 mm per tooth

$F = N \times f \times T$

Where F is the feedrate (mm/min)

N is the number of revolutions of the cutter (rev/min)

f is the feed per tooth (mm)

T is the number of teeth in the cutter

$F = 440 \times 0.1 \times 4$

Feedrate is **176 mm/min**

CALCULATION 1

UP-CUT MILLING AND DOWN-CUT MILLING

In the milling process the workpiece can be fed into the cutter in two ways:

1 With the direction of rotation of the cutter.
2 Against the direction of rotation.

This is most apparent in a peripheral milling operation.

Up-cut milling

This is also called *conventional milling*. In this form of milling the workpiece is fed against the direction of rotation of the cutter. In this situation the chip thickness starts at zero and increases to a maximum towards the end of the cut. This is shown in FIGURE 12.

The cutting action has a lifting effect on the workpiece, tending to lift it out of the workholding device. It is important therefore to ensure proper clamping of the workpiece. The main advantage of up-cut milling is that it tends to eliminate any effect of free play in the table leadscrew. This results in a smoother cutting action.

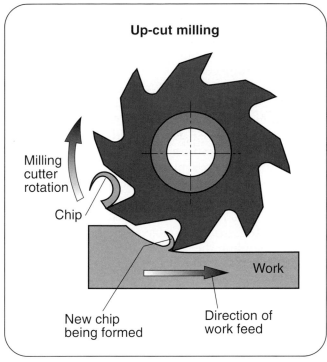

FIGURE 12   *Up-cut milling.*

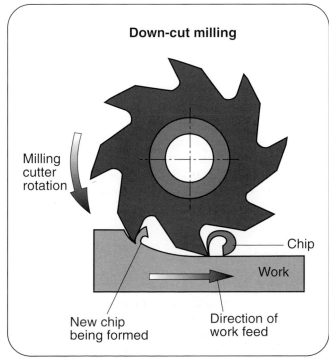

FIGURE 13   *Down-cut milling.*

Down-cut milling

This method is also called *climb milling.* When the workpiece is fed in the same direction as the cutter rotation, the method is known as down-cut milling. Here the chip thickness is at a maximum immediately after the start of the cut and tapers out to zero at the end of the cut.

Because of the feed direction in down-cut milling, the cutter tends to grab the work and pull it forward. Machines have to be fitted with a special device known as a *backlash eliminator* if down-cut milling is to be safely carried out. The backlash eliminator removes the free play in the leadscrew. Down-cut milling should never be attempted on milling machines which are not fitted with this device.

Down-cut milling has the advantage that the machined surface tends to show less tooth marks than up-cut milling so the surface finish is better. The clamping forces of the workholding device are helped by the rotation of the cutter. The cutting forces are directed downward onto the machine table. Down-cut milling is shown in **FIGURE 13**.

WORKHOLDING

In the milling operation the cutter often exerts very high forces on the workpiece. It is important then to hold the workpiece by the most suitable method. The method you use to hold the workpiece will usually depend on:

- **The shape of the workpiece**
- **The type of milling operation to be carried out on it.**

There is a variety of workholding methods but you will have to decide which of these you should use after considering the two factors just referred to. If the workpiece is not rigidly clamped it may vibrate. This may cause bad surface finish due to chatter. It may also cause the cutter to dig in and possibly break. Care must be taken not to distort the workpiece with high clamping forces. In general the clamping and restraining forces should be decided following an analysis of the direction and magnitude of the cutting forces.

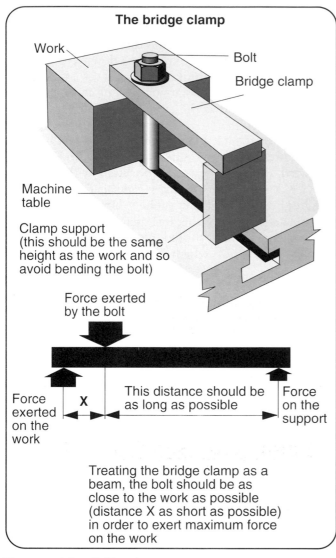

The bridge clamp

Work

Bolt

Bridge clamp

Machine table

Clamp support
(this should be the same
height as the work and so
avoid bending the bolt)

Force exerted
by the bolt

Force
exerted
on the
work

X

This distance should be
as long as possible

Force
on the
support

Treating the bridge clamp as a
beam, the bolt should be as
close to the work as possible
(distance X as short as possible)
in order to exert maximum force
on the work

FIGURE 14   *Bridge clamp.*

Methods of workholding

The more common methods of workholding are:

- **Direct clamping**
- **Gripping in the machine vice**
- **Holding in the dividing head**
- **Clamping to the rotary table**
- **Mounting on magnetic chucks**
- **Holding in special fixtures.**

Direct clamping

The table of the milling machine has a number of T-slots running its full length. With T-bolts fitted into these slots you can bolt a bridge clamp down on to the workpiece.

FIGURE 14 shows a bridge clamp. You should always ensure that the clamping force is sufficient to hold the workpiece. You should not clamp the workpiece in a position where it might possibly distort. When using a bridge clamp it is important that the T-bolt should be as close as possible to the work. Also the clamp support should be as far away from the T-bolt as possible. The clamp itself must be parallel to the machine table, otherwise there is a danger of bending the T-bolt.

The machine vice

The machine vice is a very convenient method of holding work on the milling machine. This vice is operated in much the same way as a bench vice. The important features of a machine vice are:

The jaws are very accurately machined
The vice can swivel on its base. The base is graduated in degrees

FIGURE 15 shows a workpiece gripped in the machine vice. Notice the parallel bars supporting the workpiece. These ensure parallelism of the surface being machined with the underside of the workpiece.

'Setting-up' work in the machine vice
When you use the machine vice to hold a workpiece make sure that no distortion of the workpiece can occur. Make sure also that the machining sequence is one which will produce accurate workpieces.

The dividing head

The dividing head shown in **FIGURE 16**, is usually used to hold workpieces which are required to have a repeated feature milled at equal spaces around its circumference. The dividing head chuck can be rotated through very precise angles and locked so that milling can take place. The most important feature of the dividing head is that the spindle is

Workholding in the milling vice

Many milling machine vices are designed so that the fixed jaw aligns the work with the cutter axis. The line of action of the force exerted by the screw is approximately opposite the centre of the fixed jaw

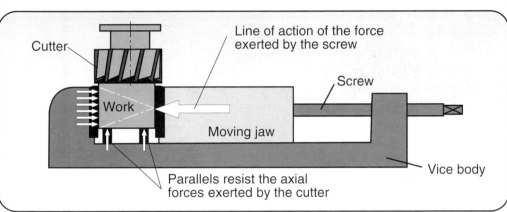

Cutter

Line of action of the force exerted by the screw

Screw

Work

Moving jaw

Vice body

Parallels resist the axial forces exerted by the cutter

FIGURE 15 *The milling machine vice.*

FIGURE 16 *The dividing head. (Courtesy: Hofmann Germany)*

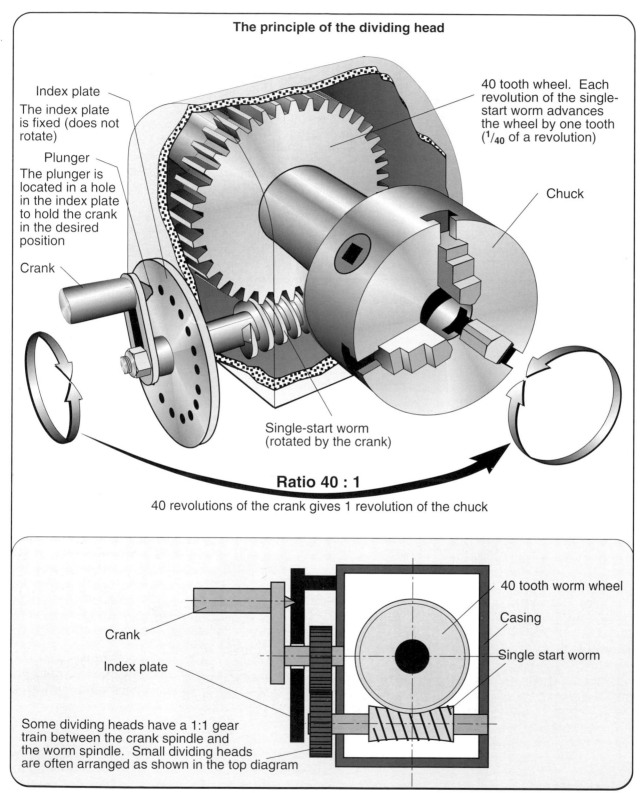

The principle of the dividing head

Index plate
The index plate is fixed (does not rotate)

Plunger
The plunger is located in a hole in the index plate to hold the crank in the desired position

Crank

40 tooth wheel. Each revolution of the single-start worm advances the wheel by one tooth ($^1/_{40}$ of a revolution)

Chuck

Single-start worm (rotated by the crank)

Ratio 40 : 1

40 revolutions of the crank gives 1 revolution of the chuck

Crank

40 tooth worm wheel

Casing

Index plate

Single start worm

Some dividing heads have a 1:1 gear train between the crank spindle and the worm spindle. Small dividing heads are often arranged as shown in the top diagram

FIGURE 17   *The principle of the dividing head.*

driven by a crank. The ratio of the movement of the crank to the movement of the spindle is:

40 turns of the crank will give 1 turn of the spindle.

This is because there is a 40 tooth worm wheel driven by a single-start worm. This is shown in **FIGURE 17**.

The dividing head can be fitted with a special driving plate or with a chuck to hold a workpiece.

Indexing
Indexing is the rotary movement of the workpiece between machining cuts. With the dividing head you can index the workpiece through any angle. A typical example is to use the dividing head to hold a bar which is to have a square milled on its end.

Each flat is 90° or $\frac{1}{4}$ of a turn from the next flat. Therefore the amount you index the work will be 90° or $\frac{1}{4}$ of a turn. A $\frac{1}{4}$ turn of the work (spindle) will require 10 full revolutions of the crank.

Methods of indexing
There is a number of ways to index. The more usual methods are:

- **Direct indexing**
- **Simple indexing.**

For direct indexing the worm is disengaged from the wormwheel. The spindle can then be rotated freely by hand. You can lock the spindle by dropping a pawl into a notch in the direct indexing plate. The direct indexing plate can be just behind the chuck or it can be at the back end of the spindle.

For simple indexing the ratio 40:1 is used. Remember it takes 40 turns of the crank to rotate the spindle once. So for $\frac{1}{2}$ of a turn of the workpiece you would need to turn the crank 20 times for each indexing movement. You will see from this that

The number of turns on the crank

$$= \frac{40}{Number\ of\ spaces\ on\ the\ work}$$

Example

Calculate the crank movement required to index 6 equal spaces on a workpiece (a hexagon, for example)

$$\text{Crank movement} = \frac{40}{\text{Number of spaces required on the work}}$$

$$= \frac{40}{6} = 6\frac{4}{6} = 6\frac{2}{3}$$

This means that for each space you turn the crank through 6 full turns $+\frac{2}{3}$ of a turn each time you index.

The index plate is used to give the $\frac{2}{3}$ of a turn. In an 18 hole circle every sixth hole is $\frac{2}{3}$ of a revolution of the crank. Therefore 12 holes will be $\frac{2}{3}$ of a revolution.

CALCULATION 2

Procedure: Index six full turns and 12 holes in an 18 hole circle. Drop the plunger into the hole to lock the crank.

From this position you index your next movement of six turns + 12 holes in 18 hole circle and so on. See **FIGURE 18**

It is possible to link the dividing head to the table leadscrew through a gear train. With this type of set-up the workpiece rotates as the table moves. In **FIGURE 19** you can see a gear with helical teeth being milled with a special form cutter.

The rotary table
The rotary table is used to hold workpieces which need to have a radius milled on them. It consists of a circular work surface which rotates when the crank is turned. See **FIGURE 20**

The base of the table is graduated in degrees. This makes it possible to rotate the table through any angle. It is possible to fix the crank in any position by pushing the plunger into a hole in the index plate. It is operated in a similar way to the dividing head.

Using the index plate to obtain $^2/_3$ of a revolution of the crank

The index plate has a large number of pitch circles, each with a different number of equally spaced holes

To measure $^2/_3$ of a revolution, a pitch circle with a number of holes divisible by 3 (18) is selected

$^2/_3$ of a revolution = $^{12}/_{18}$ = 12 holes in an 18 hole circle. (Count 12 holes from the position of the plunger. It is important to note that **you do not count the hole that the plunger is already in**)

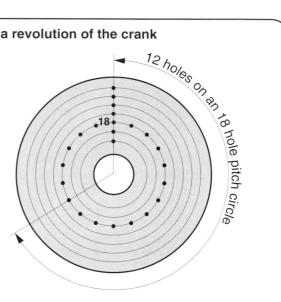

12 holes on an 18 hole pitch circle

18

FIGURE 18   *Indexing.*

FIGURE 19   *Milling a helical gear with the aid of the dividing head. (Courtesy: Bridgeport Machines Ltd.)*

FIGURE 20 *The rotary table. (Courtesy: Hofmann Germany)*

FIGURE 21 *Holding a workpiece on a milling machine using a magnetic chuck. (Courtesy: Eclipse Magnetics Ltd.)*

Magnetic chuck

A magnetic chuck can be used to hold large batches of similar workpieces on the milling machine. Workpieces whose shape would make it difficult to grip in the machine vice can sometimes be mounted on a magnetic chuck. A magnetic chuck is shown in FIGURE 21.

Holding in special fixtures

Fixtures are used when large batches of a particular component have to be machined on a milling machine. The fixture is designed and manufactured to suit the rapid loading and unloading of the component. It is also designed to exert the correct clamping forces in the most appropriate part of the component. Using fixtures reduces changeover times (time taken to remove a machined component and clamp an unmachined component to the fixture). They are also a very precise and accurate method of clamping workpieces.

SUMMARY

Milling is a metal cutting process in which a surface is generated by a revolving cutting tool. The cutting tool used in milling is known as a milling cutter. The work can be fed into the rotating cutter or the cutter fed into the work.

The chip produced in milling does not have a uniform thickness due to the combined cutter rotation and work feed.

The two main categories of milling are peripheral milling (sometimes called slab milling) and face milling.

There are different types of milling machines including general purpose column-and-knee types, bed type, planer type and special purpose machines.

The column-and-knee type milling machines are:

1 Horizontal – which has a horizontal spindle.
2 Vertical – which has a vertical spindle.
3 Turret – which has a quill-type spindle. The head of the turret milling machine incorporates the motor and gearbox and it can be swivelled and tilted in many directions.
4 Universal – which has a swivel table.

The main parts of the milling machine are the base, the column, the knee, the saddle, the table and the spindle.

Milling cutters can be divided into two main categories:

1 Arbor-mounted cutters which include cylindrical, side and face, slitting saws, angle cutter and form cutters.
2 Chuck-mounted cutters which include end mills, slot drills, angle cutters, form cutters, tee-slot cutter, dovetail cutters and many more.

Arbor-mounted cutters have a hole through the centre and are secured to the arbor by means of a screw or nut. The cutter is driven by a key in the arbor.

Chuck-mounted cutters have a shank with a screwed end. They are fitted into a special collet which in turn is secured in a chuck. These chucks are very accurate and they ensure that the axis of the cutter aligns with the axis of the spindle.

Cutting data is a collective term for spindle speed, cutting speed, depth of cut and feed rate.

Spindle speed is calculated using the formula

$$N = \frac{1000S}{\pi D}$$

Where N = Spindle speed (rev/min)
S = Cutting speed (m/min)
D = Cutter diameter (mm)

Feed rate per minute is calculated by multiplying the following:

Spindle speed x feed per tooth x number of teeth in the cutter.

Up-cut and down-cut milling are terms given to the relative movement between the work and the cutter.

In up-cut milling the work feeds against the cutter rotation. In down-cut milling the work feeds in the same direction as the cutter rotation. A backlash eliminator is required when down–cut milling as any looseness in the leadscrew will allow the table to be pulled forward by the cutter. The effect would be a sudden momentary change in feed rate and could cause the cutter to shatter with serious consequences. In a peripheral milling operation, the cutting forces in up-cut milling tend to lift the workpiece out of the vice. Down-cut milling with the same cutter directs the forces towards the table.

Work is secured in a number of ways in milling. It can be clamped or bolted to the machine table. It can be gripped in a machine vice or held on a magnetic chuck. The dividing head is used when the work (particularly cylindrical work) is to have a repeated feature milled at regular intervals around its circumference. The dividing head can be indexed through small or large equal increments. It can also be rotated through any specific angle. The crank movement is calculated to give the correct chuck movement for each increment by using the formula

$$Crank\ movement\ = \frac{40}{Number\ of\ spaces\ on\ the\ work}$$

The rotary table performs a function similar to the dividing head but it is used mainly for curved feature milling. The table is rotated by a crank and an index plate is used to ensure accurate angular movement.

Precision Grinding

INTRODUCTION

There are many methods of precision grinding. Each method is designed to produce accurate dimensions and give smooth surfaces on engineering components. The following types of precision grinding are amongst those commonly used in manufacturing.

- **Surface grinding – for producing flat surfaces**
- **Cylindrical grinding – for producing cylindrical shapes**

FIGURE 1 *A precision surface grinding machine. (Courtesy: Jones and Shipman PLC)*

- **Internal grinding – for producing internal diameters.**

The type of surface to be ground usually determines the type of grinding machine required. A surface grinding machine is shown in **FIGURE 1**.

THE GRINDING PROCESS

Grinding is sometimes referred to as *abrasive machining*. It is one of the oldest machining processes. Tools used by ancient civilisations were made by rubbing stones against other materials to produce sharp edges.

The cutting element in the grinding process is the grinding wheel. It rotates (usually at high speed) while the table movements combine to feed the work into it. **FIGURE 2** shows the grinding process. Here you can see small abrasive grains, which are the "cutting edges" of the grinding wheel, cutting very tiny chips from the workpiece. The depth of cut is usually small. A smooth surface and accurate sizes on the workpiece are the main reasons for using this process.

GRINDING WHEELS

A grinding wheel is made up of:

1 The *abrasive* grains or grit.
2 The *bond*.

The abrasive

This forms the cutting edges. It is an extremely hard material. It is carefully selected for both type and size to suit the material being ground and the quality of the surface finish required on the work. Chips of metal are cut from the workpiece by the individual grains which project from the periphery of the wheel.

ABRASIVE	SYMBOL	APPLICATION
Aluminium Oxide	A	Carbon steels
Silicon Carbide	C	Cast iron
Diamond	D	Tungsten carbide
Cubic Boron Nitride	CBN	High speed steels

TABLE 1

Types of abrasive

There is a variety of abrasive materials, each of which is suited to grinding particular workpiece materials. TABLE 1 will give you an indication of how abrasives are selected. Each abrasive is identified by a symbol.

The size of the abrasive grains

The quality of the surface finish depends to some extent on the size of the abrasive grains. The larger the grains the rougher will be the ground surface. The grains are 'sized' by passing the abrasive material through a series of sieves. The sieves have a number of meshes per unit length. The sizes of the grains range from 8 (which is a very coarse mesh) to 600 (which is a fine mesh). See FIGURE 3

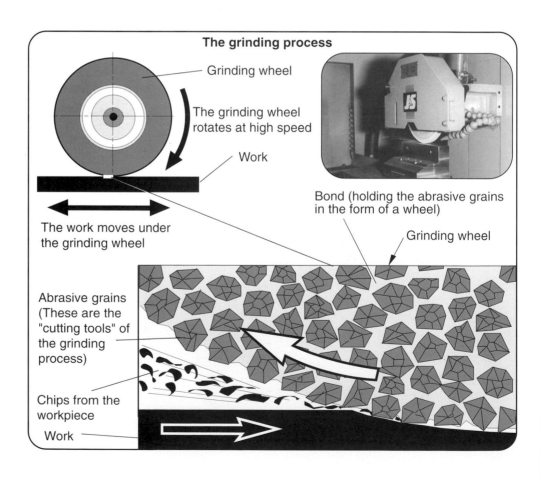

FIGURE 2

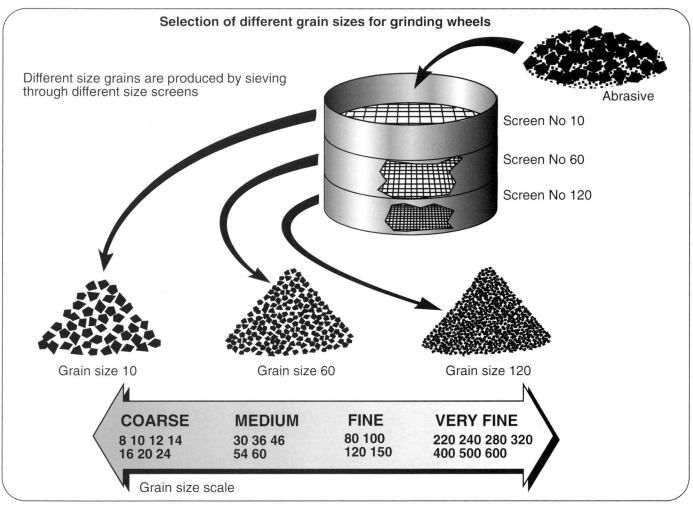

Selection of different grain sizes for grinding wheels

Different size grains are produced by sieving through different size screens

Abrasive

Screen No 10

Screen No 60

Screen No 120

Grain size 10

Grain size 60

Grain size 120

COARSE	MEDIUM	FINE	VERY FINE
8 10 12 14 16 20 24	30 36 46 54 60	80 100 120 150	220 240 280 320 400 500 600

Grain size scale

FIGURE 3

The bond

There are five main types of bond in use. The bond holds the abrasive grains together in the form of a wheel (similar to the way in which cement holds sand in concrete).

Bond type

TABLE 2 gives you the names and typical applications of the more commonly used bond types.

BOND TYPE	SYMBOL	APPLICATION
Vitrified	V	General work on carbon steels
Resinoid	B	Rapid metal removal, fettling
Rubber	R	Cutting off with very thin wheels
Shellac	E	Cutting off
Silicate	S	Tool grinding (cool cutting)

TABLE 2

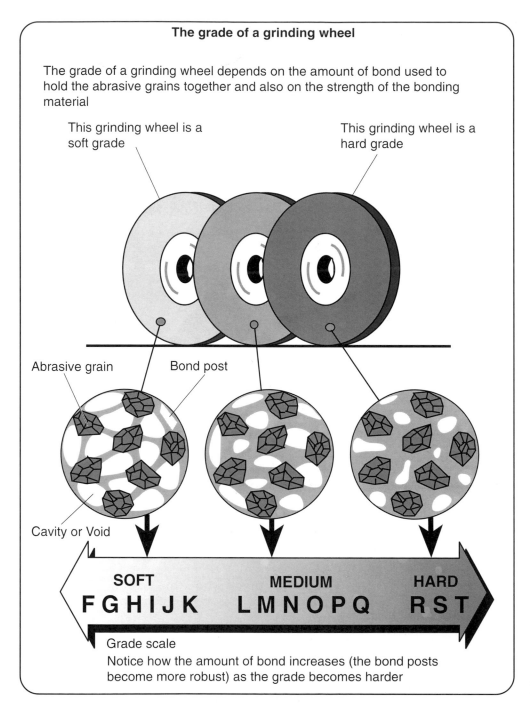

The grade of a grinding wheel

The grade of a grinding wheel depends on the amount of bond used to hold the abrasive grains together and also on the strength of the bonding material

This grinding wheel is a soft grade

This grinding wheel is a hard grade

Abrasive grain   Bond post

Cavity or Void

SOFT   MEDIUM   HARD
F G H I J K   L M N O P Q   R S T

Grade scale
Notice how the amount of bond increases (the bond posts become more robust) as the grade becomes harder

FIGURE 4

The grade (or bond strength) of a grinding wheel
This is a measure of the *hardness* of a grinding wheel. A hard wheel is one in which the bond has high strength. A soft wheel on the other hand has a weaker bond. The strength of the bond depends on two factors.

1 The strength of the material itself.
2 The amount of bond present (This is explained in **FIGURE 4**).

The bond plays a very important part in the grinding process. While grinding, the abrasive grains

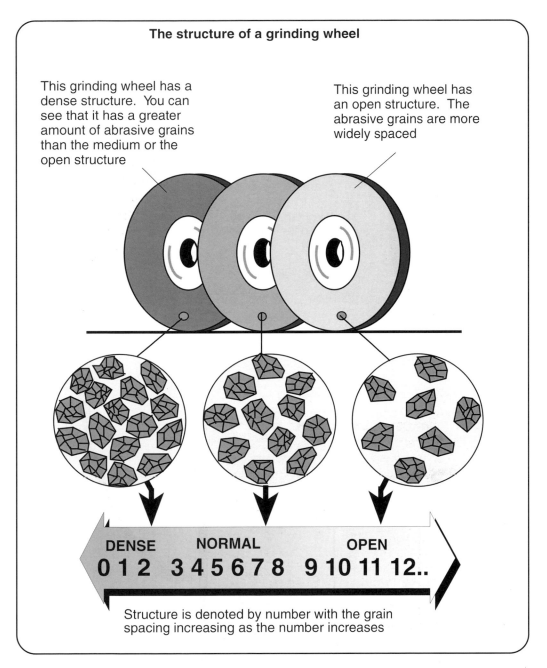

The structure of a grinding wheel

This grinding wheel has a dense structure. You can see that it has a greater amount of abrasive grains than the medium or the open structure

This grinding wheel has an open structure. The abrasive grains are more widely spaced

DENSE   NORMAL   OPEN

0 1 2   3 4 5 6 7 8   9 10 11 12..

Structure is denoted by number with the grain spacing increasing as the number increases

FIGURE 5

become worn. The bond should then allow these worn grains to break away. As the worn grains break away they expose new sharp grains underneath. The breaking away of the grains from the bond is part of a process known as *self dressing*. A grinding wheel which has been specially selected to match the grinding conditions and the workpiece material will self dress and will cut properly.

Remember: The hardness or grade of a grinding wheel has nothing to do with the hardness of the abrasive.

The structure of a grinding wheel
The structure is the proportion of the abrasive grain to the bond. In an open wheel the abrasive grains are widely spaced. There may also be voids or pores

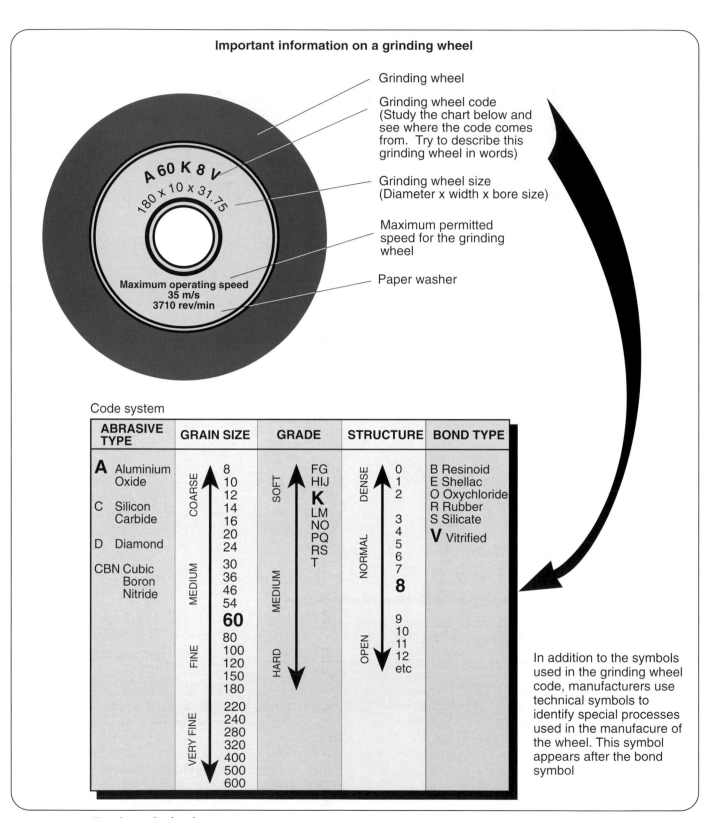

FIGURE 6   *Grinding wheel code system.*

in the bond. This type of wheel is cool-cutting and it is suitable for high rates of metal removal. In a dense structure the grains are closer together. A dense structure is preferable where long wheel life (with low metal removal rates) and high quality surface finish are required.

The structure range is from *dense* to *open*. In FIGURE 5 you can see the difference between dense and open structure.

Selection of grinding wheels

A grinding wheel, like any cutting tool, must be carefully selected to match the following:

1 The workpiece material it is expected to grind. These can be hard materials or soft materials.
2 The conditions under which it is expected to operate. These include the speed at which the grinding wheel rotates and the condition of the grinding machine.

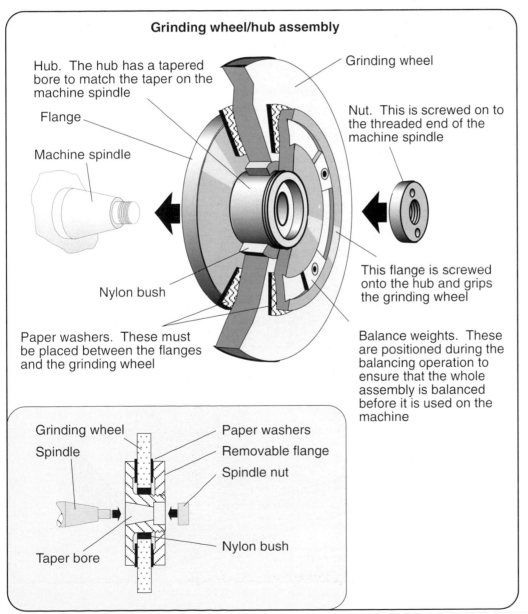

Grinding wheel/hub assembly

Hub. The hub has a tapered bore to match the taper on the machine spindle

Flange

Machine spindle

Grinding wheel

Nut. This is screwed on to the threaded end of the machine spindle

This flange is screwed onto the hub and grips the grinding wheel

Nylon bush

Paper washers. These must be placed between the flanges and the grinding wheel

Balance weights. These are positioned during the balancing operation to ensure that the whole assembly is balanced before it is used on the machine

Grinding wheel
Spindle
Paper washers
Removable flange
Spindle nut
Nylon bush
Taper bore

FIGURE 7 *Grinding wheel/hub assembly.*

The workpiece material
Hard materials cause the abrasive grains to wear quickly. The worn grains should break away and expose new sharp grains underneath. To allow the worn grains to break away, the bond should be soft.

Soft materials can be cut fairly easily. The abrasive grains remain sharp for longer periods. In this case the bond can be hard.

Working conditions of the grinding wheel
The faster a grinding wheel rotates, the more difficult it becomes to dislodge the worn grains. The wheel takes on the characteristics of a hard wheel. A slow running wheel behaves as a slightly softer wheel.

Worn bearings, poor rigidity and out-of-balance wheels are some of the causes of poor surface finish and excessive wheel wear.

Grinding wheel marking system
There is a very large variety of abrasive and bond combinations possible. Grinding wheels are given a special mark or *code* which identifies the wheel type. The system is explained in **FIGURE 6**.

Grinding wheel mounting
Grinding wheels on precision grinding machines are first fitted and secured on a special hub. The hub has a fixed flange on one side and a loose (detachable) flange on the other side. A large, soft paper washer is placed on either side of the wheel so that the flanges do not crush it. The paper squeezes into the spaces between the abrasive grains and ensures that the flanges take a good grip on the wheel. In **FIGURE 7** you will see how the grinding wheel is mounted on the hub.

Grinding wheel balancing
It is not possible to grind satisfactorily if the grinding wheel is out-of-balance. If you do not balance the

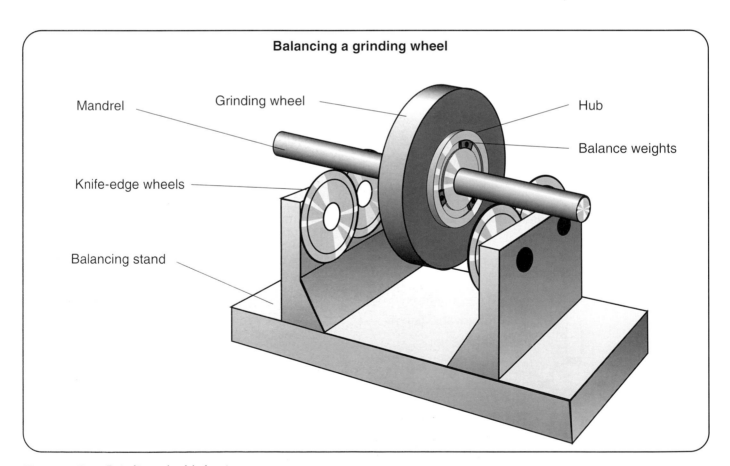

Balancing a grinding wheel

Mandrel — Grinding wheel — Hub — Balance weights — Knife-edge wheels — Balancing stand

FIGURE 8   *Grinding wheel balancing.*

wheel the spindle will vibrate. These vibrations will cause a bad surface finish on the workpiece.

On precision grinding machines the wheel is balanced on a balancing stand. The balance weights that you can see in **FIGURE 8** are moved around the flange and locked in position when the wheel assembly is completely balanced.

Grinding wheel condition

A grinding wheel should only be used within the manufacturer's recommendations. All of the information regarding the wheel type and correct spindle speed can be found on the paper washer on the wheel. Failure to use the wheel correctly can result in poor cutting and it can also be a serious risk to the safety of the operator.

The main faults which can develop are:

- **Loading**
- **Glazing.**

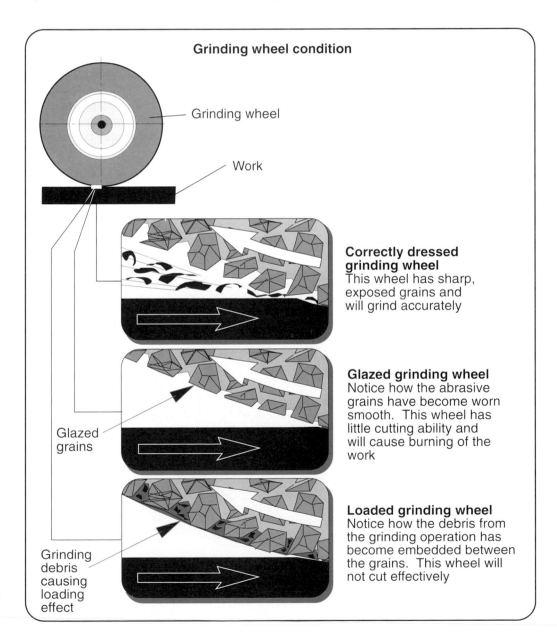

Grinding wheel condition

Grinding wheel

Work

Correctly dressed grinding wheel
This wheel has sharp, exposed grains and will grind accurately

Glazed grains

Glazed grinding wheel
Notice how the abrasive grains have become worn smooth. This wheel has little cutting ability and will cause burning of the work

Grinding debris causing loading effect

Loaded grinding wheel
Notice how the debris from the grinding operation has become embedded between the grains. This wheel will not cut effectively

FIGURE 9 *Comparison between dressed, glazed and loaded wheel.*

A wheel becomes *loaded* when small particles of grinding debris become trapped in the surface of the wheel between the abrasive grains. Any attempt to grind with a loaded wheel will result in poor cutting and a tendency to overheat and possibly burn the workpiece.

You can recognise a *glazed* wheel by its shiny appearance. If the worn or dulled abrasive grains fail to break free of the wheel then the wheel is said to become glazed. A glazed wheel will not grind efficiently and will burn the workpiece. In FIGURE 9 you can compare a properly *dressed* grinding wheel with glazed and loaded wheels.

Grinding wheel dressing

The cutting surface of a grinding wheel should be maintained sharp and true. A diamond traversed across the wheel will correct any irregularities, e.g. out-of-roundness and undulations in the face. FIGURE 10 shows how a wheel is dressed.

Self dressing

Self dressing was referred to briefly under the heading of *Grade*. There it was stated that when the abrasive grains become worn they should break free of the bond and expose new sharp grains underneath. Another way that self dressing occurs is when abrasive grains break along cleavage planes and produce very sharp edges. This effect would be similar to breaking a smooth sandstone. There would be very sharp edges on the broken fragments.

SURFACE GRINDING

Surface grinding is a metal cutting process. Its purpose is to generate flat surfaces on the workpiece. The surfaces produced by surface grinding are extremely smooth and because of this it is often considered to be a finishing process. It is used effectively on both hard and soft workpiece materials.

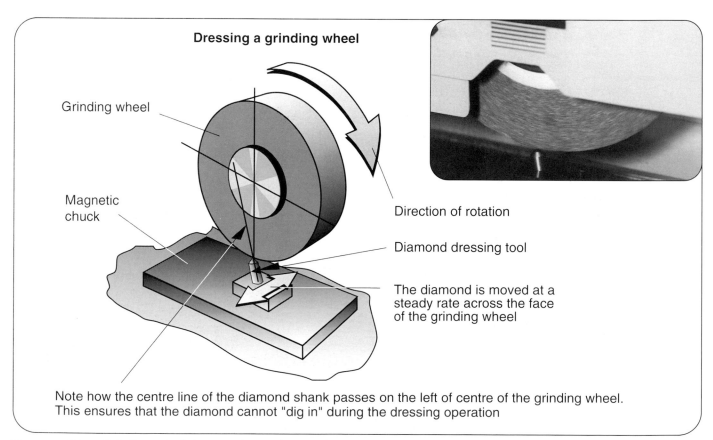

Dressing a grinding wheel

Grinding wheel

Magnetic chuck

Direction of rotation

Diamond dressing tool

The diamond is moved at a steady rate across the face of the grinding wheel

Note how the centre line of the diamond shank passes on the left of centre of the grinding wheel. This ensures that the diamond cannot "dig in" during the dressing operation

FIGURE 10   *Grinding wheel dressing. (Inset photograph courtesy: Jones and Shipman Plc)*

There are many different types of surface grinding machines. One type has a reciprocating table and may use either a vertical spindle or a horizontal spindle as shown in **FIGURE 11**.

MAIN PARTS AND MOVEMENTS OF THE SURFACE GRINDING MACHINE

All surface grinding machines have certain features in common.

- **Rotary movement of the grinding wheel**
- **Table movement for feeding the workpiece into the grinding wheel**
- **Movement for setting the depth of cut.**

The base
The base of the surface grinding machine is a hollow casting. It is reinforced on the inside by ribs. This is to ensure that there is no vibration during grinding. The base contains the fluid for the hydraulic power and also the hydraulic pump.

The column
The purpose of the column is to carry the wheelhead and to allow the wheelhead to be moved up and down. (The depth of cut is increased by moving the grinding wheel downwards.) A motor at the bottom of the column drives the spindle by means of a belt which runs inside the column.

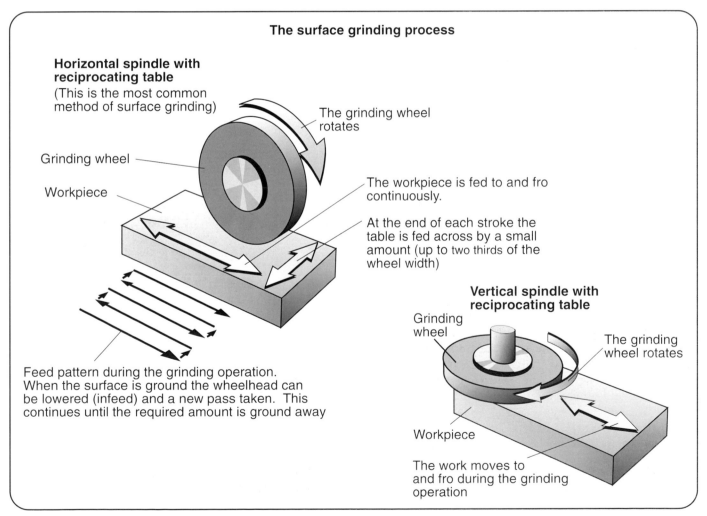

FIGURE 11 *The surface grinding process.*

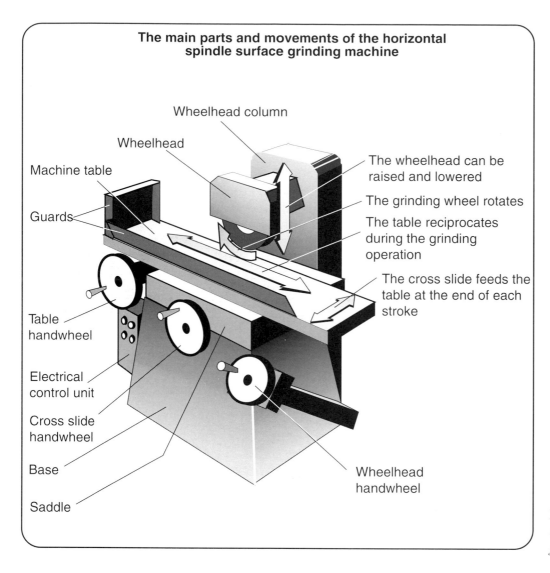

The main parts and movements of the horizontal spindle surface grinding machine

Wheelhead column

Wheelhead

Machine table

Guards

The wheelhead can be raised and lowered

The grinding wheel rotates

The table reciprocates during the grinding operation

The cross slide feeds the table at the end of each stroke

Table handwheel

Electrical control unit

Cross slide handwheel

Base

Saddle

Wheelhead handwheel

FIGURE 12 *Main parts and movements of the surface grinding machine.*

The wheelhead
The spindle is mounted in precision bearings in the wheelhead. The wheelhead is at the top of the column. The spindle which projects from the wheelhead has a tapered end. This taper carries and drives the grinding wheel hub.

The table
The table is located on special slideways. You can move it by rotating a handwheel or you can put it on automatic feed. On automatic feed, the table reciprocates at a steady speed each way. The table speed is infinitely variable. It is operated by a hydraulic cylinder.

The table can move in two directions in the horizontal plane.

Vertical movement, to provide wheel infeed, is on the wheelhead. The wheelhead can move up and down. The wheel axis always remains parallel to the work surface of the table. **FIGURE 12** shows the main parts and movements of the surface grinding machine.

WORKHOLDING

The usual means of holding workpieces for surface grinding is on the *magnetic chuck*. There are some

FIGURE 13   *The magnetic chuck and principle of operation. (Courtesy: Eclipse Magnetics Ltd.)*

important factors which must be considered before attempting to use the magnetic chuck.

- **The work must be a magnetic material**
- **The work must have a flat surface in order to make good contact with the chuck**
- **The surface of the work and the surface of the chuck must be clean.**

The magnetic chuck

The most important characteristic of magnetic workholding is that the force of attraction, or pull, depends entirely on the *magnetic flux* that can be induced in the workpiece by the chuck.

The magnetic chuck can be switched "on" and "off". The method of switching is called *flux diversion*. The chuck has a moving magnet system. By operating a control handle this magnet can be moved under the top plate. It is similar to sliding a *keeper* between the magnet and the workpiece. You can see a magnetic chuck in **FIGURE 13**.

Adaptor plates

Magnetic chucks with large 'poles' are not suitable for gripping light workpieces. Adaptor plates (like the one you can see in **FIGURE 14**) are available which provide much smaller poles. An adaptor plate is constructed of alternate layers of brass and mild steel strips. The mild steel strips are shaped so that alternate ones pick up flux from opposite poles on the chuck face.

FIGURE 14   *Adaptor Plate. (Courtesy: Eclipse Magnetics Ltd.)*

FIGURE 15 *The use of chuck blocks to support a workpiece. (Courtesy: Eclipse Magnetics Ltd.)*

Chuck blocks

These are special magnetic blocks (**FIGURE 15**) which are parallel. They are assemblies of alternate layers of mild steel and epoxy resin. Chuck blocks may be machined to the shape of the workpiece.

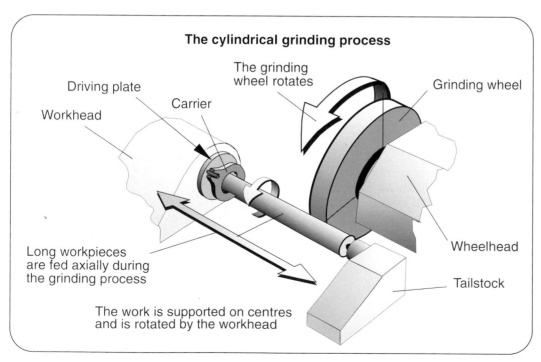

The cylindrical grinding process

Driving plate

Workhead

Carrier

The grinding wheel rotates

Grinding wheel

Wheelhead

Tailstock

Long workpieces are fed axially during the grinding process

The work is supported on centres and is rotated by the workhead

FIGURE 16 *The principle of cylindrical grinding.*

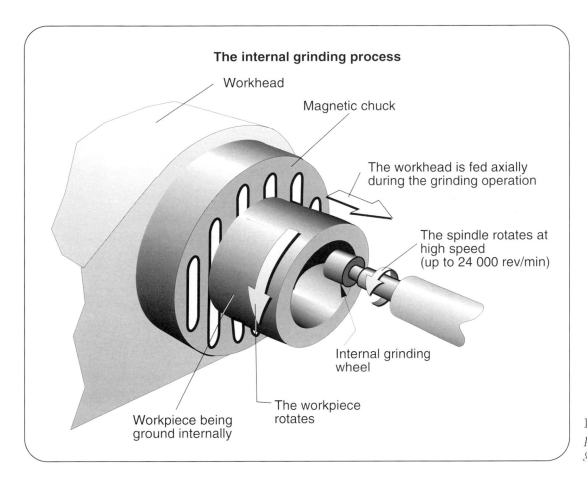

The internal grinding process

Workhead

Magnetic chuck

The workhead is fed axially during the grinding operation

The spindle rotates at high speed (up to 24 000 rev/min)

Internal grinding wheel

The workpiece rotates

Workpiece being ground internally

FIGURE 17 *The principle of internal grinding.*

The universal vice

This means of workholding should be used only when there is no likelihood of distorting the workpiece. A vice used for grinding should not be used for any other purpose.

The sine chuck

The sine chuck is used to hold workpieces on which an angle is to be ground. The sine chuck is essentially a magnetic chuck which can be tilted on its base. The angle of tilt is calculated in the same way in which the angle of a sine bar is calculated. The chuck is then set up on slip gauges and locked in position.

CYLINDRICAL GRINDING

This grinding operation is used to produce cylindrical workpieces. The workpiece is gripped in a chuck or is mounted between centres and is made to rotate at a constant speed. The grinding wheel, when brought into contact with the workpiece, will grind it into a near perfect cylinder. The work table of the cylindrical grinding machine reciprocates so that long workpieces can be ground. The wheelhead can be moved towards the workpiece to provide infeed. The table can be swivelled to enable tapered work to be ground. The principle of cylindrical grinding is shown in **FIGURE 16**.

INTERNAL GRINDING

This is a method of producing accurately-sized internal diameters. The workpiece is gripped in a chuck and rotated at a constant speed. A small diameter grinding wheel on a long spindle is used. Because of its small diameter the grinding wheel rotates at a very high speed (often as high as 24 000 rev/min). The principle of internal grinding is shown in **FIGURE 17**.

SUMMARY

Grinding is sometimes referred to as abrasive machining. This is because the grinding process makes use of small particles of an extremely hard material acting as tiny cutting tools. The hard particles (or grit) are bonded together in the form of a wheel. This wheel can be fitted to the spindle of a grinding machine. The wheel rotates at high speed and the work is brought into contact with it. Careful control of the work position and movement allows very accurate sizes and high quality surfaces to be generated by the grinding wheel.

There are two main constituents in a grinding wheel:

1 The abrasive (this is the grit).
2 The bond (this holds the abrasive in a rigid shape).

There are also small pockets, or voids as they are known, within the wheel. These are important because the more voids that are present, and the bigger they are, the easier it is to dislodge the abrasive from the wheel.

The abrasive forms the cutting edges. Usually, a particular abrasive type is selected to suit the material being ground. The surface finish required on the work influences the size of the abrasive grains chosen.

The bond, while designed to hold the abrasive in the form of a wheel, also must release the grains when they become worn. There will be greater pressure on a grain from the work if it has lost its cutting ability so it will become dislodged exposing sharper grains underneath. This process is called *self-dressing*. Grains can break along cleavage planes creating sharp corners. This is also part of the self-dressing action.

There are different types of bond for different grinding applications. A bond which releases the abrasive after a small amount of wear would be a soft bond. A grinding wheel of this nature would be regarded as a "soft wheel". One which resists the release of grains for longer periods would be regarded as a "hard wheel".

The grade of a grinding wheel refers to the strength of the bond. The strength of the bond depends on:

- **The strength of the material itself**
- **The amount of the bond present. (If the voids are large there is less bond.)**

Grinding wheel structure is the proportion of abrasive to bond. The greater the amount of abrasive the more dense the wheel is. An open wheel has less abrasive.

As a general rule, hard materials are ground with a soft wheel and soft materials are ground with a hard wheel. Hard materials will dull the abrasive quickly so they need to be dislodged or "cleaved" (broken along cleavage planes) to keep the wheel sharp. Soft materials will not cause the abrasive grains to wear so quickly so the bond should retain them longer.

Grinding wheels are identified by a code which indicates:

- **The abrasive type**
- **The grain size**
- **The grade**
- **The structure**
- **The bond type.**

Before using a grinding wheel on the machine it should be:

- **Checked for flaws**
- **Tapped lightly to check for soundness (ringing)**
- **Mounted on the hub**
- **Balanced**
- **Trued on the machine (and possibly re-balanced)**
- **Dressed.**

Grinding wheel faults
The main faults which occur are:

- **Loading**
- **Glazing.**

Loading is the result of particles of dust and metal from the grinding process becoming trapped between the grains. The abrasive will no longer be able to make contact with the work if this happens.

Glazing is the result of the abrasive becoming worn smooth and having no ability to cut the workpiece material.

Methods of precision grinding

The following are the main types of precision grinding. Other methods are usually variations of these two basic processes.

• **Surface grinding**
• **Cylindrical grinding.**

In surface grinding, a flat surface is ground on the work. In one type, the machine table holding the work, moves to and fro under the rotating wheel.

In cylindrical grinding the work is in contact with the wheel in an arrangement similar to the lathe. The work rotates and its diameter is altered when the rotating wheel cuts material from it.

There are many workholding devices for grinding machines. Because there are very low cutting forces on the work, magnetic workholding devices are very often used.

The Shaping Machine

INTRODUCTION

The shaping machine, shown in **FIGURE 1**, is used to generate flat surfaces. It uses a single-point cutting tool similar to the lathe tool. The shaping machine is capable of machining surfaces parallel to the machine table. It can also machine surfaces perpendicular to the table or at any angle between those two extremes.

THE SHAPING PROCESS

To generate a flat surface with a single-point tool, there must be at least two relative motions. In the

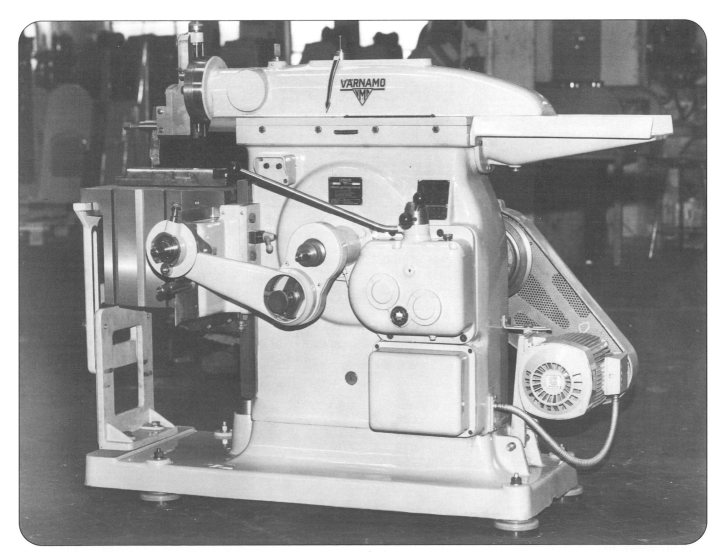

FIGURE 1   *The shaping machine. (Courtesy: Värnamo Sweden)*

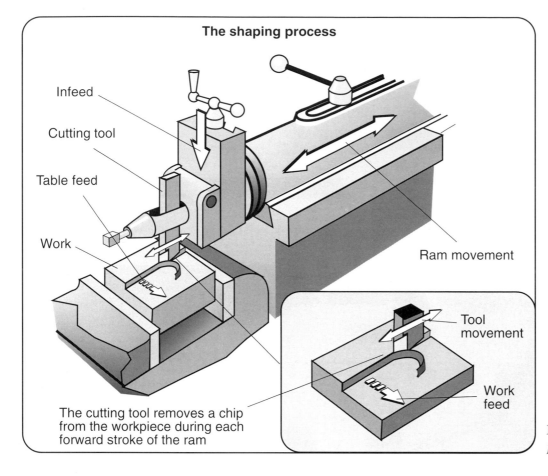

The shaping process

Infeed

Cutting tool

Table feed

Work

Ram movement

The cutting tool removes a chip from the workpiece during each forward stroke of the ram

Tool movement

Work feed

FIGURE 2 *The shaping process.*

shaping process the tool reciprocates in one plane. This is one motion. The workpiece is fed at right angles to the movement plane of the tool. This is the second motion. During each forward movement of the tool, a chip is removed from the workpiece. As the tool returns to take the next cut, the workpiece is moved a small amount.

The only method of machining a flat surface at the beginning of the nineteenth century was to mount it on the faceplate of the lathe. The demand grew for machines which were more suited to machining flat surfaces. Richard Roberts invented a planing machine which could handle large surfaces. Other inventors who contributed were Matthew Murray (in 1814) and Joseph Clement (in 1825). The shaping machine as it is at present was first shown at the Great Exhibition of 1851. It was made by Joseph Whitworth.

In **FIGURE 2** you can see the shaping machine removing a chip from the workpiece. The movement of the tool as it is removing a chip is known as the cutting stroke. The workpiece does not move during the cutting stroke. When the tool is travelling back to start, the movement is referred to as the return stroke.

THE MAIN PARTS AND MOVEMENTS OF THE SHAPING MACHINE

Refer to **FIGURE 3** while you are studying this section.

The base
The base of the shaping machine is made from cast iron.

The column
The column is a rigid hollow casting. The main

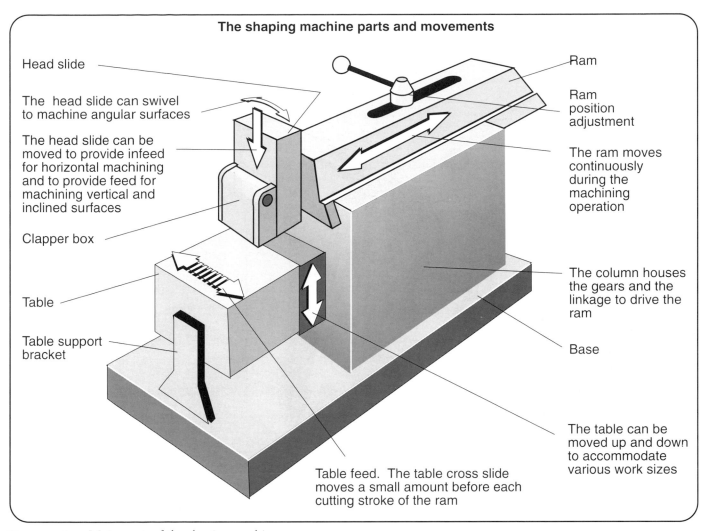

The shaping machine parts and movements

Head slide

The head slide can swivel to machine angular surfaces

The head slide can be moved to provide infeed for horizontal machining and to provide feed for machining vertical and inclined surfaces

Clapper box

Table

Table support bracket

Ram

Ram position adjustment

The ram moves continuously during the machining operation

The column houses the gears and the linkage to drive the ram

Base

The table can be moved up and down to accommodate various work sizes

Table feed. The table cross slide moves a small amount before each cutting stroke of the ram

FIGURE 3 *Main parts of the shaping machine.*

drive elements are housed inside the column. These include a gearbox to provide a range of cutting speeds, and the mechanism to drive the ram. There are two sets of slideways on the column.

1 On top are the slideways for the ram.
2 On the front are the slideways for the table.

The driving motor is usually bolted to the back of the column.

The ram
The ram is fitted in the slides on top of the column. These are dovetail slides and they ensure that the ram travels in the same plane each time it moves.

Lifting tendencies due to overhang and the cutting forces are resisted by the shape of the slides. The end of the ram carries the head slide assembly.

The head slide
There are two parts in the head slide assembly.

1 The slide is the means of moving the tool into contact with the work (infeed). In vertical or angular machining the slide can be used to provide feed. (It is important to understand the difference between 'feed' and 'infeed'.)
2 The clapper box holds the tool. It is attached to the head slide by a hinge mechanism. On the forward stroke of the ram the tool removes a chip

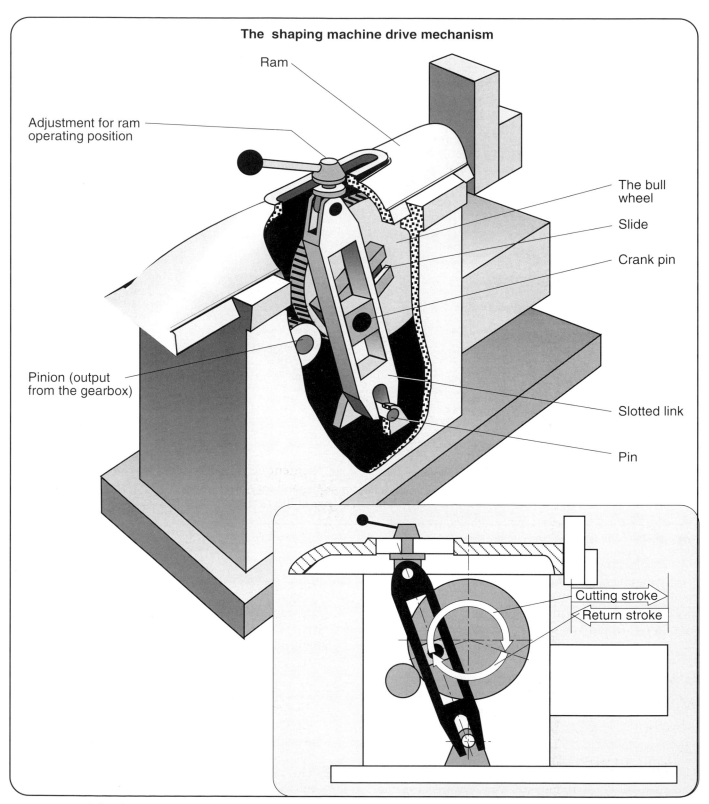

The shaping machine drive mechanism

Ram

Adjustment for ram operating position

The bull wheel

Slide

Crank pin

Pinion (output from the gearbox)

Slotted link

Pin

Cutting stroke

Return stroke

FIGURE 4 *The shaping machine drive mechanism.*

from the workpiece. On the return stroke the clapper box flips the tool upwards off the work to allow the table to feed the work across for the next cut. This ensures that the point of the tool does not break on the return stroke of the ram.

The table

The machine table is mounted on a saddle which can move across the machine. It can also be raised and lowered. A leadscrew on the crossrail moves the table across. The leadscrew is operated by a crank for positioning the table or it can be moved by a power feed when machining flat surfaces in the horizontal plane.

In a universal shaping machine the table can be tilted through various angles.

Tee slots in the surface of the table make it possible to bolt workpieces directly to it or to mount a machine vice on it. To prevent sagging of the table, a support bracket is fitted to the front. The height of this support bracket is adjustable.

The shaping machine drive mechanism

The ram of the shaping machine is driven by a quick-return mechanism. A quick return is required because the tool cuts on the forward (cutting) stroke only and idles on the return stroke. To make the machine more efficient you try to reduce the return time as much as possible. Most reciprocating machine tools are distinguished by their ingenious quick-return mechanism. The shaping machine is no exception.

You can see the main elements of the drive mechanism in FIGURE 4.

The pinion is driven by the driving motor through the gearbox. The pinion rotates the bull wheel. The slotted link is pinned to the ram position adjuster at the top end, and is constrained by the fulcrum pin at the bottom end. When the bull wheel rotates, the crank pin causes the slotted link to move back and forth. The position of the crank pin can be changed to operate on a large or small radius. It is mounted on a slide on the bull wheel. A leadscrew, which is rotated by a bevel gear, moves the crank pin along the slide. Changing the position of the crank pin has the effect of moving the ram through a longer or shorter stroke.

The angle through which the bull wheel rotates on the cutting stroke is greater than the angle through which it rotates on the return stroke. You can see this in FIGURE 5, A is larger than B. It is reasonable to say that because the bull wheel rotates at a constant speed, it will take less time to rotate through the angle B than it will take to rotate through the angle A. The ram will therefore move faster on the return stroke than it will on the cutting stroke.

The table feed mechanism

As you have already seen, the table of the shaping machine is fed in small increments. Each feed movement takes place during the return stroke of the cutting tool. The mechanism shown in FIGURE 6 allows you to feed the table in either direction.

The bracket carrying the pawl is rocked to and fro by the eccentric. The pawl engages the teeth in the ratchet and moves it through a part of a revolution. The ratchet is fixed to the table leadscrew. The pawl 'skips' over the ratchet teeth as it rocks backward and the cycle is repeated.

By rotating the pawl through 180° you can cause the leadscrew to be moved in the opposite direction.

The amount by which the table moves on each increment depends on the number of teeth taken by the pawl on each movement. The lowest feed rate would be one tooth each time.

ALIGNMENTS OF THE SHAPING MACHINE

The movement of the shaping machine ram is used as the basic alignment reference.

1 The working surface of the table must be parallel to the movement of the ram.
2 The table cross traverse movement should be perpendicular to the ram movement.

SHAPING OPERATIONS

Shaping involves generating a flat surface using a single-point tool. The surface produced can be:

1 Parallel to the machine table.
2 Perpendicular to the machine table.
3 At any angle between 1 and 2.

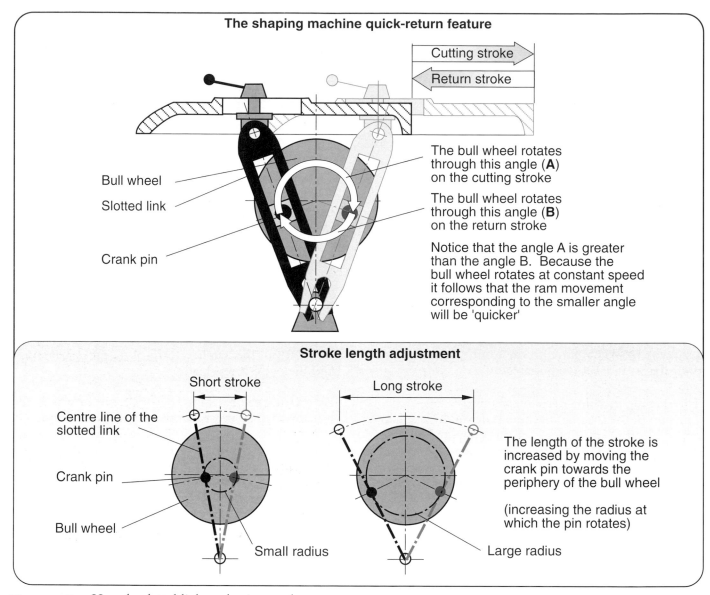

FIGURE 5 *How the slotted link mechanism works.*

On each cutting stroke the tool removes a chip from the step between the rough (unmachined) surface and the machined surface.

Shaping vertical surfaces
The feed in this situation is controlled by the head slide.

Shaping inclined surfaces
Here again the feed is controlled by the head slide. In both of these situations, the clapper box has to be set to ensure that the tool will lift off the workpiece on the return stroke.

SETTING UP THE SHAPING MACHINE

It is important to set up the shaping machine correctly. There are three aspects to setting up:

1 Setting the stroke length.
2 Setting the stroke position.
3 Workholding.

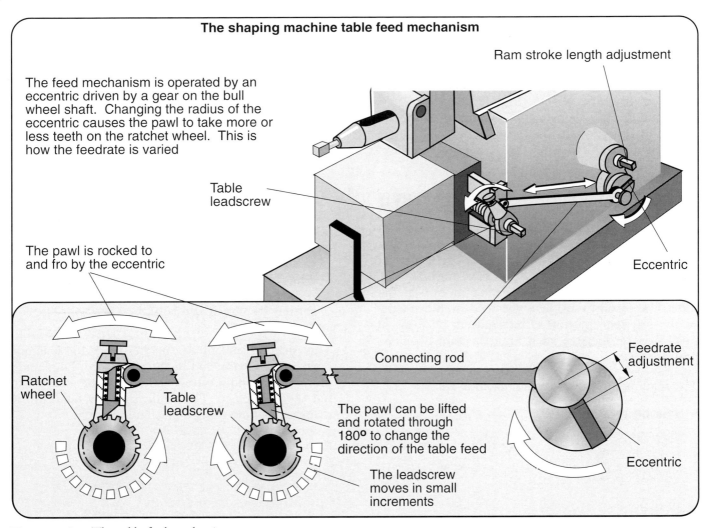

The feed mechanism is operated by an eccentric driven by a gear on the bull wheel shaft. Changing the radius of the eccentric causes the pawl to take more or less teeth on the ratchet wheel. This is how the feedrate is varied

Ram stroke length adjustment

Table leadscrew

The pawl is rocked to and fro by the eccentric

Eccentric

Connecting rod

Feedrate adjustment

Ratchet wheel

Table leadscrew

The pawl can be lifted and rotated through 180° to change the direction of the table feed

The leadscrew moves in small increments

Eccentric

FIGURE 6   *The table feed mechanism.*

Setting the stroke length
The total length of the stroke should include a small overrun at the start and finish of the stroke. The speed of the ram is at a maximum at the centre of the stroke. At the beginning and end of the stroke the speed of the ram is building up and slowing down respectively. An overrun at the start and end of the stroke helps towards achieving a more constant speed over the work. It is also necessary that the tool clears the work at each end of the stroke. Too much overrun on the other hand makes the operation inefficient.

Setting the stroke position
The tool has to be set in the correct position relative to the position of the work. The ram can be moved in either direction and locked relative to the slotted link. In **FIGURE 4** you will have seen the feature for setting the operating position of the ram.

Workholding
The workpiece can be bolted directly to the shaping machine table or held in the machine vice.

A spirit level can be used to check that the workpiece is parallel to the machine table. This is assuming that the machine table is 'level' in the first instance.

The machine vice
This is the most convenient method of gripping the

workpiece. You should make sure that the vice jaws are accurately aligned with the ram movement. The alignment of the workpiece can be checked using a dial indicator.

Shaping machine tools

The cutting tools used on the shaping machine are similar to lathe tools at the cutting edge. The shank of the shaping machine cutting tool is often goose-necked to prevent digging-in.

SUMMARY

The shaping machine is used to generate flat surfaces on workpieces. It uses a single point cutting tool which is similar to a lathe tool. To generate flat surfaces the shaping machine has two motions. The primary motion is the reciprocating motion of the tool. The second motion is the feed motion of the work. The feed motion is intermittent. It feeds in small steps – one step each time the tool is on the return stroke.

The main parts of the shaping machine are:

- **The base**
- **The column which contains the main drive mechanism**
- **The ram which carries the headslide**
- **The headslide which carries the clapper box and tool post**
- **The table which can move on both horizontal and vertical slides**
- **The drive mechanism. The quick-return mechanism of the shaping machine is a most important feature. The tool does not cut on the return stroke and therefore the time during this "idle" stroke should be as short as possible. The quick-return mechanism provides a cutting stroke and at a suitable speed for the tool and a return stroke which is faster**
- **The table feed mechanism is designed to move the table in short steps during the return stroke of the tool.**

The shaping machine can be used to machine horizontal, vertical and inclined surfaces. The length of the stroke and position the tool can be adjusted to suit the workpiece. The work is usually held on the shaping machine using a machine vice.

ENGINEERING TECHNOLOGY

Metal Cutting

INTRODUCTION

Metal cutting is the process of removing or cutting unwanted metal from a workpiece. The metal is cut away in the form of chips or *swarf* using a cutting tool. Metal cutting gives the workpiece its correct shape, its correct size and its desired surface finish.

The tools used to cut the metal are basically wedge shaped. The machine which performs the cutting operation provides the motions, power, toolholding capability and workholding capability required to force the tool into the work. In **FIGURE 1** you can see a chip being cut from a workpiece on a lathe. This is just one of many different types of metal cutting operations.

THE PRINCIPLES OF METAL CUTTING

To understand the basic principles of metal cutting, a good place to start is with the cold chisel. The

FIGURE 1 *A metal cutting operation.*
(Courtesy: Sandvik Coromant)

Cutting tool angles

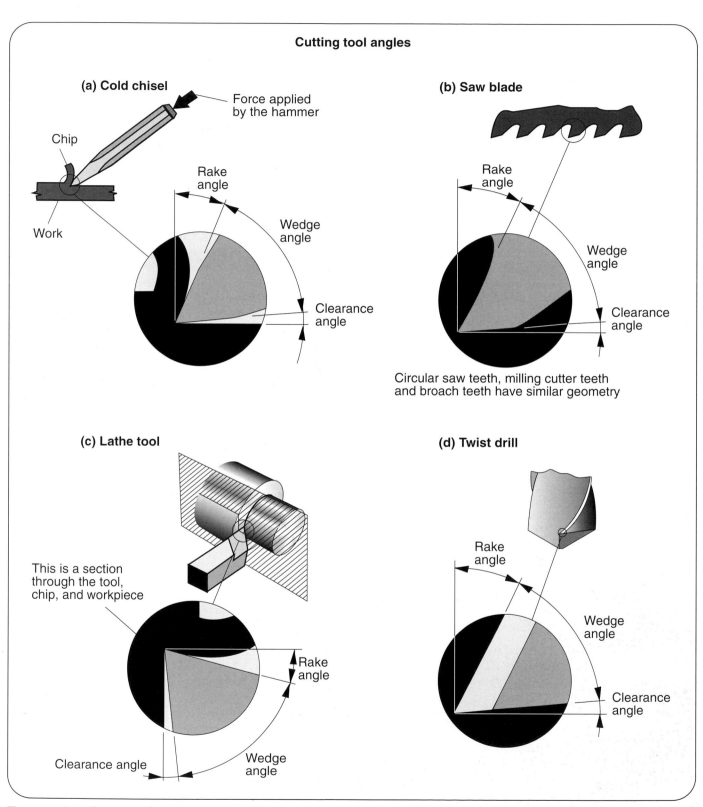

(a) Cold chisel

Force applied by the hammer

Chip

Work

Rake angle

Wedge angle

Clearance angle

(b) Saw blade

Rake angle

Wedge angle

Clearance angle

Circular saw teeth, milling cutter teeth and broach teeth have similar geometry

(c) Lathe tool

This is a section through the tool, chip, and workpiece

Rake angle

Clearance angle

Wedge angle

(d) Twist drill

Rake angle

Wedge angle

Clearance angle

FIGURE 2   *Cutting tool angles.*

point of the cold chisel has the shape of a wedge. The chisel is held so that the underside of the wedge forms a small *clearance angle* between it and the workpiece. If you study **FIGURE 2** you can see this. You can also see how the top of the wedge forms a *rake angle*. The clearance angle ensures that only the cutting edge is in contact with the newly cut surface of the work. The rake angle helps the chisel to dig into the metal and it directs the chip away from the workpiece.

Any metal cutting operation has to have a method of providing the relative movement between the work and the tool and also the power needed to remove the chip. When metal cutting with the cold chisel the relative movement is achieved by clamping the work in a vice and forcing the chisel to move through the metal using hammer blows as the power source. The chisel is hand–held. This is how its direction is guided and the rake and clearance controlled. All other metal cutting operations are based on this example. As you study the chapters on the various metal cutting processes – shaping, turning, milling and grinding – note particularly how the relative movement between the work and the tool is achieved and controlled in each case. Notice also that while these processes look quite different in general terms, they are all very similar in the tool/work zone. In order to achieve this, almost all metal cutting tools have similar geometry. The geometry basically consists of:

- **The wedge angle**
- **The rake angle**
- **The clearance angle.**

You can see some examples in **FIGURE 2**

THE SINGLE POINT CUTTING TOOL

This is the simplest form of cutting tool. It has a wedge shape. The rake and clearance angles are ground into the tool. It is held so that when it is removing a chip it retains the correct rake and clearance angles with respect to the work. **FIGURE 3** shows the geometry of the single point cutting tool.

The rake angle
The rake angle is ground to suit the metal which the tool is required to cut. For example, to cut mild steel the rake angle on a high-speed steel tool might be 20° but to cut harder steel the rake angle might be as low as 5°. A large rake angle reduces the wedge angle. This makes the tool "sharper" but weak at the cutting edge. A small rake angle increases the angle of the wedge making the cutting edge strong. Small rake angles are used when cutting hard materials.

The clearance angle
If the flank of the tool came into contact with the work, the cutting edge could not take off a chip. The clearance angle ensures that only the cutting

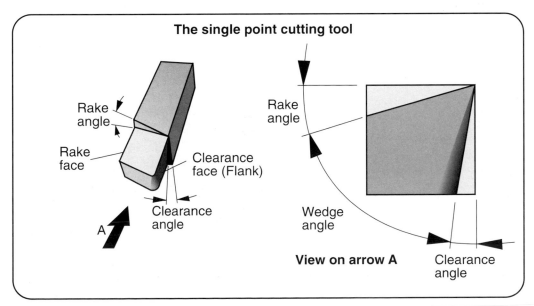

FIGURE 3   *Single point cutting tool.*

edge touches the workpiece. The clearance angle is affected by the shape of the workpiece. This will be obvious when you study the chapters on specific machining processes.

THE THEORY OF METAL CUTTING

In metal cutting the chip is sheared from the workpiece. If you study the photo micrograph in **FIGURE 4** you will see that the shearing action takes place along a line. This line runs from the cutting edge of the tool to where the chip meets the work. This line is in fact a plane because the cutting tool is engaged in the workpiece by the "depth of cut". This plane is known as the *shear plane.*

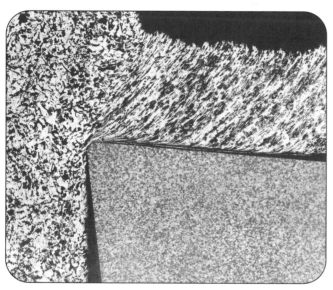

FIGURE 4   *A photo micrograph showing a cutting tool removing a chip from a workpiece.*
(Courtesy: Sandvik Coromant)

It is important to note that the thickness of the chip just formed by the tool is greater than the feed rate. Study these points in **FIGURE 5**.

The shear plane angle
The angle of the shear plane is affected by the rake angle of the tool. If the rake angle is large then the shear plane angle is large. A large shear plane angle gives a reduced shear area. Reducing the angle of the shear plane (smaller rake angle) causes the shear area to be increased. It would be reasonable to assume that it would require less force to shear a

small area than a large area. This is why it is easier to cut with a tool having a large rake angle (small wedge) than it is to cut with a tool whose rake angle is small. Therefore:

- **A large rake angle gives a small shear area — easy to cut**
- **A small rake angle gives a large shear area — more difficult to cut.**

CHIP FORMATION

The principal types of chip formed in metal cutting are:

- **A continuous chip**
- **A discontinuous chip**
- **Another type is one which is often referred to as a chip with a built-up-edge.**

A continuous chip is formed when a ductile metal is machined. As the name suggests this chip remains unbroken while the cutting action continues. Continuous chips tend to become entangled in the work and the tool. This can be very dangerous and should on no account be touched by hand. **FIGURE 6** gives an idea of how a continuous chip can become wrapped around a workpiece. If this should happen the machine should be stopped, the power isolated and a special "swarf rake" used to remove the chip.

A discontinuous chip will be formed when brittle materials are machined. Brass and cast iron are examples of materials which produce a discontinuous chip. The chip is sheared from the workpiece and falls away in small pieces.

THE BUILT-UP-EDGE

A built-up-edge is the name given to a form of pressure-welding of small particles of the workpiece to the rake face of the tool. The particles come from the underside of the chip. The build-up on the tool continues during the cutting action. The material building up on the tool work hardens and is capable of acting as a cutting edge. It continues to build during the cutting operation but eventually reaches a stage when it becomes unstable and breaks off. The process of building up starts again. The alternate

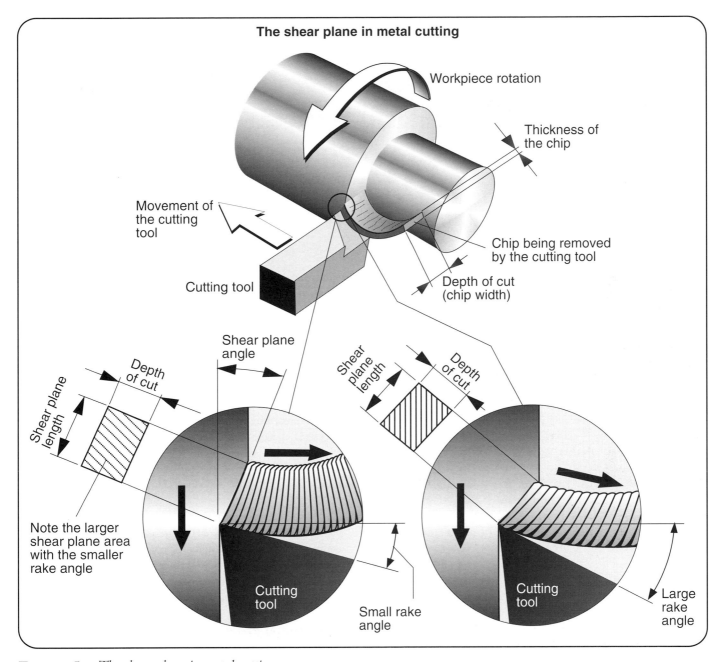

The shear plane in metal cutting

Workpiece rotation

Thickness of the chip

Movement of the cutting tool

Chip being removed by the cutting tool

Cutting tool

Depth of cut (chip width)

Shear plane angle

Depth of cut

Shear plane length

Shear plane length

Depth of cut

Note the larger shear plane area with the smaller rake angle

Cutting tool

Small rake angle

Cutting tool

Large rake angle

FIGURE 5   *The shear plane in metal cutting.*

building up and breaking off of material on the tool has the effect of changing the position of the cutting edge. This can cause dimensional inaccuracy and a bad surface finish on the workpiece. The main causes of the built-up-edge are:

The high pressure of the chip on the tool

The high temperatures caused by the friction of the chip rubbing on the rake face of the tool.

The built-up-edge can be avoided to some extent by using coolant to remove the heat from the cutting zone. **FIGURE 7** shows the different types of chips formed in metal cutting.

FIGURE 6 *A continuous chip wrapped around a workpiece. (Courtesy: Sandvik Coromant)*

To remove a chip, the tool has to be pressed into the workpiece. This requires force. The forces are supplied by the primary cutting motion of the machine and the feed motion of the tool or work. Most of the energy supplied by the motor in a machine tool goes to cut the chip from the workpiece. In FIGURE 8 you can see how the forces act in a metal cutting situation. (The example is based on the turning process.)

There are two important force systems in metal cutting. For the purpose of studying the forces a turning operation is used.

1 Orthogonal cutting – this is a two-force system.
2 Oblique cutting – this is a three-force system.

Orthogonal cutting is a form of metal cutting where there are two forces on the tool. These are:

The tangential force which is caused by the pressure of the chip on the tool.

The axial force which is caused by the workpiece resisting the feed motion of the tool.

The tangential force acts at a tangent to the workpiece. It is given the symbol **Ft**.

The axial force acts parallel to the axis of the workpiece. It is given the symbol **Fa**.

Oblique cutting is a three-force system. Two of the forces are similar to orthogonal cutting. The third force is caused by a plan approach angle on the tool, shown in FIGURE 8. This force is the radial force. As the radial force increases, the axial force decreases. The radial force is given the symbol **Fr**.

The plan approach angle

The plan approach angle is useful in some metal cutting situations. It has the effect of reducing the thickness of the chip for any given depth of cut. The chip thickness is reduced but the cutting action is spread over a greater length of the cutting edge.

MEASURING THE FORCES ON THE CUTTING TOOL

The forces on a tool can be measured using a tool force dynamometer. One type of tool force

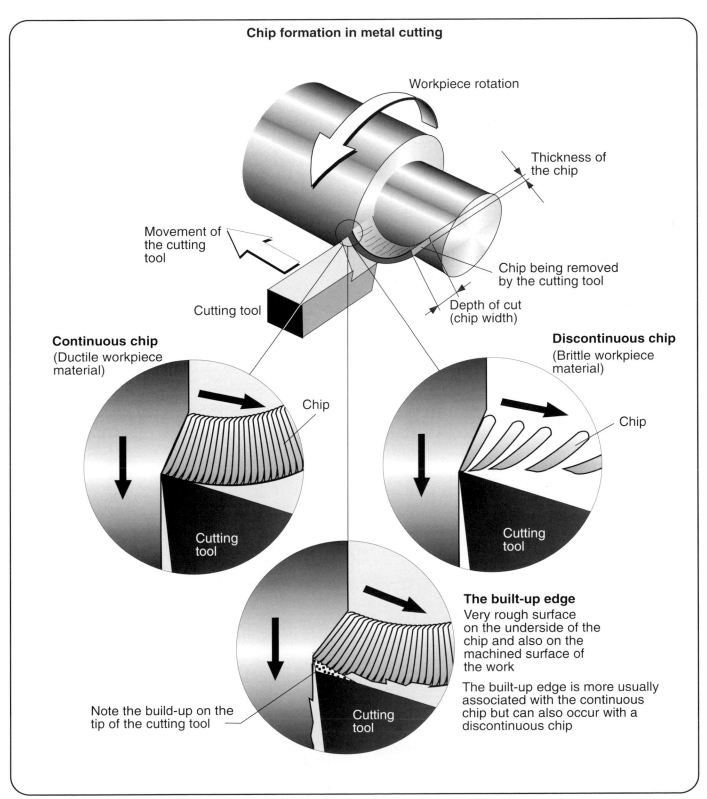

FIGURE 7 *Chip formation in metal cutting.*

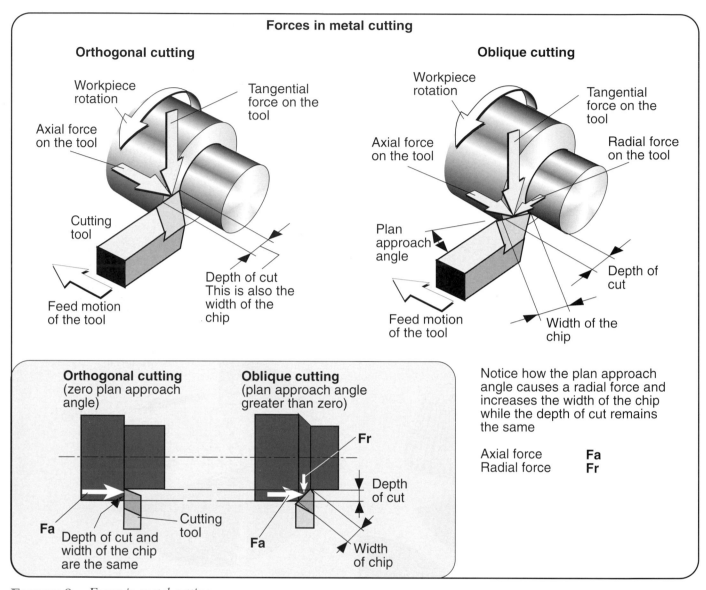

FIGURE 8 *Forces in metal cutting.*

dynamometer is a special tool holder which can deflect when the cutting forces act on the tool. The deflection is measured in millimetres and converted into units of force. The principle of a lathe tool dynamometer is shown in **FIGURE 9**.

THE POWER CONSUMED IN METAL CUTTING

The greater the forces at the tool the greater will be the demands on power. If the forces can be reduced at the tool, less power will be required from the motor. The cutting forces can be reduced in a number of ways.

By increasing the rake angle. The shear area reduces as the rake angle increases as shown in **FIGURE 5**. The smaller shear area will require less force to cut it, so less power will be required.

Using a lubricant will make it easier for the chip to slip over the rake face of the tool so the force required to overcome friction will be reduced. Less power will be required.

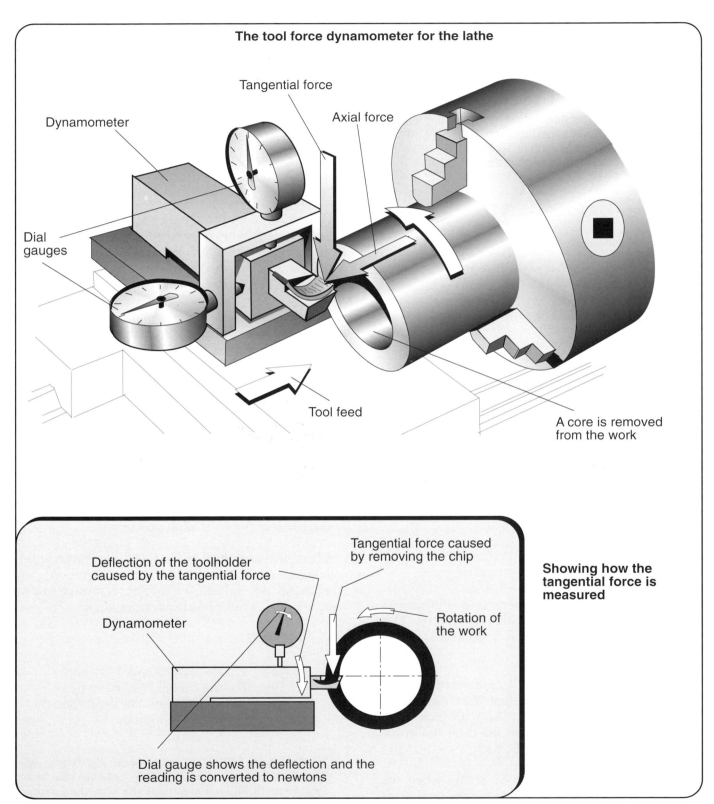

The tool force dynamometer for the lathe

Tangential force

Axial force

Dynamometer

Dial gauges

Tool feed

A core is removed from the work

Deflection of the toolholder caused by the tangential force

Tangential force caused by removing the chip

Dynamometer

Rotation of the work

Showing how the tangential force is measured

Dial gauge shows the deflection and the reading is converted to newtons

FIGURE 9   *Tool force dynamometer (lathe).*

**Power (kW) =
Tangential force (Ft) x Cutting speed (S)**

Example

Calculate the power consumed at the cutting edge of a lathe tool if the tangential force is 1785N and the cutting speed is 28m/min

Solution

Power = Ft x S

where Ft = the tangential force (N)

S = the cutting speed (m/sec)

$$Power = \frac{1785 \times 28}{60}$$

= 833 Watts

= 0.833 kW

CALCULATION

TOOL WEAR

A cutting tool can wear in a number of ways.

- **Flank wear**
- **Crater wear**
- **Spalling or chipping**
- **Plastic deformation.**

The tool wears on the flank because it is in contact with the moving surface of the workpiece. This causes a wear land to develop. A large wear land will cause bad surface finish.

The rake face of the tool can become cratered from continuous rubbing by the chip. You can see in FIGURE 10 that a large crater causes an increase in the rake angle and this weakens the tool. It also has an effect on the geometry of the tool.

Spalling or chipping of the tool occurs when the tool material is not tough enough for the workpiece material and the cutting conditions. Chipping can

sometimes be caused by vibration. Also very large rake angles can weaken the cutting edge and this may result in chipping.

Plastic deformation can be caused by very high temperatures in conjunction with high pressure at the cutting edge. High cutting speeds can be a reason for the high temperatures. A lack of hardness in the tool material can also contribute to plastic deformation.

TOOL LIFE

The period of time a cutting edge survives in a metal cutting operation is referred to as tool life. This term can be expressed in different ways. It can have slightly different meanings to those who are concerned with the life of a tool in a manufacturing situation.

It can be expressed as the actual length of time for which the tool will remove swarf before it needs to be reground again.

It can also be expressed in terms of the number of workpieces which can be produced between tool regrinds.

Tool life is concerned with actual chip removal times. It is not concerned with non-machining times (known as down-time).

Tool life is often based on the amount of flank wear (the width of the wear land) on the tool.

When this wear land increases to a predetermined amount, say 0.2 mm, the tool is removed and reground. An estimate of the life of a tool can be made using Taylor's Equation for tool life.

$$VT^n = C$$

Where: V is the cutting speed (m/min).
T is the tool life (min).
n and C are constants depending on the cutting conditions.

In the early 1900s, an American, Frederick W. Taylor discovered a relationship between the heat treatment of alloyed steel and the way the cutting edge stood up to metal cutting.

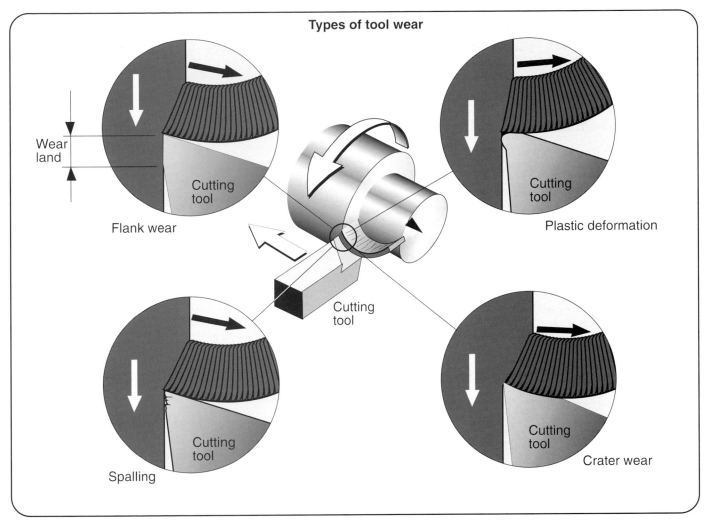

FIGURE 10 *Types of tool wear.*

MACHINABILITY

Machinability is a term used to describe the ease (or difficulty) with which a material may be machined. There is, however, no precise meaning to this term. The machine operator may regard a material as having "good machinability" if the tool lasts for a long time between regrinds, or if it is possible to produce a good surface finish, or if it is possible to produce a large number of components per hour and so on. The difficulty in trying to put a precise meaning to the term machinability arises when, for example, the cutting tool material is changed — causing the tool to last for a longer or shorter time between regrinds, or if the cutting conditions (cutting speed, feed rate) are changed. In an attempt to determine the machinability of a material one or more of the following may be used:

- **Tool life**
  The amount of material which a tool will remove, under certain conditions before the tool becomes dulled and needs to be reground. If the material is difficult to machine (poor machinability), the tool may not cut for very long before it needs to be reground. On the other hand if the material is easier to machine (good machinability) the tool will last longer

- **Cutting forces**
  The forces needed to remove a chip. (These forces can be measured using a dynamometer.) If the forces are very high for a particular set of machining conditions the machinability might be regarded as poor. Low cutting forces under the same cutting conditions would indicate good machinability

- **Surface finish**
  The quality of the surface finish produced on the workpiece is sometimes regarded as an indicator of machinability. Good surface finish might indicate good machinability while bad surface finish might indicate bad machinability.

If possible, all the above criteria (and sometimes additional ones) are taken into consideration when discussing machinability.

SUMMARY

Metal cutting is the removal of unwanted portions of a workpiece by cutting it away as swarf. Tools used for metal cutting are shaped like a wedge. At either side of the wedge lie the rake and clearance angles. The rake angle helps to lift the chip from the workpiece while the clearance angle ensures that only the cutting edge is in contact with the work.

In metal cutting the chip is sheared from the workpiece on the shear plane. The area of the shear plane is controlled by the depth of cut and the rake angle. The greater the depth of cut the larger the shear area. This makes machining more difficult. A larger rake angle gives a large shear plane angle but smaller shear plane area. This makes machining less difficult.

A large rake angle gives small shear area.
A small depth of cut gives small shear area.
A small rake angle gives large shear area.
A large depth of cut gives large shear area.

The main types of chips formed in metal cutting are:

Continuous – from ductile workpiece materials. The chip is long and unbroken. This chip can be very dangerous should it become wrapped around the work.

Discontinuous (segmented) – from brittle workpiece materials. This chip leaves the tool as a spray of separate small pieces of swarf.

Chip with built-up-edge. Unfavourable cutting conditions can cause chips to start a built-up-edge on the tool. The built-up-edge is caused by particles from the underside of the chip becoming welded to the rake face of the tool.

Forces are present in metal cutting because the tool is forced into the work to lift a chip. There are two main forces in orthogonal cutting – tangential force and axial force. In oblique cutting there are three main forces – tangential force, axial force and radial force.

Oblique cutting arises where the cutting edge is not at 90° to the movement of the tool. This angle, the plan approach angle, can be varied to spread the chip over a greater length of the cutting edge for a given depth of cut. Increasing the plan approach angle can sometimes have the effect of slightly increasing the life of the tool.

Forces in metal cutting can be measured using a tool force dynamometer.

The power consumed in metal cutting can be altered by changing the rake angle and also by using a lubricant in the tool/work zone.

There are four main types of tool wear:

Flank wear – a wear land appears on the clearance face.
Crater wear – a crater appears on the rake face.
Spalling or chipping – the edge chips or breaks away.
Plastic deformation – the edge becomes plastic and rounded.

Tool life is determined by the formula:

$$VT^n = C$$

Where: V is the cutting speed (m/min).
T is the tool life (min).
n and C are constants depending on the cutting conditions.

Tool life is a measure of how long the tool will last while cutting a workpiece.
Machinability is an estimate or measure of how easy or difficult it is to cut a particular material.

Cutting Tool Materials

INTRODUCTION

Efficient metal cutting depends to a large extent on selecting a cutting tool material to suit the workpiece material to be cut. It is necessary to have different tool materials because there is such a variety of materials that need to be machined. It is necessary also because the conditions under which the tool operates are so varied. It is understandable, therefore, that a range of cutting tool materials has been developed. Each of these materials has its own special properties and capabilities. Cutting tool materials are selected with the workpiece materials and the cutting conditions in mind.

The development of modern cutting tool materials has been achieved through a process of trial and success. Ever since humans felt the need to cut material there has been a search for the ideal tool material. The ideal tool material would be one which would be:

- **Hard – harder than the material it is required to cut so that it will resist wear**
- **Tough – it must be able to withstand the very high forces which are common in metal cutting and resist breaking**
- **Able to withstand high temperatures and pressures.**

A great variety of materials were tried and tested over the years. The ones which survive today are the ones which:

- **Have a good (long) working life**
- **Can remove large amounts of metal in a given time (metal removal rate)**
- **Can produce a good surface finish on the workpiece.**

Most of the cutting tool materials available today fall into one or other of a number of groups. The main groups are:

1 Carbon steel.
2 High speed steel (HSS).
3 Cemented carbide.
4 Cast alloys.
5 Ceramics.
6 Cubic Boron Nitride (CBN).
7 Diamond.

CARBON STEEL (sometimes called TOOL STEEL)

Carbon steel contains up to about 1.5% carbon. It can be hardened by heating to a temperature above 723°C and quenching, (see the chapter on heat treatment). The tool is then tempered to suit the cutting conditions.

You can see from **FIGURE 1** that a rise in temperature in carbon steel produces a corresponding drop in the hardness value. The temperature produced by metal cutting, therefore, causes a serious deterioration in the hardness of carbon steel. For this reason carbon steel is rarely used as a cutting tool on modern machine tools. To ensure a reasonable life for a carbon steel tool, the cutting speed on steel would need to be around 6 m/min. This cutting speed makes carbon steel unsuitable for machining because the machining time would be too long and expensive. Carbon steels are still used for cutting tools where the cutting speed is very low, for example, certain hand tools and some wood-working tools.

HIGH SPEED STEEL (HSS)

High speed steel is capable of retaining most of its hardness at the very high temperatures produced by metal cutting. You can compare the hardness curves of carbon tool steel and high speed steel in **FIGURE 1**. The ability of a tool material to retain its hardness while red hot is known as *red hardness.*

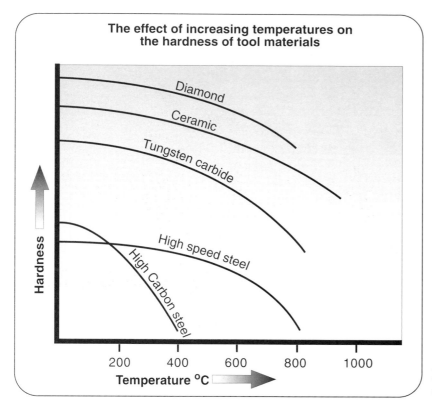

FIGURE 1 *Effect of increasing temperature on hardness of tool materials.*

Alloying elements

The heat treatment of basic high speed steel consists of heating to approximately 1250°C and cooling to 620°C in a bath of molten lead. The material is then tempered between 550°C and 600°C. Tempering of high speed steel is often called *secondary hardening.*

There are many different high speed steel compositions available today. Modern heat treatment methods of high speed steel are very precise and carefully controlled. A well known high speed steel contains 0.75% carbon with:

18% tungsten
4% chromium
1% vanadium

This is often referred to as '18-4-1 steel'.

These three elements combine with the carbon to form carbides. As the temperature is raised these carbides tend to dissolve and go into solution in the iron. The more the temperature is increased the more carbide particles go into solution, but some of them remain intact and prevent grain growth in the steel.

Around 1868 the first successful attempt was made to produce a better tool material by adding alloying elements. This steel was self-hardening which meant that it could be cooled in air and did not have to be quenched in water. It was the scientist Robert Mushet who pioneered this steel and it was given the name *Mushet Steel*.

This steel had a carbon content of 1.2% to 2.5% and contains the alloying elements:

Tungsten 6% – 10%, Manganese 1.2% – 2%, Chromium 0.5%

The addition of the manganese and chromium gave the steel its "self-hardening" quality.

F W Taylor, an engineer, and M. White, a metallurgist, developed high-speed steels. After exhaustive testing, the optimum composition of this material was regarded as iron containing:

Carbon 0.6%, Tungsten 19%, Chromium 5.5%, Manganese 0.11%, Vanadium 0.29%

Taylor-White tools were demonstrated at the Paris Exhibition of 1900. These tools continued to cut steel while the point was red hot.

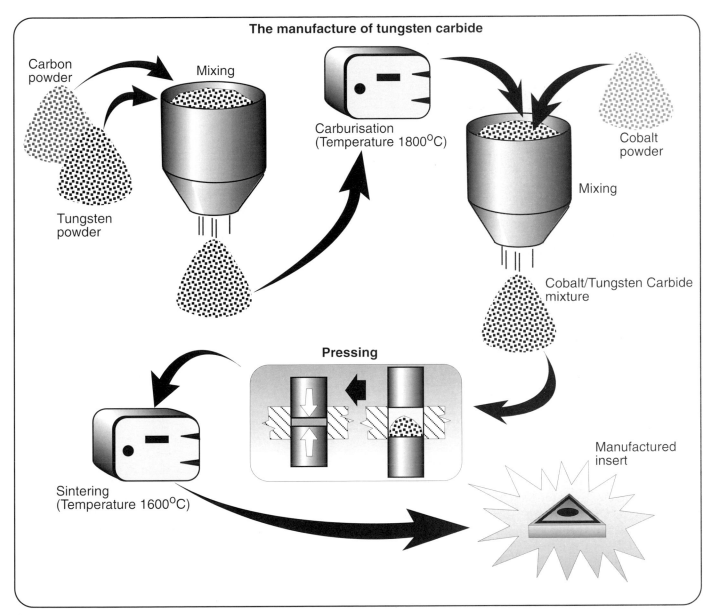

The manufacture of tungsten carbide

Carbon powder

Mixing

Carburisation (Temperature 1800°C)

Tungsten powder

Cobalt powder

Mixing

Cobalt/Tungsten Carbide mixture

Pressing

Sintering (Temperature 1600°C)

Manufactured insert

FIGURE 2   *Manufacture of tungsten carbide.*

Their essential purposes are:

- **To promote toughness in the steel**
- **To discourage grain growth (a fine grain structure is less brittle) while the vanadium increases wear resistance in the tool.**

The chromium provides the material with hardenability. Even if it is cooled relatively slowly, the material will form a hard structure. This is very important when large masses of high speed steel are to be hardened and uneven cooling rates may be inevitable.

TUNGSTEN CARBIDES

Tungsten carbide is a material made by powder metallurgy. This means that the material starts out as metal powders. The powders are then processed in a way that an extremely hard and tough tool material is formed.

FIGURE 3   *An array of special tool holders and (inset) a selection of tungsten carbide inserts (Courtesy: Sandvik Coromant).*

The first stage in the process is to produce the hard carbide particles. Tungsten and carbon powders are mixed and heated to about 1800°C. This process produces tungsten carbide. Tungsten carbide powder is now mixed with a binder powder. The binder is usually cobalt. Measured quantities of this mixture are then pressed in dies which are the shape of the finished tool. The pressings or *compacts*, as they are known, are then sintered (baked) in an oven at about

Cemented carbides were first made around 1920. The introduction of cemented carbides was revolutionary, in that the cutting speeds changed and machining times were reduced dramatically. In the 1930s the use of cemented carbide as a cutting tool became widespread. Continued research and development since the introduction of cemented carbides has produced many grades to suit different materials and machining conditions. In 1950 there was a great improvement in the grades and in 1970 coated carbide tools were introduced.

1500°C. The manufacture of tungsten carbide is shown in **FIGURE 2**.

Metal cutting with tungsten carbides

Tungsten carbides are important as tool materials in metal cutting. This is mainly because of their excellent resistance to wear. They also have a red hardness which is higher than high speed steel. Tungsten carbide tools are usually little more than a cutting edge clamped or brazed to a steel holder or shank because it is a relatively expensive material to produce. These inserts, as they are called, are made in a great variety of shapes, sizes and grades (toughness/hardness). **FIGURE 3** gives you an indication of the variety of shapes in which inserts are available.

Grading of tungsten carbides

In the manufacture of tungsten carbides it is possible to vary the proportions of hard particles (carbides) and the binder (cobalt). The proportion could be as

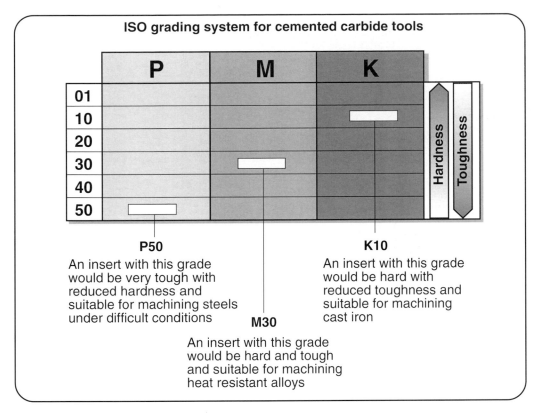

ISO grading system for cemented carbide tools

P50
An insert with this grade would be very tough with reduced hardness and suitable for machining steels under difficult conditions

M30
An insert with this grade would be hard and tough and suitable for machining heat resistant alloys

K10
An insert with this grade would be hard with reduced toughness and suitable for machining cast iron

FIGURE 4 *Simplified ISO classification chart.*

high as 90% of hard particles and 10% of binder. This would give a very hard material but lacking in toughness. In general

- **The higher the *cobalt* content the *tougher* the material**
- **The higher the *tungsten carbide* content the *harder* the material.**

The proportions of the constituents of tungsten carbides are varied to suit the workpiece materials being machined and the working conditions of the tool. There is now a range of inserts which are coated with titanium and other materials. These coated inserts are capable of even higher rates of metal removal.

The ISO classification system

P, M and K are three groups of tungsten carbide. The P group is used mainly for steels. The M group is used mainly for alloys. The K group is used mainly for cast iron. The numbers 1 to 50 give an indication of the relative toughness and hardness of

the tungsten carbide. A simplified version of the ISO classification chart is shown in **FIGURE 4**

Other tungsten carbide metal cutting tools

There is a wide range of metal cutting tools made from tungsten carbides. These include:

- **Drills**
- **Milling cutters**
- **Burs**
- **Rock drills**
- **Metal forming tools.**

Drills can be made of high speed steel with brazed-on tungsten carbide cutting edges. Drills are also made with clamped tips. **FIGURE 5** shows a selection of drills with inserted cutting edges. Notice the one in the centre of the picture. This is a trepanning tool. This cutting tool cuts a narrow groove and leaves a piece of the work material in a core. This saves material where large holes are required.

Milling cutters – end mills for example – can be made

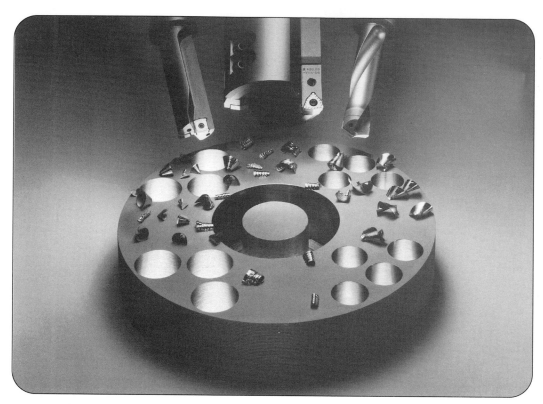

FIGURE 5 *A selection of metal cutting drills with tungsten carbide inserts. (Courtesy: Sandvik Coromant)*

FIGURE 6 *Inserted tooth milling cutter. (Courtesy: Sandvik Coromant)*

338

certain grades of tungsten carbide making it an excellent rock drill tool.

Metal forming means changing the shape of metals through pressure. The properties of tungsten carbides make them suitable for use in a host of metal forming processes. Common examples are:

- **Wire drawing – the reduction of the diameter of wire by passing it through a tungsten carbide die**
- **Cold heading – a method of forming the head on a bolt. Special dies made from tungsten carbide form the bolt head by squeezing the end of the bolt blank. The space in the die is the exact shape of the bolt head. The process is performed at very high speed in a machine.**

CAST ALLOYS

"Stellite" is the trade name of a non-ferrous material. It is an alloy of cobalt, chromium and tungsten. It has a higher red hardness than high speed steel. Stellite is normally cast into shape and then ground if it is to be used as a cutting tool. When cast, this material is extremely hard. It will not soften by heating.

CERAMICS

Ceramics are used in metal cutting in a number of ways:

- **As grinding wheels. This is covered in detail in the section on grinding**
- **As cutting tool inserts. These are used in a similar way to cemented carbide inserts.**

The main advantage in using ceramic inserts is that they can withstand extremely high machining temperatures. They also have a high resistance to abrasion.

Ceramic cutting tools can be used to machine 'difficult' materials at really high cutting speeds – sometimes over 2000 m/min. Compare this with the cutting speed for carbon steel cutting tools – 6 m/min. Ceramic cutting tools are very brittle. They can be used only on machines which are extremely rigid and free of vibration.

FIGURE 7   *Rotary Bur. (Courtesy: Sandvik Coromant)*

from solid tungsten carbide. Large side and face cutters and face mills usually have clamped-in tips which can be replaced when the edge becomes chipped or dull. **FIGURE 6** shows an inserted tooth milling cutter.

Burs are like very small milling cutters with many small teeth. They are used where small amounts of metal have to be removed. The motor for driving burs are high-speed air driven motors. (Speeds of up to 75,000 rev/min are not uncommon.) Special safety precautions have to be taken when using burs because of the very tiny chips and the high speeds at which they can fly off the cutter. **FIGURE 7** shows a rotary bur. It is about 8 mm in diameter.

Rock drilling calls for a combination of wear resistance and impact resistance. This is possible with

FIGURE 8 *Diamond grinding wheels. (Courtesy: BMS Ireland)*

CUBIC BORON NITRIDE (CBN)

CBN is second only to diamond in hardness. As a cutting tool a 0.5 mm layer of CBN is bonded to a base of cemented carbide. This material is capable of machining fully-hardened steels.

DIAMOND

Diamond is a super hard material. Synthetic diamonds are made in very large presses and are used to machine hard materials such as tungsten carbides. They are also used in the machining of copper, aluminium and other non-ferrous metals. A common use of diamond is in the form of grinding wheels. **FIGURE** 8 shows a range of diamond wheels. There is only a small layer of diamond bonded to an aluminium wheel.

SUMMARY

The material used in a cutting tool is selected for a number of reasons:

- **It must suit the material to be cut or machined**
- **It should suit the cutting conditions.**

An ideal tool material would be *hard* to resist wear and *tough* to resist breaking.

The common tool materials are:

Carbon steel	Ceramics
High speed steel	Cubic Boron Nitride
Tungsten carbide	Diamond

Carbon steels contain up to about 1.5%C and are hardened and tempered. This material softens at high cutting speed and is therefore unsuitable for use on modern machines.

High speed steel contains 0.75% Carbon with 18% Tungsten, 4% Chromium and 1% Vanadium. These provide toughness, fine grain structure and hardenability. This is known as 18-4-1 steel. Other alloying elements are also used in other high speed steel. This steel has the ability to remain hard at higher temperatures than carbon steel. It has a higher red-hardness.

Tungsten carbide is made by powder metallurgy. This means that powdered metals are mixed in the correct proportions, pressed in a die and sintered in an oven at 1500°C. At this temperature the powders fuse resulting in a very hard and tough tool material. One of the powders, tungsten carbide, provides the hard particles and the other powder, cobalt, acts as a binder. The hardness/toughness of the tool can be predetermined by varying the proportions of the powders in the mix – more tungsten carbide provides greater hardness, more cobalt greater toughness.

Tungsten carbide is used extensively in industry. It is capable of machining at much higher speeds and much longer cutting times than high speed steel.

Ceramics are capable of withstanding even higher speeds. These tools are often used to machine metals that are difficult to cut. Cubic Boron Nitride is a material which can be bonded to cemented carbide. It is extremely hard and can cut for long periods.

Diamond is the hardest known material. It has many uses including machining non-ferrous metals and dressing grinding wheels.

Cutting Fluids

INTRODUCTION

An important part of the metal cutting process is the application of a cutting fluid. Frederick W. Taylor discovered that a large flow of water onto the tool/work zone allowed him to at least double the cutting speed. For obvious reasons plain water is not used on modern machine tools. Cutting fluid is a combination of liquids, minerals and chemicals. It is applied to the tool and the workpiece for the following reasons:

- **To lubricate and reduce the friction between the tool and the chip**
- **To keep the machining process cool**
- **To flush away the chips.**

There is a high degree of sliding friction in most machining processes. For example, the chip slides along the rake face of the tool and the cutting edge is in frictional contact with the machined surface. Increased friction causes increased temperatures. You have seen in Cutting Tool Materials that increasing temperatures can reduce the hardness of tools. Cutting fluids, therefore, can have the effect of maintaining the hardness of the tool by keeping its temperature low.

The cutting fluid is used in some machining processes to control the swarf. In a drill with coolant ducts, coolant is pumped into the ducts at the shank end, and as it exits at the point, it forces the swarf up the flutes of the drill. Feeding coolant to the point of an ordinary twist drill is difficult as the swarf is coming up the flutes while the fluid is trying to go in the opposite direction.

A variety of cutting fluids have been produced for special machining operations. Details of these are available from each manufacturer. Cutting fluids, however, fall into four broad categories:

1 Synthetic cutting fluids.
2 Semi-synthetic cutting fluids.
3 Neat oils.
4 Emulsion-type cutting fluids (soluble oils).

Synthetic cutting fluids
These cutting fluids contain little or no oil and are transparent in appearance. The ingredients are dispersed in water. These are good fluids for grinding.

Semi-synthetic cutting fluids
These cutting fluids may contain up to 40% oil. They are usually translucent in appearance when they are mixed with water.

Neat oils
These cutting fluids are not mixed with water. They are normally a carefully blended mixture of mineral oils and chemicals. They are normally used where materials are very tough and difficult to machine.

Emulsion-type cutting fluids (soluble oils)
These cutting fluids usually contain a high percentage of oil. When they are combined with water they have a 'milky' appearance. Oil and water will not mix. An emulsifier breaks the oil down into tiny droplets and disperses them throughout the water. This is known as *emulsion*. Chemicals are added to prevent contamination of the fluid by bacteria. The two main problems caused by bacteria are:

- **Rancidity**
- **Skin problems.**

Rancidity means that the bacteria have broken down the additives to other chemicals that have a foul smell. To prevent rancidity the machine and fluid must be kept in a clean condition. Rancidity is also discouraged by keeping the cutting fluid at the proper strength.

The chief skin problem which results from contact with soluble oil is *irritant contact dermatitis*. This

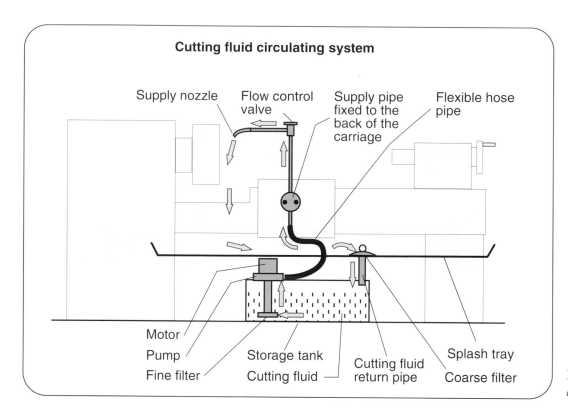

Cutting fluid circulating system

Supply nozzle   Flow control valve   Supply pipe fixed to the back of the carriage   Flexible hose pipe

Motor
Pump
Fine filter
Storage tank
Cutting fluid
Cutting fluid return pipe
Splash tray
Coarse filter

FIGURE 1 *Fluid circulating system.*

manifests itself as redness, swelling, scaling and cracking of the skin. You can avoid prolonged contact with the cutting fluid by using splash guards on the machine and also by using a suitable barrier cream on your hands.

The application of cutting fluid
Cutting fluid is normally delivered to the tool/work zone at low pressure through a nozzle which is shaped to suit the machining operation. Sometimes the cutting fluid is fed through the tool itself and makes its exit at the cutting edge.

The cutting fluid circulating system
The cutting fluid is stored in a tank. This tank is usually located underneath the machine splash tray. In the case of a milling machine it is stored in its hollow base. The cutting fluid is pumped up through a pipe which has a regulating valve to control the flow rate. When the cutting fluid runs off the tool/work it falls into the splash tray. From there it is piped directly, through a filter, into the tank. A cutting fluid circulating system is shown in
FIGURE 1

SUMMARY

Cutting fluids are important in metal cutting because they reduce friction, cool the work and flush away the chips cut by the tool.

There are many different types of cutting fluids in use. The more important ones are:

• **Synthetic cutting fluids (used in precision grinding)**
• **Semi-synthetic cutting fluids**
• **Neat oils (used where materials are difficult to cut)**
• **Soluble oils (used for general machining).**

Cutting fluids should be maintained in good condition. They should not be allowed to become contaminated in the machine splash tray or in the storage tank.

The cutting fluid is delivered to the tool-work zone through a nozzle which can be fixed in the most suitable position. It is pumped from the storage tank through a flexible hose pipe to the nozzle.

ENGINEERING TECHNOLOGY

Mechanical Joining

INTRODUCTION

Many machining processes are designed to produce finished parts from blank material. There are advantages in making components in one piece. There are situations, however, where you need different mechanical properties at various points in a product.

A product may be subject to high wear in one point, high or low temperature in another, high tensile stress in another and so on. No single material can be made to cope with all these demands. The problem cannot always be solved by altering the microstructure of the part by heat treatment. The heat treatment process used may affect the entire part and this may be undesirable.

It is usually necessary to make individual parts, each with the properties that are needed, and then join them together. There are many examples of assemblies of parts made from different materials. The average family car is made from approximately 15,000 individual parts, all of which are joined together in many different ways. Some joints are rigid, some are free to move or swivel. Some joints are permanent while others can be dismantled. The engine shown in FIGURE 1 is an assembly of parts made from:

- **Toughened steel**
- **Hardened steel**
- **Aluminium**
- **Polymers**
- **Brass**
- **Copper**
- **Zinc.**

FIGURE 1 *A car engine. (Courtesy: Opel Ireland Ltd.)*

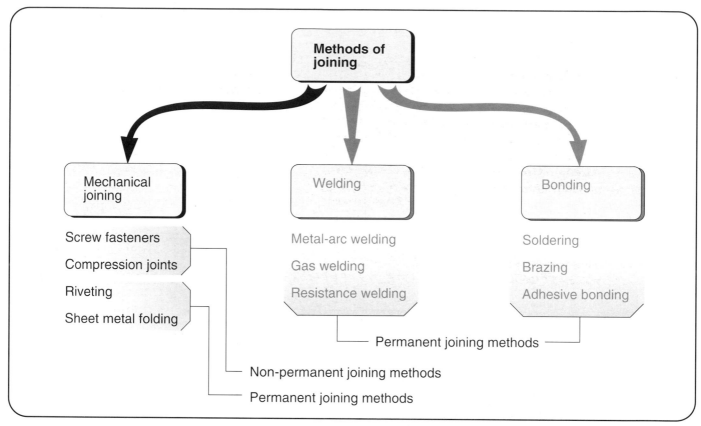

FIGURE 2 *Methods of joining.*

Materials can be joined in a number of ways. **FIGURE 2** shows the different categories of joining processes. This chapter, however, deals with mechanical joining. The others will be examined in the following chapters.

JOINT DESIGN

The most important thing about joining is that the joint should not fail when the product is in use. Sometimes certain features of the joint make it weak. Holes for screws and rivets, for example, can make the parts weak. (If you pull a page from a ring binder the page will almost always tear at the punched holes.)

The points that designers consider when joining parts include:

1 The joint should remain intact throughout its working life – it should not fail.
2 Material which would automatically cause galvanic corrosion at the joint faces should not be joined together. Direct contact between brass and aluminium, for example, should be avoided. Copper parts should not be joined with steel screws.
3 A suitable joining method should be chosen for the materials. The joint should be designed so that the joining medium will hold the joint intact. This will be explained later.

METHODS OF MECHANICAL JOINING

Some joining methods result in *permanent joints* being formed while others result in joints which are non-permanent (capable of being dismantled).

Screw fasteners

a. A selection of screw fasteners

Stud   Cap screw   Set screw   Bolt

b. Forces exerted by screw fasteners

Compressive forces at the interface

Washer to spread the load

Shear forces

Shear forces resisted by frictional contact between the plates

Shear forces

Tensile force in the shank

Force exerted by the bolt or screw

c. Use of a dowel pin

Dowel pin

Cap screws and dowel pins are often used in precision assembly

Shear forces

Shear forces

Shear forces resisted by dowel pin

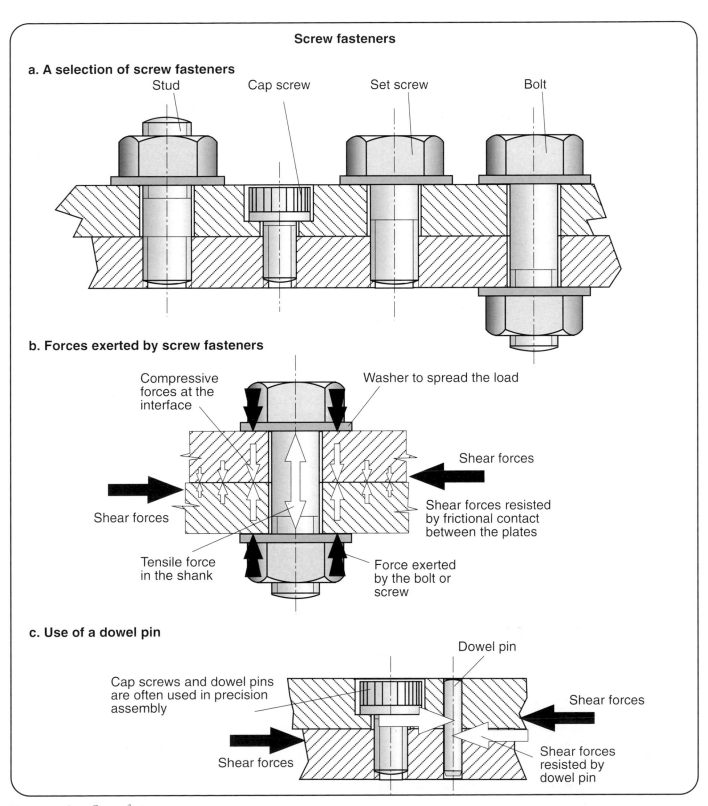

FIGURE 3   *Screw fasteners.*

These are sometimes referred to as *temporary joints.* Mechanical joining includes a wide variety of techniques and fastening devices, each developed to suit the particular requirements of the joint. The more usual methods in this category are:

- **Screw fasteners (bolts, studs, set screws)**
- **Rivets**
- **Folded sheet metal**
- **Compression joints (pipework in domestic plumbing)**
- **Interference fits (press fits, expansion/ shrink fits).**

Other methods include:

- **Pins**
- **Staples**
- **Wire stitching.**

SCREW FASTENERS

The screw thread is one of the most important elements in engineering. Screws are used in a vast range of applications including the assembly of machines and structures. The advantage of using screws to assemble parts is that the parts can be dismantled for repair or replacement. This makes screw fastening a temporary joining method. Without screws almost every machine in existence would cease to function. It is of interest to note that the screw is one of the five simple machines defined in Physics.

Screw fasteners join parts by exerting a force and pulling the joint faces tightly together. A selection of screw fasteners is shown in FIGURE 3 (a). When a screw is used to fasten parts together, the load is

Some early examples of the screw thread were wooden screws which were used on presses in Pompeii. Pompeii was an Italian city which was buried by volcanic debris when Vesuvius erupted in 79 AD. The city was discovered again in 1746 and was later excavated.

Screw bolts were used in suits of armour in the fifteenth century. The screw bolt is the ancestor of the modern nut and bolt.

taken by the head of the screw, or by the nut, depending on the type. Tightening the screw causes a tensile stress or stretching effect in the shank of the screw. The tensile stress in the shank causes a compressive stress in the components being joined. This forces the joint faces into close contact. The stress in the shank is applied through the threads when the screw is tightened. In FIGURE 3 (b) you can see the forces in a screw fastener. Sliding of the joint faces over each other is prevented by frictional contact. The shank of a screw is usually not a tight fit in the holes in the parts.

In precision assembly it is important that parts can be dismantled and reassembled in exactly the same position. Dowel pins are often used with the screws to make this possible. FIGURE 3 (c) shows a dowel pin in an assembly. It is a very tight fit in a precisely reamed hole. The dowel pin itself is very accurately made and it has high strength. The dowel pin is able to resist the forces that might otherwise shear a screw.

Torque
The correct force on a screw fastener is determined by using special equipment to tighten the screw. Torque wrenches and torque screw drivers are tools which will indicate to the operator how much *torque* or tightening force is being applied. In FIGURE 4 you can see the meaning of torque. FIGURE 5 shows a range of modern torque wrenches. The correct torque for a screw fastener can be calculated. The calculation takes into consideration the strength of the screw and the strength of the materials being joined.

Screw manufacture
The heads of high quality screw fasteners are cold forged – a process known as *cold heading.* This ensures a continuous grain flow from the shank to the head. When a screw is subjected to a tensile load, the threads are in shear. High quality machine screws have *rolled threads.* Rolling gives the threads a continuous grain flow which resists shearing. The radius between the screw shank and the head is important. An incorrect radius may cause the screw to fracture at that point. The principles of both cold heading and thread rolling are shown in FIGURE 6.

Types of screws
Screws are identified mainly by the shape of the

Torque

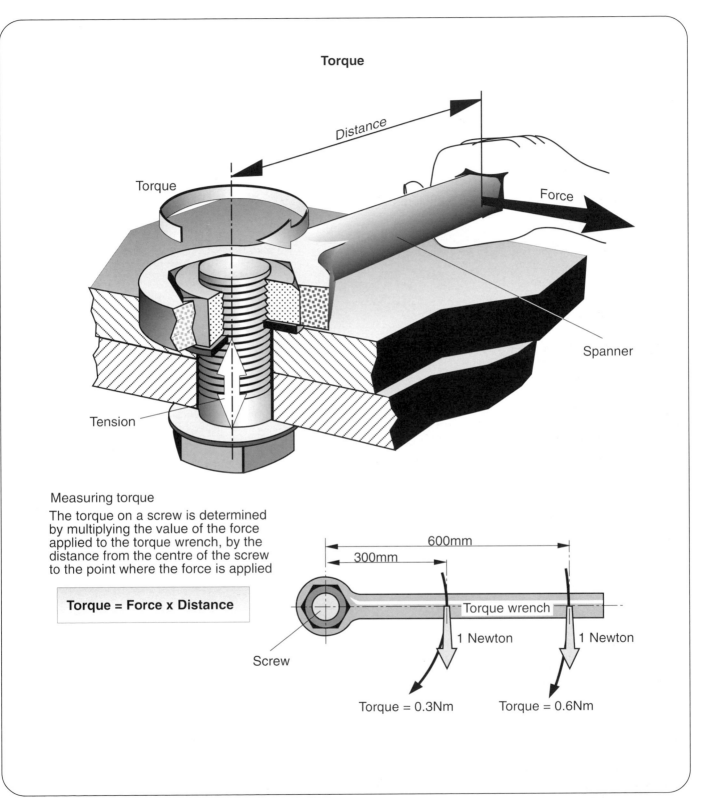

Measuring torque

The torque on a screw is determined by multiplying the value of the force applied to the torque wrench, by the distance from the centre of the screw to the point where the force is applied

Torque = Force x Distance

FIGURE 4   *Torque.*

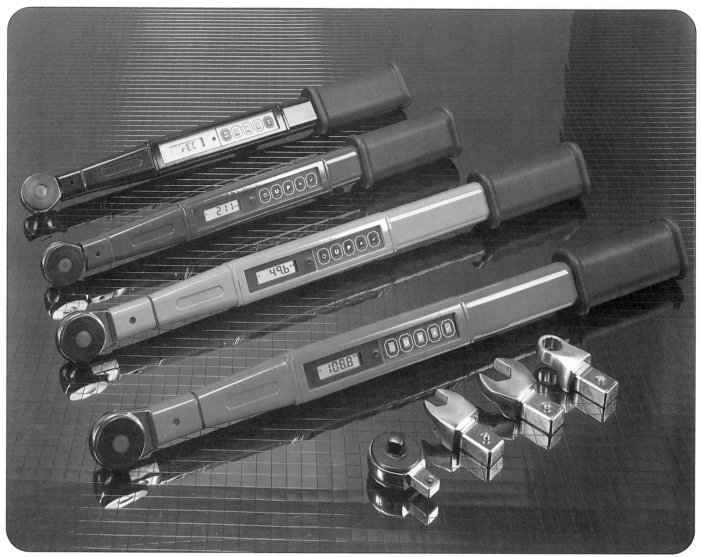

FIGURE 5   *Torque wrenches. (Courtesy: BMS Ireland)*

head. Other differences include the shape of the point and the length of the threaded portion of the shank. **FIGURE 7** shows some common screw head shapes. The following is a list of the more common screw types.

1 Socket screws
Socket screws get their name from the hexagonal socket in the head. A hexagonal shaped key fits into the socket to turn the screw. These screws are made from special alloy steel. They are cold-forged and have high strength.

2 Hexagon head bolts and screws
Hexagon head bolts are used with a nut. These are used where high strength is required. Bolts are threaded for only part of their length. The unthreaded portion of the bolt should pass most of the way through the joint faces. One of the parts to be fastened is tapped and acts as the nut for hexagon head screws.

3 Self-tapping screws
Self-tapping screws are hardened fasteners which make their own threads in one of the components

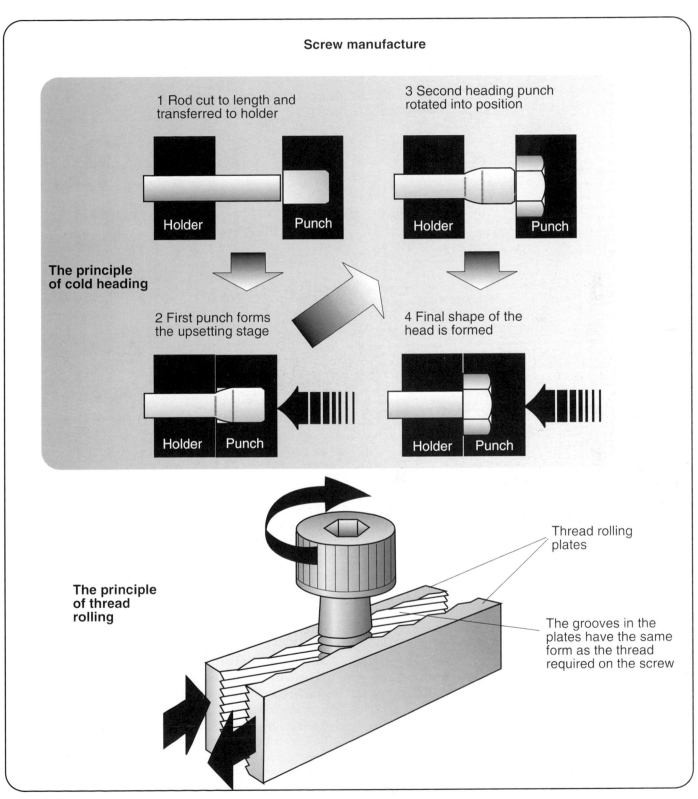

Screw manufacture

The principle of cold heading

1 Rod cut to length and transferred to holder

Holder   Punch

2 First punch forms the upsetting stage

Holder   Punch

3 Second heading punch rotated into position

Holder   Punch

4 Final shape of the head is formed

Holder   Punch

The principle of thread rolling

Thread rolling plates

The grooves in the plates have the same form as the thread required on the screw

FIGURE 6 *Screw manufacture.*

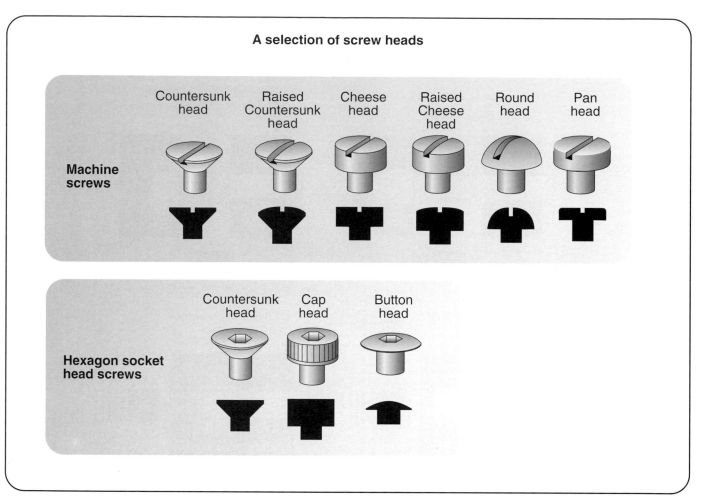

A selection of screw heads

Machine screws

Countersunk head Raised Countersunk head Cheese head Raised Cheese head Round head Pan head

Hexagon socket head screws

Countersunk head Cap head Button head

FIGURE 7 *A selection of screw heads.*

being joined. This acts as a nut. They are most often used in sheet metal joining and are a convenient way to secure removable panels on washing machines and other domestic appliances.

4 Thread-forming screws
Thread-forming screws displace the material and form the thread in the metal without removing any swarf. These screws are suitable for joining very ductile materials.

5 Thread-cutting screws
Thread-cutting screws have flats, grooves or flutes which make cutting edges. When the screw is forced into the metal it behaves like a tap. This type is used on harder materials.

6 Studs
Screwed studs are used where joints are dismantled regularly. Because the stud remains in one of the joint elements, it provides a means of locating the parts quickly.

Screws and vibration
When screws are used on parts which are subject to vibration there could be a danger of a screw becoming loose. To prevent this possibility a locking device should be used. Many of the screws used in the assembly of components are locked so that they cannot become loose. Locking devices include:

• **Spring washers**
• **Nuts with nylon inserts which grip on the bolt**

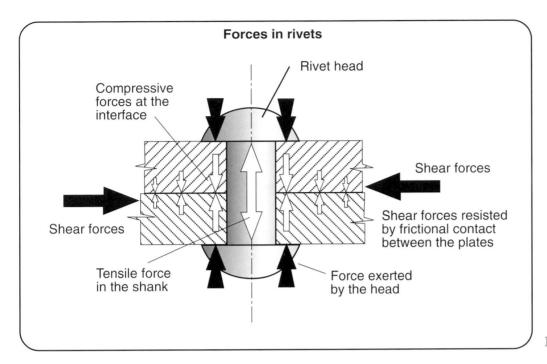

Forces in rivets

- Rivet head
- Compressive forces at the interface
- Shear forces
- Shear forces resisted by frictional contact between the plates
- Shear forces
- Tensile force in the shank
- Force exerted by the head

FIGURE 8   *Forces in rivets.*

- **Pins inserted in holes drilled through the nut and bolt assembly**
- **Nuts locked against each other (locknuts).**

RIVETS

Riveting had a special place in early engineering fabrication, especially in boiler making, steel construction and shipbuilding. Rivets were used extensively in bridge building. There are many riveted railway bridges still in existence around the country. Riveting is a permanent joining process. Rivets generate sufficient force on the joint faces to ensure that they do not come apart or slide over each other. This force is the result of tension in the shank of the rivet. The heads on either end of the rivet pull the plates firmly against each other.

Riveted joints

The riveted joint is made by drilling the plates and inserting the rivet. A second 'head' is formed on the shank of the rivet by applying pressure, usually by hammering. The rivet head is supported on a bolster and the end of the shank is formed into a second head using a special former of the required shape. Riveting machines are used on large rivets.

Hot formed rivet heads can exert very high compressive forces on the plates. Heating the rivet makes the head easier to form but it also expands the shank. Once the head is formed, and the rivet begins to cool, the shank contracts. This causes a tensile stress which exerts a very high compressive force on the plates. This is shown in **FIGURE 8**.

Quick riveting systems such as pop rivets are sometimes used where the cost of assembly should be kept low. Pop rivets are often made from soft material such as aluminium. This material has a low tensile strength so it will not exert much force on the plates. The method of forming the head of a pop rivet causes the plates being joined to be pulled tightly together before the pin snaps. The rivet will then hold the plates in this position.

SHEET METAL JOINTS

Light gauge sheet metal can be joined without the use of mechanical fasteners. The edges of the metal sheets are folded and interlocked. These joints are sometimes used in the manufacture of food and liquid containers. To prevent leakage of liquids, joints in containers of this type are sealed with a

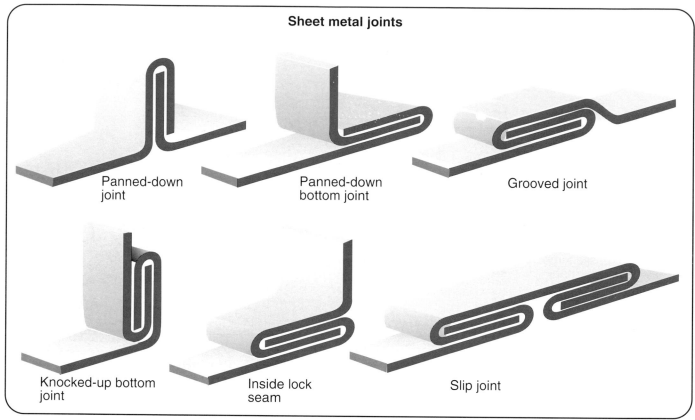

Sheet metal joints

Panned-down joint

Panned-down bottom joint

Grooved joint

Knocked-up bottom joint

Inside lock seam

Slip joint

FIGURE 9 *Sheet metal joints.*

sealant or soft solder. **FIGURE 9** shows some common folded sheet metal joints.

PIPE JOINTS

Liquids and gases have to be transported through pipe lines from their containers to where they are used. The pipes may be metal or polymer tube. Sometimes the piping system is part–metal and part–polymer tubing. Pipe lines may have to withstand high pressures. The liquids carried by pipe lines often cause a scale to build up on the inside of the pipe. This may mean that the pipe line has to be dismantled regularly for cleaning. As a result there are many ways of joining pipes. Some of these can be seen in **FIGURE 10**.

Unions are used on steel piping in which the wall is thick enough to have a thread cut on it.

Compression joints are used on small bore piping with a thin wall.

There are two types of flanged joint. In the high pressure joint the seal is placed between the ends of the pipes. The flanges do not come into contact. When the bolts are tightened the entire force exerted by the bolts comes directly on the pipe ends. The low pressure joint on the other hand has a gasket between the flanges. A flange can be screwed on to a pipe end or it can be welded to it.

INTERFERENCE FITS

Parts can be joined mechanically by introducing a dimensional change to one or both of the parts. The two parts to be joined are made so that their dimensions, where they are intended to fit together, would produce an interference fit. (See limits and

Pipe joints

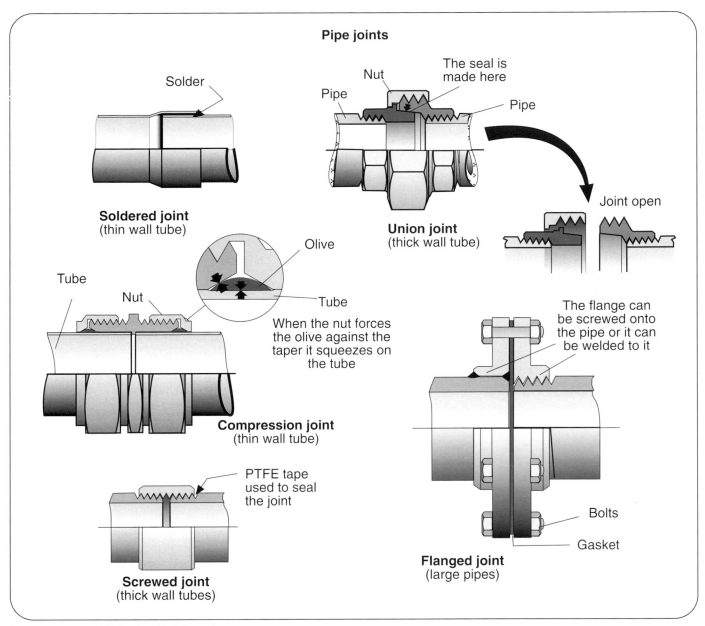

Solder

Soldered joint
(thin wall tube)

Nut

Pipe

The seal is made here

Pipe

Joint open

Union joint
(thick wall tube)

Tube

Nut

Olive

Tube

When the nut forces the olive against the taper it squeezes on the tube

Compression joint
(thin wall tube)

The flange can be screwed onto the pipe or it can be welded to it

PTFE tape used to seal the joint

Bolts

Gasket

Flanged joint
(large pipes)

Screwed joint
(thick wall tubes)

FIGURE 10 *Methods of joining pipes.*

fits, page 133.) The parts can be assembled in a number of ways:

- The outer part can be expanded by applying heat until it is large enough for the inner part to fit easily into it. As the outer part cools to the temperature of the inner part, it shrinks and forms an extremely strong joint between the two

- The inner part can be shrunk by cooling until it is small enough to fit easily into the outer part. As the inner part returns to the temperature of the outer part it expands into it and forms a strong joint

- The parts can be assembled by pressing the two together with a mechanical force. This results in a joint which is equally as strong as the shrink/expansion types.

SUMMARY

Mechanical joining is important in engineering. Almost all of the appliances and machines we use every day are assemblies of different component parts. Each part in an assembly has its own special properties which enable it to carry out its special function.

Joint design is very important in joining.

- **The joint should be designed in such a way that it should not fail when the product is in use.**
- **Materials should be carefully chosen**
- **You should not put materials which would cause galvanic corrosion directly in contact with each other**
- **A suitable method of joining should be used in all situations.**

Mechanical joining includes techniques that use:

- **Screw fasteners**
- **Rivets**
- **Folded sheet metal**
- **Compression joints**
- **Interference fits**
- **Pins**
- **Staples**
- **Wire stitching.**

Screw fasteners and rivets join parts by pulling the joint faces into very close contact with each other. Sliding of the parts over each other is prevented by frictional contact between the joint faces. Sometimes dowel pins are used for this purpose as well as making dismantling and precise reassembly of the parts possible.

Torque wrenches can ensure that all the screws in a component are tightened with the correct force. This is very important in automobile and aerospace work. The studs on the head of an engine, for example, must be carefully tightened with a torque wrench to ensure an even pressure over the entire joint area.

Cold heading and cold rolling are techniques used to manufacture high quality screws. These processes produce a suitable grain structure in the screw which gives it high strength.

Screws are prevented from becoming loose through vibration by locking devices. These include spring washers, pins, nylon inserts.

Light gauge sheet metal can be joined by folding the edges of the parts into each other. Such joints can be made liquid and gas proof by sealing with solder or other sealant.

Pipes can be jointed in a number of ways. The type of joining device usually depends on

- **The thickness of the wall of the pipe**
- **The material which the pipe is made from**
- **The pressure in the pipework system.**

Parts can be mechanically joined by making them to an interference fit and causing a change in the size of one or both parts before assembly. Changing the size is possible in metal parts by changing the temperatures. Usually, as temperature increases dimensions increase. As temperature drops, size decreases. Internal parts can be chilled (temperature lowered) or external parts can be heated before assembly. When the parts return to normal temperature a shrink fit and a strong joint is obtained.

Welding

INTRODUCTION

Welding refers to a group of processes in which parts are joined by fusing them together. Fusion is brought about by a combination of heat and pressure between the parts being joined. Some special joining requirements are carried out by pressure welding. In normal welding processes very high temperatures and no pressures are used.

To successfully weld two parts together the following conditions would be regarded as ideal.

Smooth joint surfaces that match each other.
Clean joint surfaces. Surfaces free from oxides, grease and dirt.
The metals to be joined should have the same microstructure.
The metals should be good quality (no internal impurities).

Before starting a weld, the joint edges should be carefully prepared. When joining large plates this may mean machining the edges to a bevel. Cleaning is very important and is sometimes carried out

An example of welding was found on an iron head rest in Tutankhamun's tomb (about 1350 BC). The method used in early welding was to heat the parts to be joined in a forge until they were soft. The joint faces were then hammered together. This method of welding is still practised for certain decorative purposes.

Chinese and Japanese sword makers used a welding technique about the 3rd century AD. They twisted together light strips of steel and pure iron and then heated them in the fire until they became soft. They then hammered this assembly until it welded into a solid piece. Using a system of bending the assembly double, and hammering again, they refined the grain structure and produced a very tough and strong material. This process was repeated up to ten times to produce the material for the sword blade.

chemically or by mechanical means. When metals are heated to high temperatures their surfaces are more easily affected by the oxygen in the atmosphere. This is known as *oxidation* of the surfaces. All fusion welding processes suffer from the problem of the joint surfaces tending to oxidise as the welding temperature is reached. To prevent this occurring, the surfaces must be shielded from the atmosphere during the welding operation. Each process has its own way of doing this as you will see when you study each one.

There are many modern welding techniques. You will recognise the differences between them by two important features:

1 The way the metal is heated.
2 The way additional *filler metal* is fed into the weld.

The more important types of welding are:

- **Gas welding**
- **Electric arc welding**
- **Electric resistance welding.**

GAS WELDING

A number of welding processes use a flame produced by burning a mixture of *fuel gas* and oxygen. The fuel gas is usually acetylene but other gases are also used. When acetylene is used as the fuel gas the process is known as *oxy-acetylene* welding.

The oxy-acetylene welding process
Oxy-acetylene welding is a common gas welding method used in industry. It is a fusion welding process. Each gas is stored in a separate cylinder and

A Swede named Gustaf Dahlen developed acetylene gas and worked with it in various ways. He designed a torch which burned acetylene in oxygen. In 1902 he demonstrated gas welding for the first time.

a hose pipe from each cylinder transports the gases to a torch. The acetylene mixes with the oxygen in the torch. As the gas mixture escapes through the nozzle of the torch, it is ignited and it burns as a very hot flame. The temperature is about 3100°C. The intense heat produced is capable of melting the metal. During the welding, heat from the flame is concentrated on the joint edges until the metal melts and starts to flow. When the molten metal from both of the joint edges meets, it fuses. As the metal freezes (when it cools down and becomes solid again) the two parts will be *permanently* joined.

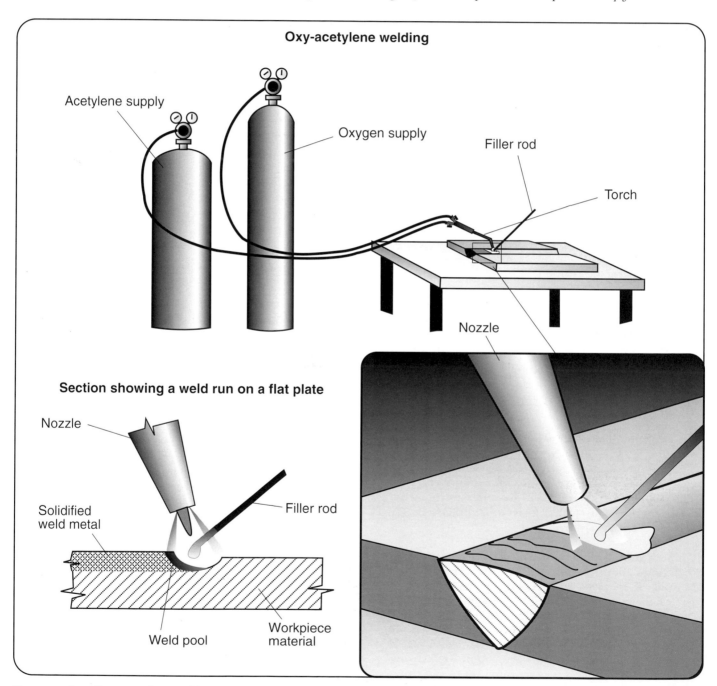

Oxy-acetylene welding

Acetylene supply

Oxygen supply

Filler rod

Torch

Nozzle

Section showing a weld run on a flat plate

Nozzle

Solidified weld metal

Filler rod

Weld pool

Workpiece material

FIGURE 1   *Oxy-acetylene welding process.*

If additional *filler* metal is required, it is fed by hand into the weld pool. The filler metal is in the form of a rod or wire. The end of the filler rod is held very close to the weld pool where the intense heat from the flame keeps it almost at melting point. During the welding it is dipped constantly at regular intervals into the weld pool. There it becomes instantly molten and a globule drops into the weld pool. The oxy-acetylene welding process is shown in **FIGURE 1**

The oxy-acetylene welding flame

The oxy-acetylene flame has two distinct zones as you can see in **FIGURE 2**. The inner zone is the hottest part of the flame and it is supported by the oxygen from the cylinder. The welding should be

performed so that the point of the inner zone is just above the joint edges. The outer zone of the flame, the secondary combustion envelope, performs two functions:

1 It preheats the joint edges.
2 It prevents oxidation by using up some of the surrounding oxygen for combustion.

Flame adjustment

The oxygen/acetylene mixture can exit from the nozzle in three possible ratios (study **FIGURE 2**).

1 Neutral flame.
2 Oxidising flame - excess oxygen.
3 Carburising flame - excess acetylene.

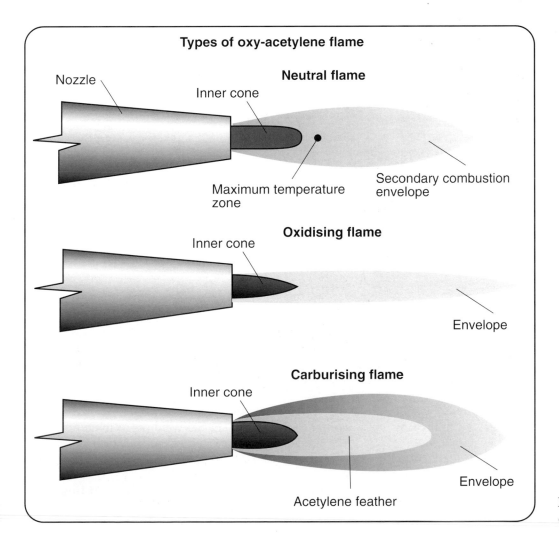

FIGURE 2 *Types of oxy-acetylene flame.*

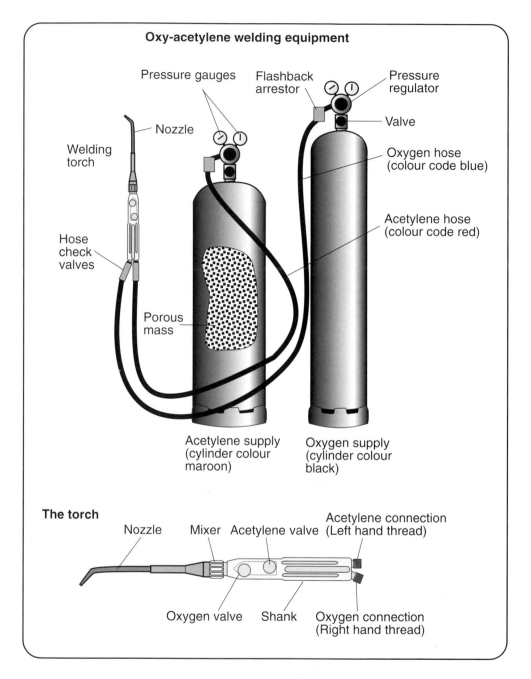

Oxy-acetylene welding equipment

Pressure gauges · Flashback arrestor · Pressure regulator

Nozzle

Welding torch

Valve

Oxygen hose (colour code blue)

Acetylene hose (colour code red)

Hose check valves

Porous mass

Acetylene supply (cylinder colour maroon)

Oxygen supply (cylinder colour black)

The torch

Nozzle · Mixer · Acetylene valve · Acetylene connection (Left hand thread)

Oxygen valve · Shank · Oxygen connection (Right hand thread)

FIGURE 3 *Oxy-acetylene welding equipment.*

The mixtures can be easily identified by the appearance of the flame. Different gas mixtures give different flame temperatures. They also have a chemical effect on the metal being welded. Most welding is done with a neutral flame. The *oxidising flame* is used in welding brass to prevent fuming and loss of zinc. It can also be used as a decarburising flame for steels. (The excess oxygen will react with the carbon in the steel.) Carburising flames are sometimes used for special welding to make sure that the metal is well protected from oxidation.

Equipment used in oxy–acetylene welding
The basic equipment required for oxy-acetylene welding is shown in **FIGURE 3**. It consists of:

- **Pressurised cylinders of oxygen and acetylene**
- **Gas pressure regulators**
- **Welding torch**
- **Gas hose pipes**
- **Flashback arrestors.**

Gases used in oxy–acetylene welding

Welding gases are compressed into cylinders at very high pressure. (Although, as you will see below, acetylene is an exception to this.) The gas cylinders always remain the property of the company who supplies the gas. Gas companies carry out very careful checks on the cylinders when they are returned for refill to make sure they are capable of withstanding the pressure. All gas cylinders have a special colour code. This is to make sure that gases are not incorrectly used by mistake.

Oxygen (O₂)
Oxygen is extracted from the air by an evaporation process at very low temperatures. It is then compressed into cylinders at high pressure. The oxygen cylinder is colour-coded black. One of the greatest dangers with compressed oxygen is that of contact with oil. Oil should never be used on any of the connecting fittings on an oxygen pipeline. The smallest spot of oil or grease inside an oxygen valve can start a fire and cause an explosion. One reason for this is that materials that are combustible in air are many times more combustible in pure oxygen.

Acetylene (C₂H₂)
Acetylene is a fuel gas. It is produced by a reaction of water on calcium carbide. Acetylene cannot be compressed as a gas directly into cylinders because it would explode at high pressures. Acetylene cylinders are packed with a porous material which is filled with acetone. When acetone is pressurised it is capable of absorbing 25 times its own volume of acetylene for each atmosphere of pressure applied to it. Acetylene in this form is known as *dissolved acetylene*. The acetylene cylinder is colour-coded maroon.

FIGURE 4 *Multi-stage gas pressure regulators. (Courtesy: the ESAB Group)*

The gas pressure regulators

The pressure of both the oxygen and the acetylene must be carefully controlled as it is leaving its respective cylinder. In **FIGURE 4** you can see multi-stage pressure regulators. The same principle is used in regulating both gases. Regulators sometimes have two gauges. One of the gauges indicates the pressure in the cylinder. The other gauge indicates the pressure in the supply pipe to the torch.

The welding torch

Oxygen and acetylene are delivered to the torch through separate hoses. Each gas can be controlled by a valve on the torch. The two gases mix in the torch and after they are ignited they burn at the nozzle.

The oxygen and acetylene hose pipes

Oxygen and acetylene are carried from the regulators through reinforced rubber hoses. Hoses are colour-coded to ensure that they are always connected to the correct regulator at one end and the correct way round to the torch. As a further insurance against incorrect assembly, all the couplings on the acetylene line have *left-hand* threads. Hose check values are fitted to the torch end of the hoses to prevent sudden feedback of gases from the torch through the hoses.

Flashback arrestors

These are positioned on both the fuel gas and the oxygen supply between the hose and the regulator. Their purpose is to prevent flashback (the return of flame through the hose) into the regulator.

SAFETY NOTES:

Oxygen should never be used instead of compressed air.

Special care is always needed when using pressurised gases and flammable gases.

Instruction is needed in the safe handling and operation of gas welding equipment.

You should always wear the correct protective clothing when welding.

Goggles protect your eyes from harmful light rays which are emitted by the welding process.

ELECTRIC ARC WELDING

In these welding processes the heat for fusion is supplied by an electric arc. An electric arc is intensely hot. Temperatures up to 7000°C are possible. All arc welding processes require an electric circuit similar to the one shown in **FIGURE 5**

The main components of the circuit are the power source, the cables, the electrode and the ground terminal. The work being welded completes the circuit. When the electric arc is formed between electrode and the work, the heat melts the joint edges. In some processes the electrode also melts and

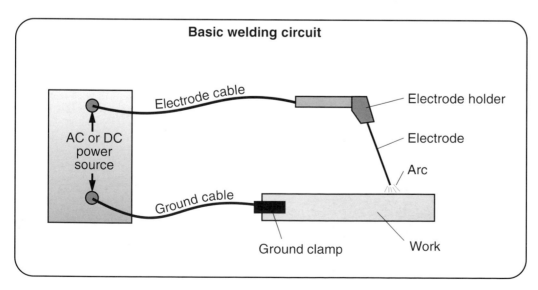

FIGURE 5 *Basic arc welding circuit.*

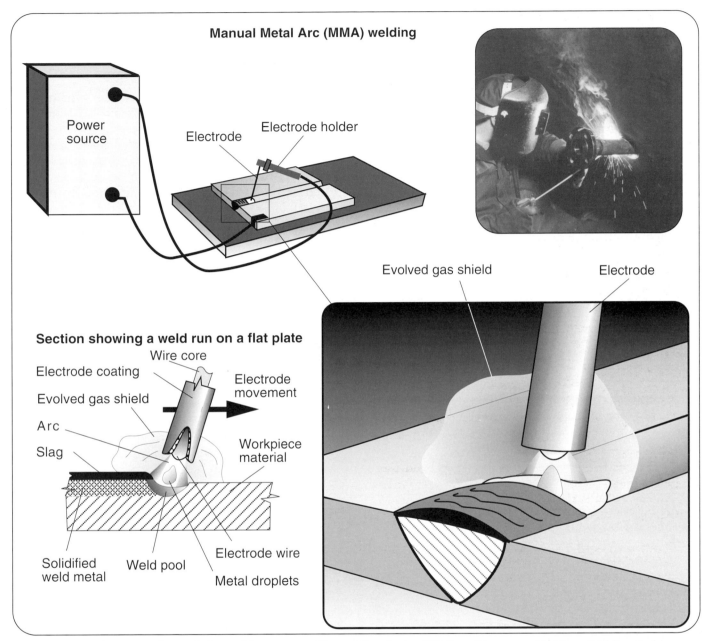

Manual Metal Arc (MMA) welding

Power source

Electrode holder

Electrode

Evolved gas shield

Electrode

Section showing a weld run on a flat plate

Electrode coating

Wire core

Electrode movement

Evolved gas shield

Arc

Slag

Workpiece material

Solidified weld metal

Weld pool

Electrode wire

Metal droplets

FIGURE 6   *The Manual Metal Arc welding process. Photo: Electric Arc Welding (Courtesy: Oerlikon Welding Ltd.)*

drops of molten electrode transfer to the weld pool. These electrodes are commonly known as *consumable* electrodes. In other processes, which you will see later, the electrode does not melt into the weld pool but merely maintains the arc. These electrodes are referred to as *non-consumable*.

The Manual Metal Arc welding process (MMA)
Manual metal arc welding is one of the most widely used welding processes in industry. In this process an electric arc is formed and maintained between the work and the electrode. The intense heat from the arc melts the joint edges. The molten metal from the

joint edges forms into a pool. When the molten metal solidifies the parts become permanently joined. See **Figure 6**.

The electrode is a metal wire covered by a coating. You may sometimes see this referred to as a *stick* electrode. The coating is a combination of chemicals. During the welding process the coating melts and it performs the following functions.

Some of the constituents of the coating produce a gas which shields the weld pool from the oxidising effects of the atmosphere.

The fluxing elements of the coating help the weld to form.

There are slag-forming elements in the coating. These unite with impurities that might be in the molten metal and float them to the top. During cooling it forms a coating over the top of the freshly made weld. This slag coating protects the weld from oxidation and it slows down the rate at which the weld cools. This prevents brittleness. The slag is later chipped off when the weld cools.

The coating sometimes contains powdered metals which add to the filler metal provided by the wire.

If special alloying elements are needed in the weld they can be added in as part of the coating. These will transfer to the molten metal during the welding to give it the required properties.

The coating also helps to maintain the arc, particularly with A.C. welding.

Manual metal arc welding has many applications, from repair work to constructional steelwork. You can see a welded constructional steel component in **Figure 7**.

Electrical terms used in the welding process

There are a few electrical terms which you should become familiar with at this point.

Direct current (DC)
This term describes an electric current which flows in one direction only around a circuit.

Alternating current (AC)
This flows first in one direction, then reverses and flows in the opposite direction around a circuit. Alternating current changes its direction as many as

Figure 7 *Constructional steel component. (Courtesy: Mr J. Lynch. Regional Technical College, Cork)*

60 times every second. You may have seen printed on electrical appliances '50 Cycles' or '50 Hertz'. Both of these mean the same thing – the power supplied to the appliance should be alternating (changing direction) 50 times per second.

Current (given the symbol 'I')
The amount of current flowing in a circuit is measured in amps (amperes).

Voltage (given the symbol 'V')
This is the force which causes an electric current to flow in a circuit. It is measured in volts.

Resistance (given the symbol 'R')
Electrical resistance is an opposition to electric current flow around a circuit. A conductor with a low resistance will carry an electric current more efficiently than a conductor with a high resistance. If one part of an electric circuit has high resistance, that part will tend to become hot. Electric heaters use this principle – the heating element has a high resistance.

Current, voltage and resistance in a circuit are related to each other by a formula called Ohm's law. It is expressed as follows:

$$voltage = current \times resistance \qquad V = IR$$

Whenever two of the basic characteristics of electricity are known Ohm's law can be used to find the third.

The transformer
The transformer is a device for transforming an alternating current at a particular voltage into an alternating current at a higher or a lower voltage. The simple transformer consists of an iron core on which two coils of wire are wound (see **FIGURE 8**). When the primary coil is connected to the electricity supply, the alternating current causes an alternating magnetic field to be set up in the iron core. This magnetic field in turn produces an alternating current in the secondary coil. If the secondary coil has a smaller number of turns (coils) than the primary coil, the *output* voltage will be lower than the *input* voltage but the output current will be higher than the input current.

In 1881 Auguste De Meritens welded with an arc from a carbon electrode. The carbon electrode was non-consumable (it did not form part of the weld). A Russian named N.G. Slavianoff successfully used a bare steel rod as a consumable electrode in 1888 and obtained a patent for metal-arc welding in 1891. The invention of the process of *manual bare-wire welding* is credited to Slavianoff. This method of welding was used for about 50 years.

There were two problems with the bare-wire electrode.
1 It was very difficult to maintain the electric arc.
2 The weld metal became contaminated by the oxygen and nitrogen in the air. This led to the development of covered electrodes. The first flux-coated electrode was introduced by a Swede named Oskar Kjellberg in the early 1900's. He was granted a patent in 1905.

Similarly, if the secondary coil has a larger number of turns than the primary coil, the output voltage will be greater than the input voltage but the output current will be lower than the input current. The principle of the welding transformer is shown in **FIGURE 8**.

Equipment used in manual metal arc welding
The principal equipment used in manual metal-arc welding includes:

- **Welding power source**
- **Cables**
- **Electrode holder**
- **Ground clamp.**

The welding plant
There are two types of welding power source used to supply current for metal-arc welding.

1 Alternating current (AC) type.
2 Direct current (DC) type.

The AC power source
This power source takes its power directly from the main electricity supply. It uses a transformer to supply the correct voltage to suit the welding conditions. A special device in the transformer allows the current in the secondary coil to be adjusted. The primary coil is connected to the electricity power

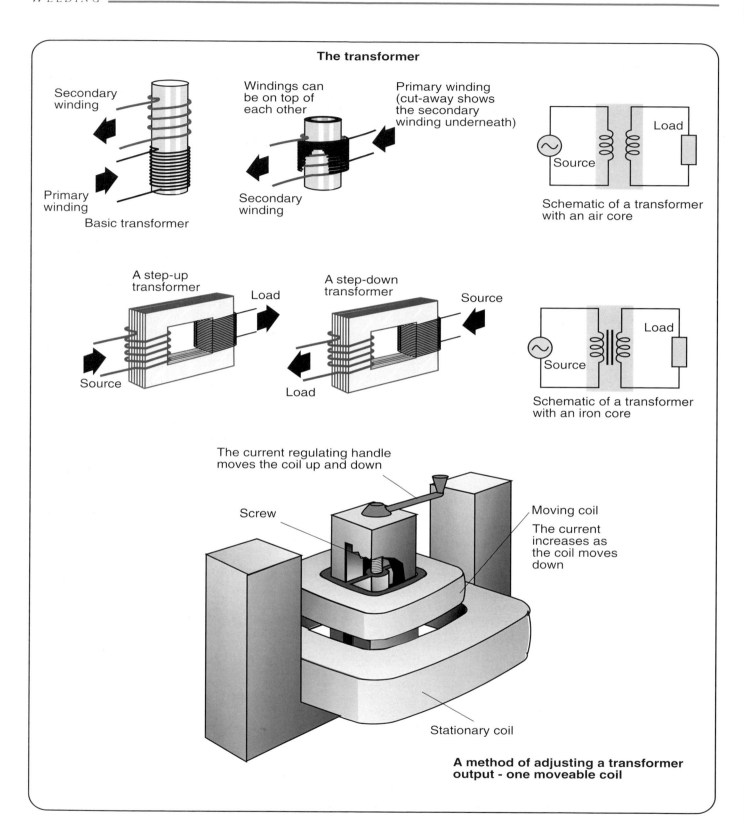

The transformer

Secondary winding

Primary winding

Basic transformer

Windings can be on top of each other

Secondary winding

Primary winding (cut-away shows the secondary winding underneath)

Load

Source

Schematic of a transformer with an air core

A step-up transformer

Load

Source

A step-down transformer

Source

Load

Source

Load

Schematic of a transformer with an iron core

The current regulating handle moves the coil up and down

Screw

Moving coil

The current increases as the coil moves down

Stationary coil

A method of adjusting a transformer output - one moveable coil

FIGURE 8   *The transformer.*

supply and the secondary coil is connected to the ground clamp and the electrode holder.

The DC power source

There are two types of DC welding plant in use:

- **DC generator**
- **Transformer–rectifier.**

DC generator

In this machine an electricity generator is driven by a motor. The motor can be electric, petrol or diesel powered. The generator provides DC current for the arc.

Transformer–rectifier

These machines are basically transformers with an electrical device for changing the alternating current into a direct current output. This device is known as a rectifier. The transformer-rectifier has the advantage that it can be made to supply AC or DC. In **FIGURE 9** you can see the principle of the rectifier.

The cables

The purpose of the cables is to carry the current required for the arc. One cable ends at the ground clamp. The other goes to the electrode holder. It is important that the cables are not too small in diameter. Small cables may have too high a resistance and they could heat up during the welding operation. Most cables contain many strands of fine copper wire. This enables them to carry the electric current and it makes them very flexible.

The electrode holder

The electrode holder is a special type of insulated clamping device which holds the electrode. It is connected to one of the cables coming from the welding plant. The current passes from the cable through the electrode holder to the electrode.

The ground clamp

This is connected to the other cable coming from the power plant. It is secured to the work by means of a screw clamp or a strong spring-operated clip.

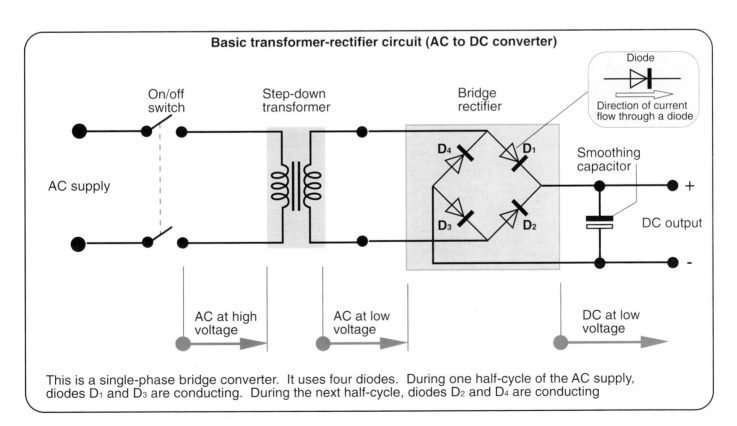

FIGURE 9 *The principle of the rectifier.*

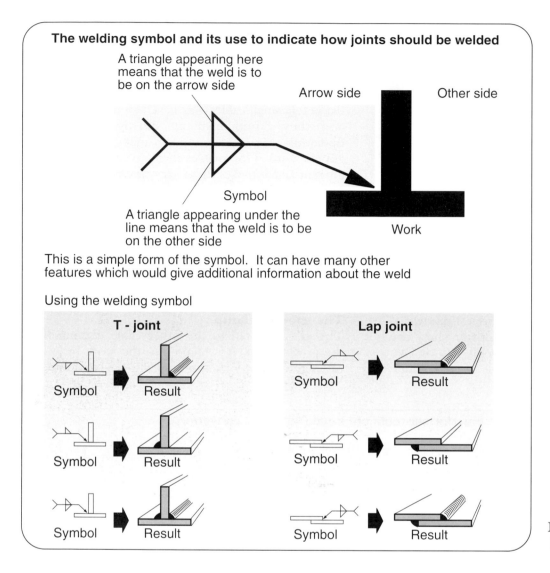

The welding symbol and its use to indicate how joints should be welded

A triangle appearing here means that the weld is to be on the arrow side

Arrow side   Other side

Symbol

A triangle appearing under the line means that the weld is to be on the other side

Work

This is a simple form of the symbol. It can have many other features which would give additional information about the weld

Using the welding symbol

T - joint

Symbol   Result

Symbol   Result

Symbol   Result

Lap joint

Symbol   Result

Symbol   Result

Symbol   Result

FIGURE 10 *Use of the Welding symbol.*

Electrode classification

There is a very wide range of electrodes manufactured for different welding applications. The core wire used in the electrode is selected so that it matches the metal in the workpiece. The coating is also important and must be carefully selected to suit the welding conditions. A code system exists for the classification of covered electrodes for MMA welding of carbon steels.

The code performs the following functions:

It identifies the mechanical value of the electrode core wire.
It indicates the make-up of the flux coating.

It specifies the suitability of the electrode for welding in certain positions.
It indicates special current requirements.

In addition to the above, information regarding the efficiency of the electrode may also be given.

The electrode selected for a welding operation must be correct otherwise the welded joint might fail.

Welding symbols

Drawings of welded assemblies should contain as much information about the welds as possible. Welding symbols can have as many as nine separate pieces of information regarding a weld but in a very

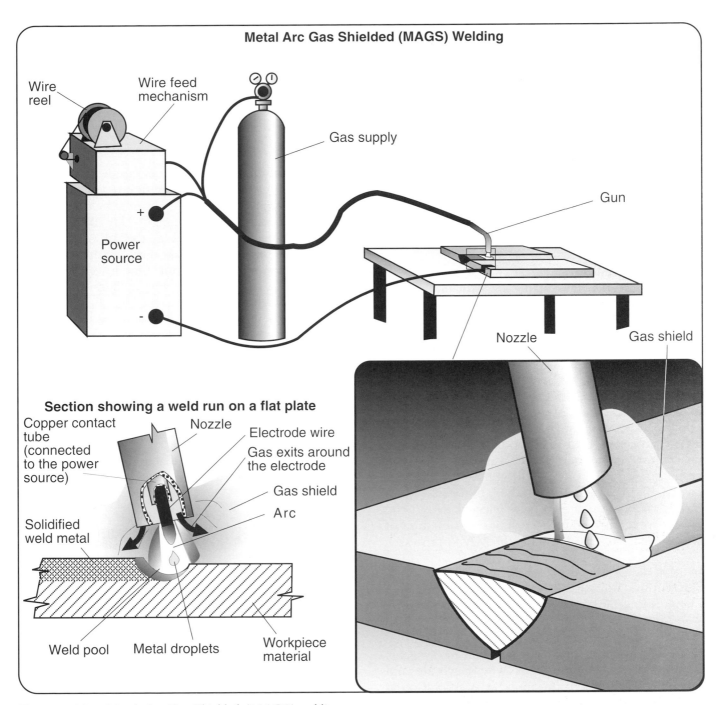

Metal Arc Gas Shielded (MAGS) Welding

Wire reel

Wire feed mechanism

Gas supply

Gun

Power source

+

−

Nozzle

Gas shield

Section showing a weld run on a flat plate

Copper contact tube (connected to the power source)

Nozzle

Electrode wire

Gas exits around the electrode

Gas shield

Arc

Solidified weld metal

Weld pool

Metal droplets

Workpiece material

FIGURE 11   *Metal Arc Gas Shielded (MAGS) welding.*

compact form. The proper use of symbols saves time writing long detailed instructions about how parts should be welded. The symbol must be understood by the welding operator and by the design engineer. **FIGURE 10** shows a basic form of the symbol.

METAL ARC GAS SHIELDED (MAGS) WELDING

This was previously known as Metal Inert Gas welding (MIG). Although it is a metal-arc welding process, it differs in many ways from the manual metal-arc process discussed above.

The electrode is a bare wire which is fed continuously from a spool through the welding gun. Shielding of the weld is performed by a continuous supply of inert gas which is stored in a cylinder. A flexible hose pipe feeds the gas through the welding gun. The gas surrounds the weld pool as it is escaping from the nozzle. This is how the shield is formed. The gas used can be argon, nitrogen, carbon dioxide or helium. It is usually selected to suit the type of welding. For some applications a mixture of gases is used. **FIGURE 11** shows the MAGS process.

In MAGS welding, a transformer–rectifier (DC) power source is used. The wire is supplied through a tube to the welding gun by a special wire-feed unit.

This is a very versatile welding process as it can be used on light sheet metal as well as on heavy plate. Because it uses a continuous wire electrode and there is no slag formed on the weld, MAGS is often performed by robots. Production welding by robots on lines such as welded assemblies for cars is common practice.

TUNGSTEN ARC GAS SHIELDED (TAGS) WELDING

This was previously known as Tungsten Inert Gas (TIG) welding. This is an arc welding process that does not consume the electrode. The electrode is made of tungsten and is referred to as a *non-consumable* electrode. As in MAGS welding, this process uses an inert gas supplied from a cylinder to shield the weld pool. If filler metal is required, a filler wire is fed into the weld pool by hand in the same way as in oxy-acetylene welding. **FIGURE 12** shows the TAGS welding process.

The arc between the tungsten electrode and the work melts the joint edges and they fuse together. In most arc welding processes the arc is started by touching the electrode against the work and quickly lifting it off to create a small gap as soon as the arc starts. TAGS welding is different in that there are two separate currents flowing in the circuit. One is for the arc and is similar to the current in any welding circuit. The other is a high frequency current specially to start and maintain the arc. The arc is started by the operator when he/she holds the electrode near the work and presses a foot pedal or torch control to switch on the high frequency supply. The high frequency current is generated by a separate unit which forms part of the welding equipment. TAGS welding normally uses a DC power source. When aluminium is being welded, however, an AC power source is used.

The TAGS process is suitable for welding most metals. It is well suited to welding aluminium and stainless steels.

SUBMERGED ARC WELDING (SAW)

In submerged arc welding a bare wire electrode is used. The flux is in powder form. It is poured over and completely covers the weld pool. This is where the name 'submerged arc' comes from. You can see a representation of submerged arc welding in **FIGURE 13**. Submerged arc welding is suitable for long, uninterrupted weld runs. An example would be the fabrication of large steel reinforcing beams for construction work.

RESISTANCE WELDING

There are different forms of resistance welding processes, the heat in the joint area is caused by the resistance to the flow of an electric current. The greatest resistance to the current flow is where the

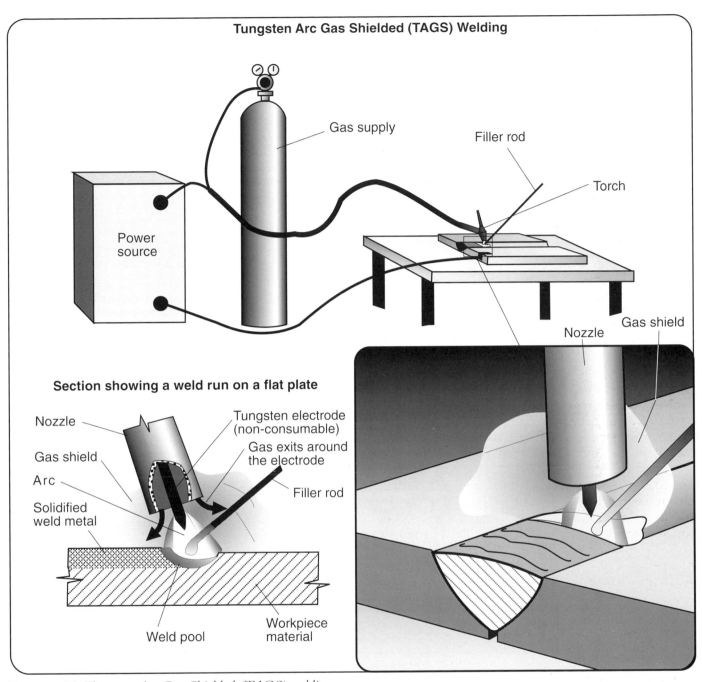

FIGURE 12 *Tungsten Arc Gas Shielded (TAGS) welding.*

joint faces meet. This causes rapid heating – up to the melting point of the metal. Fusion then takes place.

Resistance spot welding

This is a common resistance welding process. It is an ideal method of joining light gauge sheet metal. The electrodes are made of copper or a similar low resistance conductor. Pressure is applied to the electrodes and an electric current is passed through the circuit. The high resistance between the joint

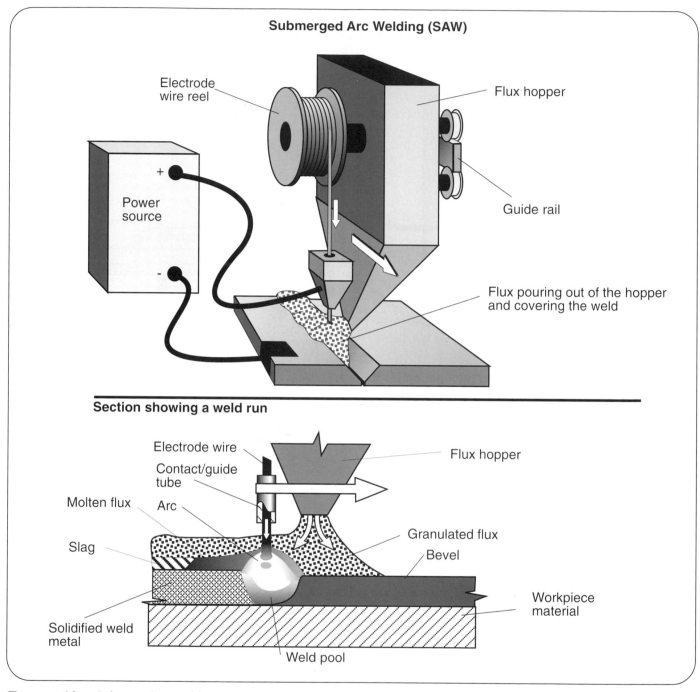

Submerged Arc Welding (SAW)

Electrode wire reel

Flux hopper

Power source

+

−

Guide rail

Flux pouring out of the hopper and covering the weld

Section showing a weld run

Electrode wire

Contact/guide tube

Flux hopper

Molten flux

Arc

Slag

Granulated flux

Bevel

Solidified weld metal

Workpiece material

Weld pool

FIGURE 13 *Submerged arc welding.*

faces causes rapid heating and fusing of a small globule of metal from both faces. You can see resistance spot welding in **FIGURE 14**.

Resistance seam welding

Continuous seams can be welded by resistance welding. There are two methods in general use. One

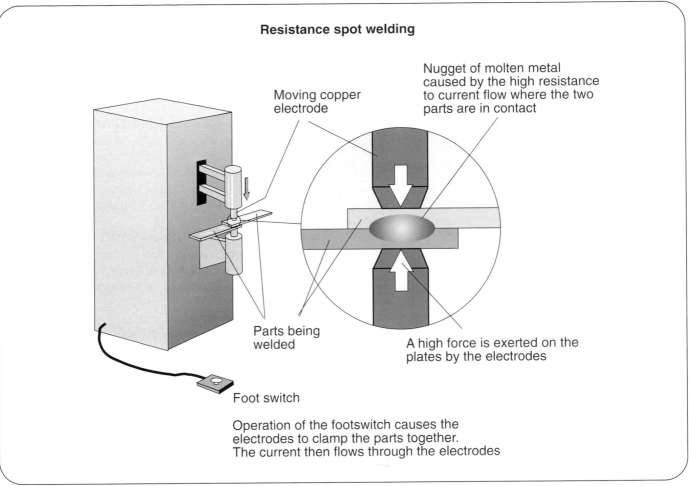

Resistance spot welding

Moving copper electrode

Nugget of molten metal caused by the high resistance to current flow where the two parts are in contact

Parts being welded

A high force is exerted on the plates by the electrodes

Foot switch

Operation of the footswitch causes the electrodes to clamp the parts together. The current then flows through the electrodes

FIGURE 14 *Resistance spot welding.*

is *stitch* welding which uses a series of overlapping spots. The other method uses rollers instead of electrodes. The rollers allow the workpiece to move through the welder continuously. A stream of electrical pulses pass through the rollers and welds the joint.

Projection welding
This is a method of resistance-welding relatively large objects. The contact area between the two parts to be welded is reduced by forming points on one of the parts. In the welding operation the projection and the part with which the projection is in contact fuse together.

SUMMARY

Welding is the process of permanently joining parts by fusing the joint edges together. Fusion results from a combination of heat and pressure. Before welding begins the parts should be clean. During the welding the joint area must be protected from the formation of oxides.

Gas welding
Oxy-acetylene welding is a method which uses a high temperature gas flame. Acetylene is the fuel gas and combustion is supported by oxygen. The gases are stored in cylinders and supplied to the torch through flexible hose pipes.

Electric arc welding

In arc welding processes heat for fusion is supplied by an electric arc. The main components in arc welding equipment are:

- **A power source**
- **Cables**
- **Electrode holder**
- **Ground terminal.**

Manual Metal Arc welding (MMA)

This process uses a short "stick" type electrode. This is a special metal rod covered by a coating of specially prepared chemicals. During the welding process an electric arc is formed between the work and the electrode. The electrode is *consumable* and as it melts it provides filler metal for the weld pool and the coating generates a gas which shields the joint area.

The power source for MMA welding is a special transformer. It has an output current which can be controlled and changed to suit the welding conditions.

Metal Arc Gas Shielded (MAGS) welding

This welding process uses a consumable, bare wire electrode. The wire is stored on a large spool in the welding plant. It is fed through a tube to the welding gun. Shielding for the weld is provided by a supply of gas from a cylinder through a hose pipe.

Tungsten Arc Gas Shielded (TAGS) welding

This welding process uses a non-consumable tungsten electrode. The arc is formed between the tungsten and the work. Additional filler metal, if required, is fed by hand into the weld pool. Shielding is similar to MAGS welding.

Submerged Arc Welding (SAW)

This process uses a bare wire consumable electrode. The electrode is continuously fed from a spool. Flux in powder form is poured over the weld area.

Resistance welding

In resistance spot welding the joint faces are clamped under pressure between two copper electrodes and the current is switched on. The high resistance between the joint faces causes a build-up of intense heat – hot enough to melt the metal.

Adhesive Bonding

INTRODUCTION

An adhesive is a substance which is capable of holding materials together by surface attachment. The use of adhesives to bond or join materials probably dates back to prehistoric times. The ancient Egyptians used glues made from animal tissue and bones to join wood. Glues were also made from gums, starch and proteins produced by certain plants.

These were essentially low-strength adhesives which carried light loads, but as in the case of paper-joining, the adhesives normally out-lived the materials which they bonded.

ENGINEERING ADHESIVES

Since the mid 1930s new types of adhesives have been developed. These are chemical compounds. They are often referred to as *engineering adhesives*. These substances are capable of bonding high-strength engineering materials such as steels, non-ferrous metals and plastics. To qualify as an adhesive, a substance must:

- **Be able to wet the joint faces completely**
- **Cure to a solid to form the bond.**

Depending on their type, adhesives are supplied in the form of solids, liquids or pastes.

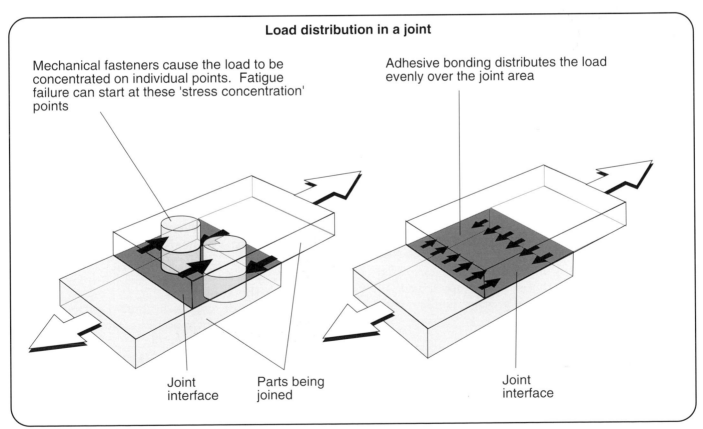

Load distribution in a joint

Mechanical fasteners cause the load to be concentrated on individual points. Fatigue failure can start at these 'stress concentration' points

Adhesive bonding distributes the load evenly over the joint area

Joint interface

Parts being joined

Joint interface

FIGURE 1   *Load distribution in a joint.*

Adhesive bonding is the expression which describes the use of adhesives to join materials. This method of joining often has many advantages over other methods:

- **It is possible to join metal to metal, metal to non-metal, non-metal to non-metal. Plastics, for example, can be joined to metals**
- **In a bonded joint the load is more evenly distributed throughout the joint**
- **An immensely strong joint is possible with adhesive bonding. The absence of mechanical fasteners often eliminates the risk of fatigue failure**
- **Adhesives can withstand stresses caused by flexing of the joint and different coefficients of expansion. (This would occur in a joint between steel and aluminium)**
- **Galvanic corrosion between dissimilar metals is reduced or eliminated**
- **Eliminating mechanical fasteners from a joint also eliminates the need to drill holes**
- **The metallurgical structure of the material being joined will not be affected**
- **A properly bonded joint will provide a good seal for gases or liquids.**

LOAD DISTRIBUTION IN A JOINT

Using mechanical fasteners, the load is usually concentrated on individual points. Fatigue failure can start at these stress concentration points. With adhesive bonding, the load is quite evenly distributed over the joint area. See **FIGURE 1**.

TERMS USED IN CONNECTION WITH ADHESIVES

In adhesive science a number of terms are used frequently. Some of these terms are given in **TABLE 1**. It is important to become familiar with these terms.

BONDING WITH ADHESIVES

To form a high-strength bond with adhesives it is very important to:

- **Design the joint so that the load can be**

Term	Meaning
Adhesive	The bonding material
Adhesion	The force which holds the adherends together
Adherends	The parts being joined
Adhesive failure	Failure of the bond at the interface between the adhesive and the adherend
Bond strength	The ability of a joint to resist a breaking load
Cohesive failure	Failure of the joint within the adhesive or within the adherend
Cure	The process during which the adhesive changes from liquid to solid (solvent-free adhesives)
Hardener	A catalyst for curing the adhesive
Substrate	The surface of an adherend
Thermoplastic adhesives	Adhesives which soften when heated
Thermosetting adhesives	Adhesives which require heat to cure. Once cured they cannot be resoftened by heating

TABLE 1   *Terms relating to adhesives.*

taken by the adhesive in the direction of its highest strength
- **Prepare the substrates properly**
- **Choose an adhesive which suits the adherends.**

Preparing the substrates
The substrates, or surfaces in direct contact with the adhesive must be scrupulously clean. Cleaning can be carried out with the use of:

- **Abrasive materials (for example, emery paper)**
- **Solvent cleaners**
- **Shot-blasting (a high pressure 'spray' of abrasive grit).**

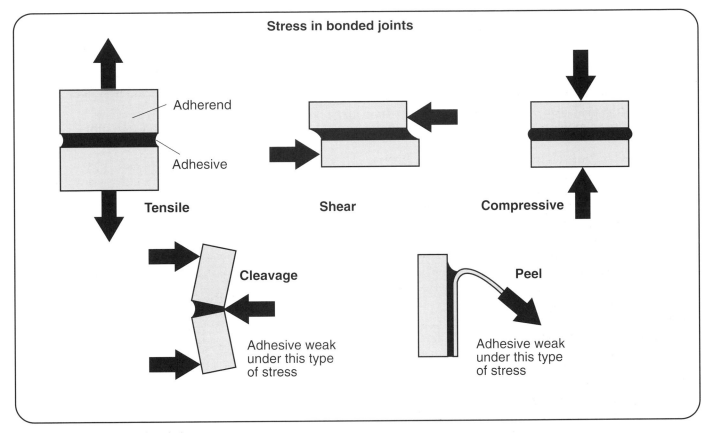

FIGURE 2 *Stress in bonded joints.*

It is sometimes necessary to etch the substrate by treatment with acid-based solutions before using an adhesive.

STRESS IN BONDED JOINTS

Before looking at the different jointing methods, it is useful to examine the ways in which a bonded joint can fail. **FIGURE 2** shows how joints could be stressed. Joints which are to be made with adhesives should ideally be subjected to compression, shear or tensile forces. If the joint is subjected to peel or cleavage forces its resistance to failure will be less. Bonded joints are strongest in compression, tension and shear.

JOINT DESIGN FOR BONDING

It is possible to join all solid materials with an adhesive. To ensure that the joint has high strength it is often necessary to use special joint designs. In **FIGURE 3** you can see the basic types of bonded joint.

CHOOSING THE CORRECT ADHESIVE

There are basically two categories of adhesives:

1 Natural adhesives.
2 Synthetic adhesives (much more important these days).

Natural adhesives

These are derived from animal tissue and bones, vegetable extracts (gum, starch, protein) and minerals.

Animal adhesives are often supplied in solid form and have to be heated until they become liquid

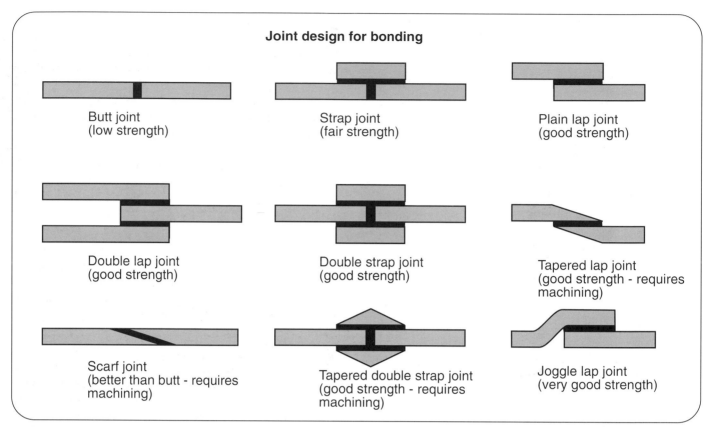

FIGURE 3 *Joint design for bonding.*

before they can be used. They were mainly used to join wood.

Vegetable adhesives are usually powdered and must be mixed to a paste with water before use. Vegetable adhesives are sometimes used in woodwork. They also have a range of applications in paper carton manufacture.

An example of a mineral adhesive is sodium silicate. This is a mineral adhesive which is valuable for its resistance to high temperatures. It can withstand temperatures as high as 850°C. This makes it suitable for use in bonding thermal insulating materials.

Synthetic adhesives
There is a very large range of synthetic adhesives and they represent the most important materials today. To categorise synthetic adhesives, it is easiest to do so by their setting or curing method. Curing methods include:

- **Chemical reaction**
- **Hot-melt**
- **Solvent evaporation.**

Chemically-activated adhesives
Anaerobics
These are one-component adhesives and they remain liquid while they are exposed to air. When they are confined to the small space between the metal faces of the parts being joined, the air is excluded and it polymerises into a resin. They cure at room temperature. The word *anaerobic* means 'functioning without atmospheric oxygen'. Anaerobic adhesives are used to bond many different materials.

Cyanoacrylates
Cyanoacrylates solidify in seconds under the influence of atmospheric moisture. They are suitable for bonding non-porous materials such as glass, rubber, metals and plastics. They are particularly well suited to

bonding flexible substrates such as rubber and many plastics. They are commonly available under the name 'super glue' for general household use.

Epoxies

These are usually two-part adhesives that consist of an epoxy resin and a curing agent or *hardener*. One-part epoxies use heat as the curing agent. Epoxies can be used to bond a wide range of materials. The bond formed has high strength.

Modified phenolics

A very strong bond between the adherends is possible using modified phenolic adhesives. To cure properly, these adhesives need pressure and heat. An example of the use of modified phenolics is the bonding of brake-lining materials to the metal shoe.

Hot-melts

These adhesives are heated until they become fluid. The adhesive is then spread on the substrate and the joint is assembled. As the adhesive cools to room temperature it solidifies and forms a bond.

Solvent-based adhesives

These are frequently rubber adhesives. The solvent carries the rubber and/or plastic. As the solvent evaporates the adhesive becomes tacky and then hardens. Rubber adhesives are not suitable for carrying sustained loads.

SUMMARY

An adhesive is a substance which is capable of holding substances together by surface attachment.

Engineering adhesives are chemical compounds which have high strength and can bond materials such as glass, steel, non-ferrous metals and plastics.

The bonding process requires that the joining substances will:

- **Completely wet the joint surface**
- **Cure to a solid to form the bond.**

Adhesive bonding has many advantages:

- **Most materials can be joined**
- **There is a uniform distribution of the load in the joint**
- **A high-strength joint is possible**
- **Flexing of the joint is sometimes possible**
- **Galvanic corrosion is eliminated**
- **No need to drill holes**
- **The metallurgical structure of the joint will not be changed**
- **A good gas/liquid seal is provided.**

Joint design

The direction in which the joint has the highest strength is important. An engineer using adhesives must know the type of load and the direction of the load which will be on the joint. He/she will then design the joint to suit that load.

Preparation of the joint

The joint surfaces must be perfectly clean before the adhesive is applied. Mechanical cleaning with abrasive materials may be necessary. Special solvent cleaners are available to ensure correct preparation of the joint surfaces. The surfaces are sometimes etched with acid-based solutions during preparation.

Types of adhesives

Natural adhesives are derived from animal tissue and vegetable extracts. Synthetic adhesives are chemical compounds. Most engineering applications use synthetic adhesives. Adhesives must be able to wet the joint surfaces and cure to a solid. Methods of curing include:

- **Chemical reaction. Reactions can be caused by air, moisture, chemicals**
- **Hot melt. These can be heated until they become fluid. When they cool and solidify they form the bond**
- **Solvent evaporation. The bonding medium is carried in a solvent. When the solvent evaporates, the adhesive hardens.**

Brazing and Soldering

INTRODUCTION

If you wish to join metals permanently, welding is not always the best solution. For example, the high temperatures of a welding process may cause damage to the parts being joined. Some metals do not weld very well because of their structure.

Brazing and soldering are useful ways to make relatively strong joints between dissimilar metals. Steel and brass are good examples of metals which can be joined together by brazing and soldering. Low temperature joining methods can often be the best solution to a joining problem. It must be remembered, however, that the brazed joint will not be as strong as a welded joint and a soldered joint will not be as strong as a brazed joint. In general, the lower the joining temperature, the lower the strength of the joint.

THE BRAZING PROCESS

Brazing is a joining process which uses a non-ferrous filler metal or alloy in the joint. The filler metal is melted and made to flow into the small space between the faces of the parts being joined. An important difference between brazing and welding is that in brazing the parts being joined do not melt. This is because the brazing alloy always melts at a temperature above 450°C but well below the melting point of the metals being joined. You can see now why there is such a difference between brazing and welding. In brazing only the filler metal becomes liquid in the joint. When the liquid solidifies the joint is made. Brazing is a *bonding* process. In welding the joint surfaces as well as the filler metal become liquid. As they solidify they fuse together. Welding is a *fusion* process.

A most important requirement for brazing is that the joint faces must be clean and free of oxides. The faces must be thoroughly cleaned. This can be done mechanically. A special flux is used to remove any remaining oxides from the surfaces. The flux also prevents the formation of oxides during heating and it helps the filler metal to become more fluid. In brazing, the flux is usually in the form of a paste and the joint faces are coated with this paste. This preparation ensures that the molten filler metal can completely *wet* the surfaces. In any bonding process, the wetting of the joint surfaces is a crucial part of the process.

Brazing relies on *capillary action* (or capillary *attraction*) to draw the filler metal into the joint. A capillary is defined as a very fine hole or narrow passage. Capillary action can be demonstrated by dipping the end of a very fine glass tube into a liquid. The liquid will quickly rise in the tube. This is mainly due to the ability of the liquid to wet the glass and creep up the wall of the tube. In order that capillary action can occur in the brazing process it is necessary that the joint faces have the *correct* gap between them. The size of this gap or space depends on the type of braze metal being used.

The parts to be joined are cleaned, fluxed and heated. They should be heated broadly – not in a small pin-point area. Air-fuel torches are excellent for brazing because it is not necessary to melt the metals being joined. They also give a broad flame. It is not as concentrated as the oxy-acetylene flame. When the work is heated the filler rod is touched to the joint at the gap. If the work is hot enough and the gap is correct, the filler metal will flow all round the joint. Continued heating of the work will cause the joint to be completely filled. The brazing process is shown in **FIGURE 1**.

BRAZE WELDING

In braze welding, also known as bronze welding, the filler metal is a copper-rich alloy. It has a melting point which is lower than the melting point of the metal being joined.

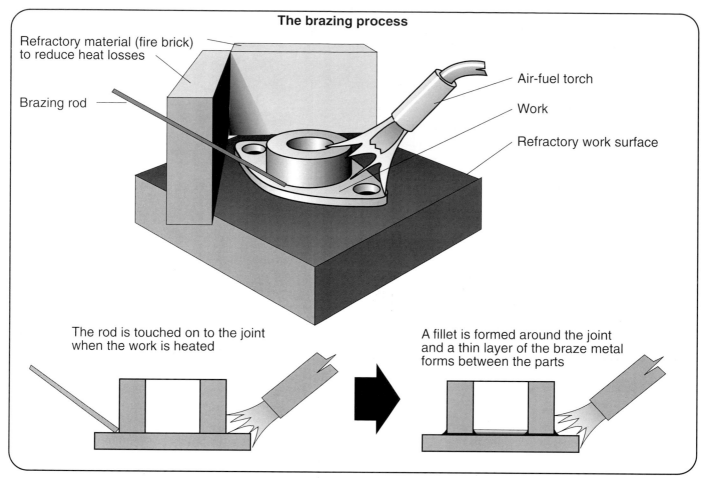

The brazing process

Refractory material (fire brick) to reduce heat losses

Brazing rod

Air-fuel torch

Work

Refractory work surface

The rod is touched on to the joint when the work is heated

A fillet is formed around the joint and a thin layer of the braze metal forms between the parts

FIGURE 1   *The brazing process.*

The technique used is similar to that used in fusion welding, except that the parent metal, unless it is of the same composition as the filler metal, is not melted. Capillary action is not involved.

Silicon, manganese and nickel bronze filler metals may be used to make sound welds between steel, cast iron and copper components. Joints between dissimilar metals like copper and steel can be made at a lower temperature than that usually employed in fusion welding.

In braze (bronze) welding powdered flux is applied with the filler rod or in some cases the filler rod is already flux-coated.

Fairly large joint gaps can be filled quite easily as capillary action is not involved. You can see braze welding, brazing and fusion welding compared in **FIGURE 2**.

Fluxes
Flux is very important in brazing. Its functions are dissolving oxides prior to heating and preventing the formation of oxides during heating. It also makes the molten filler metal more fluid by reducing its surface tension. Borax was commonly used as a brazing flux. There are now fluxes available which are more suitable than borax and are more efficient in removing oxides.

Braze metals
The filler metals used in brazing are mainly:

Copper and copper alloys – for brazing steels, copper, nickel, stainless steels

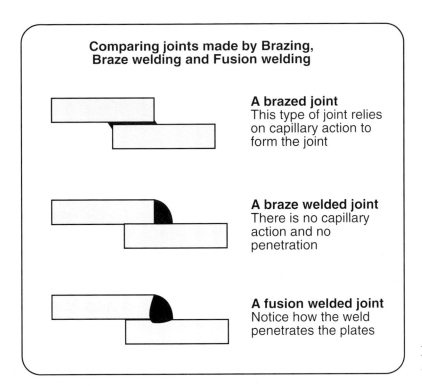

Comparing joints made by Brazing, Braze welding and Fusion welding

A brazed joint
This type of joint relies on capillary action to form the joint

A braze welded joint
There is no capillary action and no penetration

A fusion welded joint
Notice how the weld penetrates the plates

FIGURE 2   *A selection of joining processes showing the filler metal in the joint.*

Silver alloys – also used for brazing the above materials in special situations. These are expensive braze metals and their use is often referred to as *silver soldering*
Aluminium alloys – for brazing aluminium.

A very common braze metal is an alloy of 60% copper and 40% zinc (60-40 brass). This is often referred to as brazing brass. Brazing brass can be used in the form of rods. It is very common, however, to produce it in the form of rings or strips which suit the shape of the joint. These are then placed in the joint before the parts are assembled. When heat is applied to the joint area, capillary action draws the molten braze metal into the narrow spaces in the joint. In preparation for brazing, parts are often provided with grooves which hold the specially shaped braze metal pieces. In a properly designed joint, the braze metal piece will be the exact amount necessary to fill the joint. **FIGURE 3** shows examples of how braze metals might be pre-shaped.

The melting points of braze metals vary with the proportions of metals in the alloy. In general the melting point is not below 450°C and can be as high as 850°C.

Heating the joint

A *gas torch*, as you have already seen, is a common method of supplying heat to the joint area. Other methods used include:

- **Induction heating (electric)**
- **Furnace heating**
- **Dip brazing.**

Induction heating

The component is placed inside a coil. The coil is carrying a high frequency current. This high frequency current induces *eddy currents* in the component causing it to heat rapidly. The braze metal and flux are already placed in the joint area. When the component reaches the required temperature the molten braze metal fills the joint cavity.

Furnace heating

The components to be joined are assembled and a pre-shaped braze metal and flux are already in the

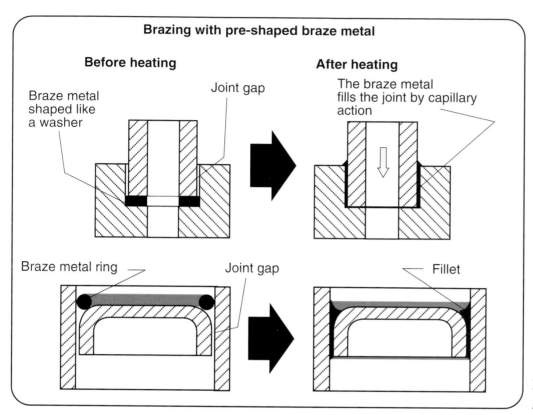

FIGURE 3 *The use of pre-shaped brazing metal.*

joint area. Batches of components can then be placed in a furnace until the joint is made.

Dip brazing

The components are immersed in a bath of molten braze metal. The molten braze metal heats the components and flows into the joints. This method of brazing is usually confined to small parts because the entire surface becomes coated.

SILVER SOLDERING

This is a joining process which is similar to brazing. The filler metal is an alloy of *silver, copper* and *zinc.* Silver solders are used to join steels, copper and nickel. Certain types of stainless steels can be joined using silver solders. Pure silver is used to join some metals. Many of the techniques used in brazing are also used in silver soldering.

SOFT SOLDERING

This is a method of joining metals by using similar principles to brazing – causing a molten bonding metal to flow into the joint. In soft soldering, the bonding metal is an alloy of tin and lead. This alloy, known as solder, has a melting point of approximately 183°C to 250°C depending on the proportions of tin and lead in it. However, an important difference between soldering and brazing is that soft solders will melt *below* 450°C.

A soldered joint has relatively low strength. For this reason the soldering process is confined to uses which do not cause the joint to be stressed. It is ideal for assembling electronic components and sealing folded sheet metal joints.

THE SOLDERING PROCESS

Under ideal conditions the molten solder wets the surfaces of the metals being joined. When the work is heated to the correct temperature the solder flows into the space in the joint. The tin in the solder and the joint surfaces react together and form an alloy. The solder adheres to the surfaces and when the heat source is removed, it solidifies and a permanent joint is formed. The solder *bonds* the two surfaces

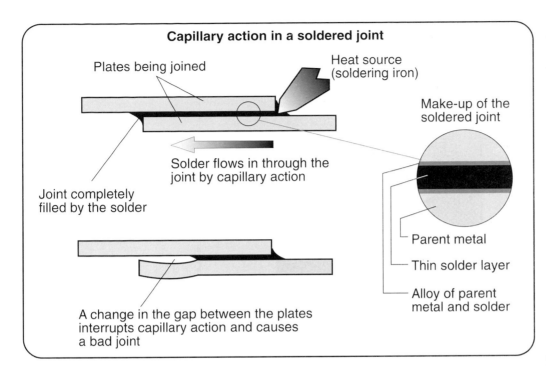

Capillary action in a soldered joint

Plates being joined

Heat source (soldering iron)

Make-up of the soldered joint

Solder flows in through the joint by capillary action

Joint completely filled by the solder

Parent metal

Thin solder layer

Alloy of parent metal and solder

A change in the gap between the plates interrupts capillary action and causes a bad joint

FIGURE 4 *The soldering process.*

together. **FIGURE 4** shows the soldering process and the composition of a soldered joint.

The conditions which are necessary to allow the solder to join the metals include:

- **Chemically clean joint faces**
- **Joint faces heated to the correct temperature.**

Cleaning the joint surfaces

If you spread molten solder over a surface which is not chemically clean the solder will not wet the surface. The tin in the solder cannot form an alloy with the surface of the metal.

Oil, dirt and oxides are examples of barriers to surface wetting. Before you apply the solder, the bare metal should be exposed by cleaning. Any of the following methods can be used:

Emery cloth or other abrasive means
Files
Scrapers.

Chemical cleaning is also possible and is an effective method of removing oil and grease.

Function of a flux

You have seen throughout the discussion on joining processes which require the application of heat, that when the unprotected clean surface of a metal is heated slightly it will become coated with an oxide film. As the temperature of the metal in the soldering process must be raised in order that the solder will melt, oxides will form on the joint surface very quickly. To prevent this a flux is used.

Fluxes can be supplied as liquid or paste to suit different soldering applications. It is also very common to have the solder in the form of a small tube with the flux filling the tube. This is particularly useful for soldering electronic components.

SAFETY NOTE:
Chemical cleaning in acid or alkali solution should be carried out with extreme caution and only by persons wearing the correct protective apparel and using the recommended equipment. Chemically cleaned materials should be adequately washed afterwards.

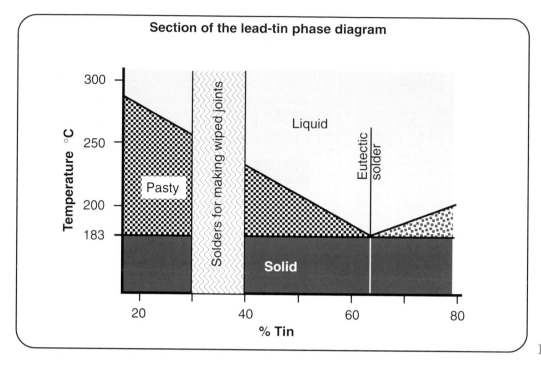

Section of the lead-tin phase diagram

FIGURE 5   *Solder metals.*

There are two types of flux in use in soft soldering.

1 Flux which cleans and protects the surface. Fluxes in this category are called *active* fluxes.
2 Flux which protects an already clean surface. Fluxes in this category are known as *passive* fluxes.

Active fluxes

These fluxes are able to dissolve oxide films and will prevent oxides reforming. Zinc chloride is an active flux. It is also known as *killed spirits.* It is a product of the chemical action of hydrochloric acid and zinc. You should always remember, therefore, that active fluxes are *corrosive.* Active flux remaining on the surface of steel after soldering will corrode the surface in a very short time. Washing in warm water containing a mild alkali followed by thorough rinsing will remove flux residues from the metal.

Passive fluxes

All of the joint surfaces must be thoroughly cleaned before using a passive flux. It does not have the ability to remove oxides from the surface.

HEATING THE JOINT IN SOLDERING

The more common methods of heating the joint in the soldering process are:

• **The soldering iron**
• **A gas flame**
• **Hot plates.**

The soldering iron

The soldering 'iron' is actually made from copper. Copper is used because this material can store large quantities of heat and it can give up its stored heat very quickly. Copper has an ability to alloy with tin. This makes it easy to coat the end of the *bit* with a layer of solder. The soldering iron collects heat from a flame (or an electric heating element) and stores it in the bit.

Soldering with a gas flame

This method is used where adequate heat cannot be supplied by a soldering iron. Examples would be:

Large areas.
Pipe joints.

Heating with a hot plate

The temperature of large components can be raised by heating them on a hot-plate. The joint surfaces must be thoroughly cleaned and coated with flux. The surfaces are then coated with solder or *tinned*. The joint surfaces are brought together and the assembly placed on the hot-plate until the solder in the joint flows. This process is known as *sweating*.

Solder metals

Solder is an alloy of *tin* and *lead* with a small amount of *antimony*. The proportions of the constituent metals vary according to the purpose for which the solder is required. Solder metals tend to be lower strength than brazing alloys. It is worth noting at this point that silver solders are mainly brazing alloys and not solders. They melt above 450°C. The exceptions are lead-silver alloys.

The different proportions of lead and tin in the solder metals has a very important effect on their behaviour. Solder containing 63% tin and 37% lead is known as Tinman's solder. It is a *eutectic* solder. A eutectic solder has no pasty stage. This solder will change from liquid to solid at 183°C. It has many uses. Higher proportions of lead gives the solder a wider pasty region. This means it will be partially solid over a wider temperature range. This is useful for certain types of soldering applications. In FIGURE 5 you will see an extract from the phase diagram for lead-tin alloys.

This shows that as the proportion of lead increases there will be a greater temperature range in which the solder will be partially solid. This was used in the past to make joints on lead piping. The plumber joined the pipes by fitting the pipes together and covering the joint with plumbers solder. Plumbers solder has a high lead content. During its pasty or partially solid state the plumber finished the joint by "wiping" the solder with a special glove. This made the solder smooth and gave the joint a pleasing appearance.

SUMMARY

Brazing and soldering are *bonding* processes. Bonding requires that the joining medium in the joint area is liquid at some point. The liquid must *wet* the surfaces. When the joining medium solidifies, a permanent joint is formed. Brazing is a process in which a brazing alloy melts and flows into the space between the joint faces. When the brazing alloy solidifies the joint is made. The brazing alloy flows into the joint by *capillary action* when the gap between the joint faces is correct. If the gap is too large capillary action will not occur and the brazing will not be a success.

The joint edges must not be melted during the brazing operation. Brazing temperatures vary with the constituents of the brazing alloy. As a general rule, brazing temperatures are above 450°C but well below the melting point of the parts being joined.

The strength of a brazed joint is lower than the strength of a welded joint.

Successful brazing depends on the following:

The joint faces must be clean and free from oxides
The joint faces must be coated with a suitable flux before brazing begins
The braze metal is suitable for the materials being joined
The gap between the joint faces must be correct to allow capillary action to draw the molten alloy into the joint.

Braze metals are alloys containing mainly copper and zinc but often containing other metals. A common brazing alloy is 60-40 brass (alloy of 60% copper and 40% zinc). Silver solders are alloys of silver and copper but sometimes including phosphorous. The flux used in brazing is in a paste form. The joint faces are coated with the flux after cleaning. Heat for the brazing process can be supplied by gas flame. Another common method is to assemble the parts with a pre-shaped brazing metal strip placed in the joint area. The assembly is then placed in a furnace or heated by an induction coil.

Braze welding is a process in which the parts are joined by a brazing metal but it does not use capillary action to fill the joint. The filler metal is deposited at the point where it is required.

Soft soldering uses capillary action to fill the joint. The soft soldering process is usually carried out by heating the joint area with a soldering iron or a gas flame. Electric hot plates can also be used. The temperature required is well below 450°C. The joint surfaces are cleaned and coated with flux before the heat is applied. When using a soldering iron, the copper bit is first tinned (coated with solder). Molten solder flows from the copper bit and completely wets the joint surface. When the solder solidifies, the parts will be joined. The strength of a soldered joint is lower than that of a brazed joint.

The flux used in soldering can be passive or active.

Passive flux will protect a clean surface from the formation of oxides. An active flux will remove residues of oxides as well as protecting the surface from the formation of new oxides when heat is applied.

The metals used in solders are alloys of lead and tin. It usually contains small amounts of antimony. A eutectic solder is an alloy containing 63% tin and 37% lead. This solder will change from liquid to solid without passing through a pasty (partially solid) stage at 183°C. Solder with greater proportions of lead have wider regions which are partially solid.

Index